W9-BNY-253

Determinants of Infant Behaviour III

Contributing Authors

GENEVIÈVE APPELL

RUTH BOBBITT

MYRIAM DAVID

B. M. FOSS

D. FREEDMAN

HAVA GEWIRTZ

J. L. GEWIRTZ

R. A. HINDE

GORDON JENSEN

GERALDINE KEENE

HARRIET RHEINGOLD

JOYCE ROBERTSON

JAY ROSENBLATT

THELMA ROWELL

Determinants of Infant Behaviour III

PROCEEDINGS OF
THE THIRD TAVISTOCK STUDY GROUP
ON MOTHER-INFANT INTERACTION
HELD AT THE HOUSE OF THE
CIBA FOUNDATION
LONDON SEPTEMBER 1963

Edited by B. M. FOSS

with a foreword by John Bowlby

LONDON: METHUEN & CO LTD
distributed in the United States
by BARNES & NOBLE, Inc.

First published 1965

Printed in Great Britain by
T. & A. Constable Ltd
Printers to the University of Edinburgh

Contents

Contents

Plates

Members of the Study Group

DR J. A. AMBROSE, Psychologist, Psychoanalyst, Tavistock Child Development Research Unit, 2 Beaumont St., London, W.1

MLLE G. APPELL, Psychologist, Institut de Service Social Pouponnière Amyot, Montrouge, Paris

DR J. BOWLBY, Consultant Psychiatrist, Member of External Scientific Staff of Medical Research Council, and Director, Department for Children and Parents, Tavistock Clinic, 2 Beaumont St., London, W.1

DR M. DAVID, Child Psychiatrist, Association pour la Santé Mentale du 13° Arrondissement, Paris

PROFESSOR B. M. FOSS, Department of Psychology, Institute of Education, Malet Street, London, W.C.1

DR J. L. GEWIRTZ, Psychologist, Child Development Section, National Institute of Mental Health, Bethesda, 4, Maryland, U.S.A.

DR M. GUNTHER, Paediatric Research Worker, University College Hospital, London, W.C.1

PROFESSOR R. A. HINDE, Sub-Department of Animal Behaviour, Dept. Zoology, University of Cambridge

DR E. P. G. MICHELL, Child Psychiatrist, Psychoanalyst, Physician-in-Charge of the Dept. of Psychological Medicine, Hospital for Sick Children, Gt. Ormond St., London, W.C.1

DR H. F. R. PRECHTL, Neurophysiologist, Academisch Ziekenhuis, Neurologiske Kliniek, Oostersingel 59, Groningen, Holland

PROFESSOR H. L. RHEINGOLD, Dept. of Psychology, Miller Hall, University of North Carolina, Chapel Hill, North Carolina, U.S.A.

MR J. ROBERTSON, Psychoanalyst, Project Officer, Tavistock Child Development Research Unit, 2 Beaumont St., London, W.1

DR J. ROSENBLATT, Psychologist, Institute of Animal Behaviour, Rutger's State University, 31 Fulton St., Newark, New Jersey 7102, U.S.A.

Members of the Study Group

DR T. ROWELL, Zoologist, Dept. of Zoology, Makerere University College, P.O. Box 262, Kampala, Uganda, E. Africa

MISS R. THOMAS, Psychoanalyst, Hampstead Child-Therapy Clinic, 21 Maresfield Gardens, London, N.W.3

Guests:

PROFESSOR M. AINSWORTH, Dept. of Psychology, Johns Hopkins University, Baltimore 18, Maryland 21218, U.S.A.

DR D. G. FREEDMAN, Psychologist, Committee on Human Development, Dept. of Psychology, University of Chicago, Illinois, U.S.A.

DR F. HALL, Zoologist, The Zoo, Regent's Park, London, N.W.1

PROFESSOR G. JENSEN, Dept. of Psychiatry, University of Washington, School of Medicine, Seattle 5, Washington, U.S.A.

PROFESSOR C. KAUFMAN, Dept. of Psychiatry, Downstate Medical Center, 450 Clarkson Avenue, Brooklyn 3, N.Y., U.S.A.

DR T. OPPÉ, Consultant Paediatrician, Paediatric Unit, St. Mary's Hospital Medical School, Praed Street, London, W.2

MRS J. ROBERTSON, Well Baby Clinic, Hampstead Child Therapy Clinic, 21 Maresfield Gardens, London, N.W.3

Editor's Note

As in previous volumes in this series, the published version of the proceedings of the study group does not follow closely what actually happened. The order of presentation is different, and the contents of the chapters have been revised, sometimes incorporating points made in the discussions which followed the original presentation of the papers. A consequence is that the discussions in printed form are drastically reduced in length. The last chapter in this volume, that by J. L. Gewirtz, is based on a paper read at the 1961 meeting of the study group, but which could not be included in the proceedings of that meeting for unavoidable reasons.

Warm thanks are due to several members of the Tavistock Clinic: to Pat Willard and Janice Edmunds for their most efficient and unstinting secretarial help; to Tony Ambrose for undertaking the preliminary arrangements of the meeting; and to John Bowlby who once more has contributed from the chair a quality of enthusiasm and purpose.

B. M. F.

Foreword

After a further interval of two years the Tavistock Seminar on Mother-Infant Interaction met for a third time in September 1963. All but a handful of the original members were able to be there and we were joined by seven guests. Once again papers were restricted in number and length to permit full discussion and impromptu contributions, and once again priority was given to papers that report the results of direct observation of what occurs between a mother and her infant, and the effects that each has on the other. As will be seen most papers were preliminary reports of work in progress.

These meetings have been convened in the belief that an understanding of mother-infant interaction in humans will come soonest if the knowledge and skills of several different groups of worker are pooled. Clinician and research worker, experimentalist and field naturalist, student of animal behaviour and student of human behaviour all have their contributions to make; and each has much to learn from the other. Within the group of participants a virus of co-operation is now strongly at work. If the published proceedings infect others with the same virus they will have achieved their purpose.

Once again we wish to record our deep gratitude to the Ciba Foundation for so generously giving hospitality to the Seminar; and to Brian Foss for bringing order to the proceedings. We are grateful also to the National Health Service and the Ford Foundation for their support of the Tavistock Child Development Research Unit.

JOHN BOWLBY

PART I

Animal Studies

The Basis of Synchrony in the Behavioral Interaction between the Mother and her Offspring in the Laboratory Rat[1]

JAY S. ROSENBLATT

Among the mammals the mother's behavior is closely synchronized with the behavior of the developing offspring. There is, of course, functional value to this; when the young are helpless and most in need of continuous maternal care, the mother is most actively maternal and, on the other hand, as the need for care diminishes in the young, maternal behavior declines. This general phenomenon as it appears in the laboratory rat is the subject of our studies. We shall be concerned with the question: how is behavioral synchrony established and maintained in the mother-young relationship in the rat?

Behavioral synchrony between mother and young is more easily seen in mammalian species bearing altricial young than in those in which the young are precocial at birth. It is present in both types of species, but among altricial mammals the young, born helpless and without vision, hearing or adequate locomotion, develop their behavioral capacities gradually. Several weeks or months may pass before they are capable of independent functioning. This affords an opportunity to observe in detail the coordination of the mother's behavior with the developing behavioral characteristics of the young.

As an example, our studies of mother-young interaction in the cat, a species bearing altricial young, revealed a pattern of synchronized changes related to the initiation of nursing-suckling during the two-month litter period (Rosenblatt, Turkewitz & Schneirla, 1961 Schneirla & Rosenblatt, 1961). Three broad phases of this feeding

[1] The studies reported and the preparation of this paper were supported by Research Grants MH-03398 and 08604 to Jay S. Rosenblatt from the National Institute of Mental Health. The assistance of Mrs Lorraine L. Roth, Mrs Pearl Weinstein, and Mr Carl Erickson in the collection of the data is gratefully acknowledged. I am also indebted to Dr Daniel S. Lehrman with whose collaboration an earlier version of this paper was written.

relationship are shown in Figure 1; the first phase is characterized by mother-initiated nursing, the second phase by mutual initiation of feeding by the mother and kitten, and the third phase by kitten-initiated feeding sessions. Elsewhere we have described seven characteristic behavior sequences observed during the first phase of mother-initiated feedings, nine different sequences found in the second phase of mutual initiation of feeding, and eight sequences in the third phase of kitten-initiated feeding (Schneirla, Rosenblatt & Tobach, 1963).

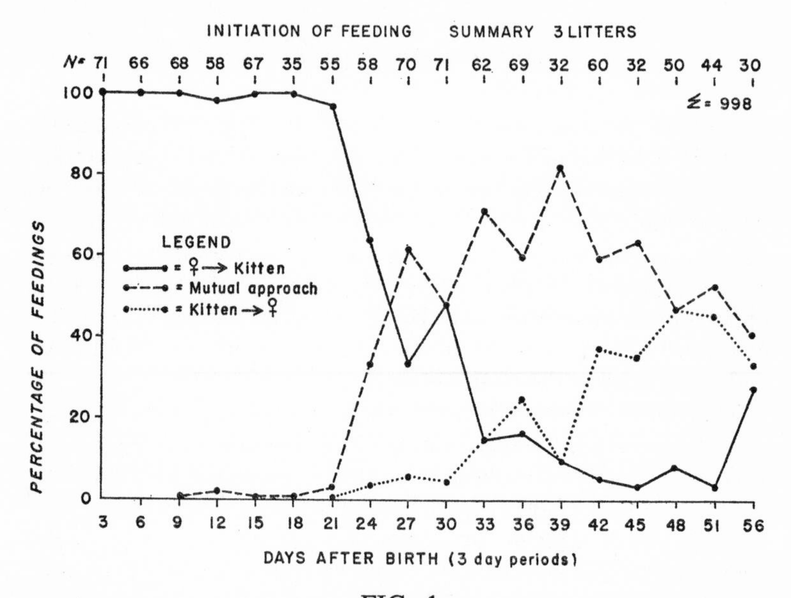

FIG. 1

Changes in the mode of initiating feeding between the mother and kitten during the two-month litter period among cats. Based upon observations reported by Rosenblatt, Turkewitz & Schneirla (1961).

The various phases of the maternal behavior cycle and the stages of behavioral development of the young can be traced in the chronological order of appearance of these twenty-four characteristic feeding interactions during the two-month litter period. Mother-initiated feedings occur in the early part of the maternal behavior cycle when the mother spends most of her time in close proximity to the home region where the kittens are huddled. A slackening of maternal care appears at the end of the third week, beginning the second phase of the feeding relationship. The female spends more time away from the litter, but remains within crawling distance of it, outside the home region. In the third phase the mother leaves the kittens for longer periods, escaping from them by climbing to a cage shelf; she descends at intervals to feed or wander throughout the cage and it is during these periods that the kittens initiate feeding by following her until they have overcome her evading actions.

On the kittens' part, during the first phase of the feeding relationship, they are confined to the home region by a dependence upon proximal sensory systems favoring contact with littermates for the maintenance of optimal thermal and tactual conditions and by development of a pattern of orientation which, being based upon olfactory deposits in the home region, prevents the kitten from moving beyond borders of the home. During the second phase of the feeding relationship improvements in locomotion, increasing dependence upon visually guided behavior, and cagewide orientation enable the kitten to approach the mother for feeding at various places in the cage. The kitten still depends upon the mother, however, to adopt a nursing posture, enabling it to suckle from her. In the third phase of the feeding relationship the kittens are more persistent and versatile in their feeding approaches than in earlier phases, attaching to a nipple while the female pauses for only a moment in her wandering in the cage, and later, climbing to the cage shelf to suckle while the female rests. Suckling declines, however, and feeding from other sources gradually increases, providing kittens with their main source of food. Social interaction among littermates increases, as exemplified by an increase in play activity, and kitten interaction with the mother is varied and more often does not involve feeding.

Continual behavioral contact between kitten and mother is required for the kitten to undergo the typical sequence of changes in the feeding interaction. Kittens that have been isolated from the mother and litter for two-week periods at various times during the development of the feeding relation, then are returned to the litter, are unable to resume suckling immediately, or at all. Not only are these kittens at a disadvantage in the development of suckling compared with kittens that have remained with the mother, but, not having had continual experience with the mother, they are unable to adjust their suckling behavior to the changes which have occurred in the mother's nursing behavior during the period in isolation (Rosenblatt, Turkewitz & Schneirla, 1961).

Among dogs, coordinated changes in the mother's behavior and the behavior of the pups has been described by Fuller & Du Buis (1961), Scott (1958), and Rheingold (1963*b*). The main features of this relationship in the dog are shown in Figure 2, the data for which were taken from the above reports.

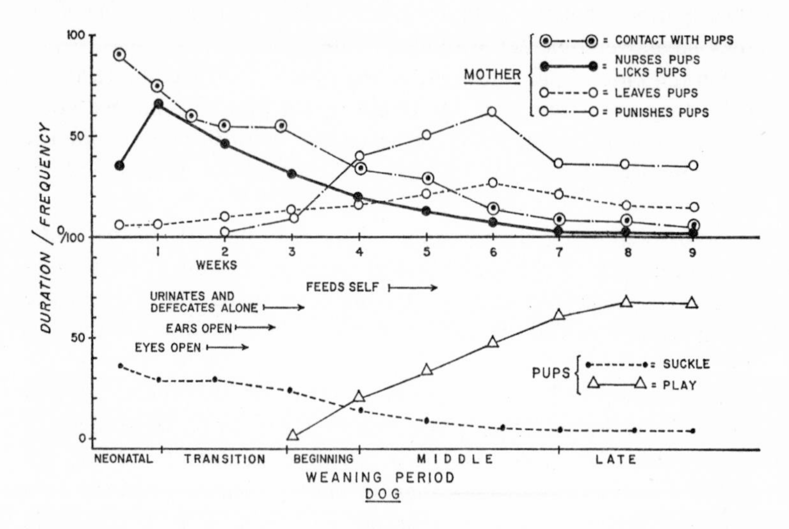

FIG. 2

Selected items of maternal behavior (upper graph) and pup development (lower graph) during the two-month litter period among dogs. Changes in maternal behavior are shown in relation to changes in the physical and behavioral characteristics of the offspring. Figure based upon data reported by Rheingold (1963*b*), *Scott* (1958), *and Fuller and Du Buis* (1962).

Temporal relations of the interaction between the mother and young are somewhat similar to those found among cats. There is an initial period lasting about three weeks during which the mother nurses the pups or otherwise remains in contact with them for a considerable portion of the observation time. During the greater part of this period the pups are without vision or hearing, move by crawling short distances, and cannot defecate or urinate alone; they are thus entirely dependent upon the mother. A second phase begins around the third week and lasts a short time. During this phase maternal departures from the litter increase in frequency and there is evidence that the mother is beginning to be disturbed by the approaches of the pups; she has been described as 'punishing' them. Vision and hearing are now available to the pups, locomotion has improved and there is the beginning of play activity. During this phase there is a decline in suckling by the pups which is matched in the mother by a decline in nursing and other types of contact with the litter. The third phase of mother-young relationship begins around the middle of the fifth week and is characterized by a further decline in the mother's responsiveness to the pups. Departures from the pups increase in frequency and duration as in the cat during the analogous period and there is a steady rise in the frequency of 'punishing' actions by the mother. This behavior may be taken to indicate an increasing disturbance of the mother by activities of the litter. The activity of the pups increases at this time as shown by the rapid rise in play activity after the fourth week. Suckling declines rapidly after the middle of the fourth week and the pups begin to feed from other sources.

The general course of mother-infant interaction among infrahuman primates represented by the rhesus monkey, langur, and baboon (Harlow, Harlow & Hansen, 1963; Jay, 1963; Devore, 1963) is similar to that found among other species bearing altricial young such as the cat and dog, which we have just described. As shown in Figure 3, the time-scale is different, extending over several months among these primates and only eight weeks in these sub-primates. The first month is a period of intense maternal care, during which the mother cradles the infant in her arms and grooms and nurses it almost continuously while the helpless neonate infant clings to the mother or remains close to her. The second phase of the relationship begins after the first month: the infant suckles less and begins to leave the mother, making contact with other infants and engaging in play. Maternal cradling, grooming and nursing decline in duration and frequency reaching a low point at the end of the second month. During the second month maternal evasion of approaches by the infant (i.e. 'rejection') appears, becoming a prominent feature of the interaction after the second month, during the third phase of maternal-young relationship. The mother also cuffs the infant and pulls its hair to discourage it from approaching her. The infant begins to feed itself from various sources and at the same time develops relationships with other infants during play and other activity which gradually weaken its relationship with the mother and enable it to remain away from her for longer and longer periods. Maternal avoidance of contact with the infant, often expressed in rather harsh treatment, rises during this period then gradually subsides as, through mutual learning, the occasions for display of avoidance behaviors become infrequent (Hansen, 1962).

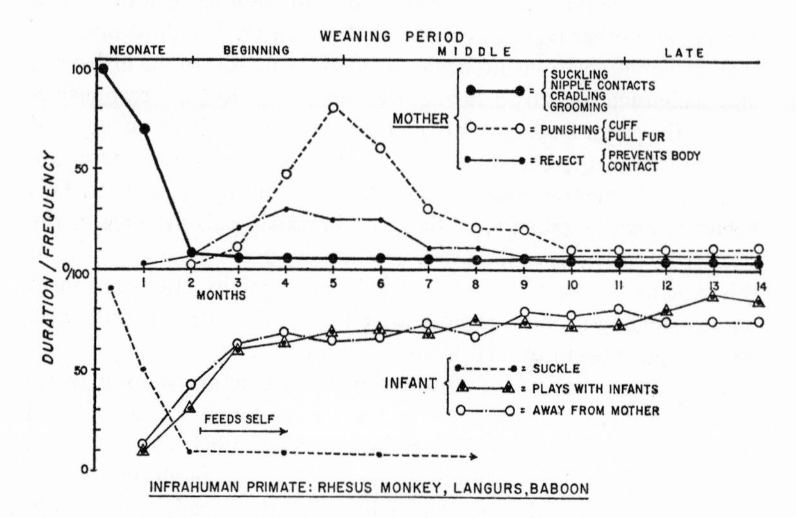

FIG. 3

Selected items of maternal behavior (upper graph) and infant development (lower graph) during the first 14 *months in the rhesus monkey, langur, and baboon. Changes in maternal behavior are shown in relation to changes in infant behavior. Figure based upon data reported by Harlow, Harlow & Hansen* (1963), *Jay* (1963), *and Devore* (1963).

Our studies were done on the mother-young relationship in the laboratory rat. The principal features of this relationship during the four-week litter period are shown in Figure 4; the upper part of the figure shows the course of maternal behavior, which consists of nursing, retrieving, and nestbuilding behavior. The lower part of the figure shows a schedule of pup development; the items are grouped as the appearance of the pups, their locomotion, sensory capacities, feeding behavior, and social behaviors of grooming and playing. We shall have occasion to refer to this figure when we present the results of our studies, now we shall describe only the main outline of the mother-young relationship in this animal.

Elements of maternal behavior first appear during parturition in the nestbuilding activity and retrieving behavior of the mother in the intervals between deliveries; occasionally nursing is also seen but

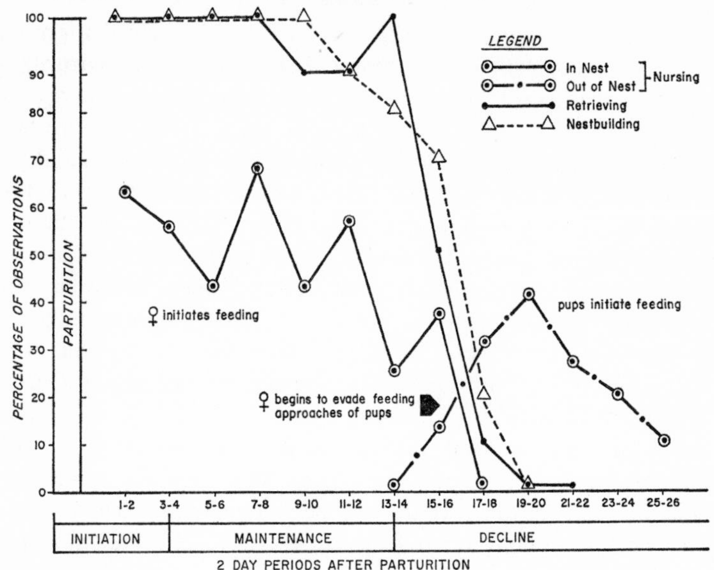

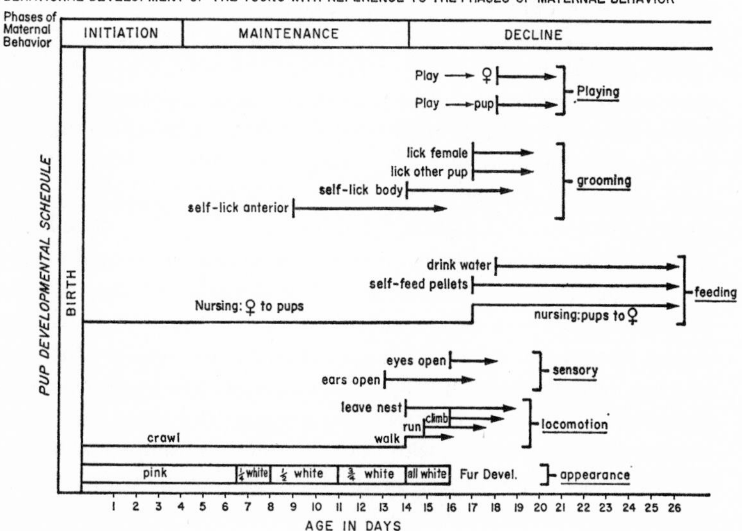

FIG. 4

Summary of observations of maternal behavior (upper graph) and pup development (lower graph) of five litters of laboratory rats during the four-week litter period. Maternal nestbuilding, retrieving, and nursing behavior are shown in relation to changes in the physical and behavioral characteristics of the pups.

continual activity of the mother, involved in delivering the fetuses, prevents nursing from occurring very often. At the end of parturition the mother gathers her pups together in the nest, rebuilds and repairs the nest, and settles in it with her pups, providing the first opportunity for the pups to engage in a long nursing session. This period and the period of several days after parturition we have called the period of initiation of the maternal-young relationship for reasons that will become apparent later in the paper. For the first two weeks maternal behavior appears regularly whenever the appropriate conditions arise in the litter situation. Nursing is regularly initiated by the mother as she enters the nest, licks the pups, thereby arousing them, then crouches over them until they attach to nipples and suckle. During nursing the mother settles her body over the litter and appears to sleep while being suckled. Changes in feeding behavior appear towards the end of the second week: the approach of the mother is a signal for the pups to crowd towards her and before she has crouched over them the young often have begun to suckle. The two-week period of maternal-young relationship following this initial period we have called the maintenance period.

During the first week the young are pink in appearance, but during the next week, as fur covers the body, they gradually take on the characteristic white color. They are without sight or hearing until the end of the second week, relying mainly upon contact stimulation; huddling is prominent providing them with a source of comfort and as an aid in thermoregulation. During the first two weeks the pups are together nearly all the time. Not until the end of the second week are the pups able to walk; before then they are able to crawl moving along a cage wall for some distance from the nest. It is rare however for pups to leave the nest before the twelfth to fourteenth day. Improvements are seen in suckling during this period: the pups respond more readily to the approach of the mother and they locate and grasp a nipple more rapidly.

After the second week the mother-relationship rapidly undergoes a change. There is a decline in nestbuilding, retrieving, and nursing on the part of the mother. In the young changes signalling the beginning of weaning occur; there is an increase in individually initiated social behavior among littermates and a general advance in independent functioning. These developments are exemplified in the change in nursing-suckling behavior at this time: increasingly, feedings are initiated by the pups who approach the female outside the nest, burrow under her body, attach to nipples and suckle while the mother simply adjusts her position to permit nursing. In the laboratory weakening of the mother-young relationship, and decline of maternal behavior starts around the second week and is completed before the end of the fourth week. In the field Calhoun (1953) assigns a later age to decline in this relationship among wild rats, noting that the mother and young remain together for about five weeks in all, until the litter emerges from the underground nest and the family group disperses.

Our studies were aimed at determining the basis of synchrony in the behavioral relationship between the mother and offspring during the principal periods of this relationship. These periods are the onset or initiation of the relationship at and shortly after parturition, the two-week maintenance period, and the period of decline in the relationship after the second week. We found that the most feasible way of analysing the mother-young relationship was through a study of the maternal behavior cycle of the mother. Our studies therefore were largely concerned with the effects of the offspring at different age-periods on the maternal behavior cycle of the female.

Studies on Maternal Behavior in the Rat

A. *The maternal behavior cycle*

The observational study described above, indicating a synchronous development of maternal behavior and growth and development of the offspring, is the basis for the studies that we carried out and upon which we shall report. It is evident that the mother undergoes changes in her behavior towards the young during the three- to four-week period of maternal care. Any characterization of these changes, beyond a simple description, already assumes that the basis for these changes is known. In fact, little is known about either the underlying causes of these behavioral changes or the physiological conditions which accompany them. It seemed wise, therefore, as a first step, to determine if the changes in the mother's behavior, during the maternal behavior cycle, are a function, simply, of the obvious changes that occur in the stimulus characteristics of the young in the course of their physical and behavioral development. The infantile characteristics of the offspring may serve to elicit maternal behavior early in the lactation period and their gradual disappearance after the second week may be the basis for the gradual disappearance of maternal behavior. If this were the case we would expect that mothers, presented with infant young, would continue to display maternal behavior at a time when they were no longer exhibiting maternal behavior towards their own pups. Our first study was undertaken to determine if this were the case and the procedure we followed was as we have just described.

Nine primiparous mothers were studied for the ability of 5- to 10-day-old pups to elicit nursing, retrieving, and nestbuilding during the four-week litter period. Each mother was observed daily with her own litter, which she continued to rear throughout the study, then with a litter of five pups of the above age, that was substituted for her own litter during a two-hour period. The nursing test consisted of placing the test pups (5 to 10 days of age) at the nest site one hour after the mother had been separated from her own pups, and the test pups had been removed from their mother. After the completion of the nursing test the pups were placed in the corner diagonally opposite from the nest and the female was released to retrieve them back to the nest. Following this the nest was removed from the cage, the pups were placed at the nest site, and the female was allowed one hour in which to collect nest material (i.e. hay and wood shavings) from bins attached to the cage wall.

We shall present data taken from the observations of nursing, the records of retrieving and the condition of the nest on the morning following the nestbuilding test. Mothers were scored as nursing if the pups remained attached to nipples for five minutes or longer; in the case of non-lactating mothers, which was a condition pertaining to studies we shall describe later, nursing was scored if the mother held the nursing posture over the pups for the same length of time. Mothers were scored as retrieving if the five pups were returned to the vicinity of the nest and nestbuilding was scored if a recognizable nest was present.

Five- to ten-day-old pups were used in the tests because of their ability to elicit maternal behavior and to respond rapidly to females that attempt to nurse them. Equally important was their inability to initiate feeding by approaching the mother at a distance, a situation that would have obscured the mother's contribution to nursing. Pups of this age remain relatively immobile when placed as a group on a cage floor, therefore they are very suitable for retrieving and nest-building tests. We have not found any instances in which mothers consistently or even occasionally refused to nurse or retrieve, or on the other hand attacked, alien pups of this age despite the fact that

Beach & Jaynes (1956a) have demonstrated the mother is able to distinguish alien pups from her own offspring at this age.

Using these procedures we were able to take daily samples of the responses of the mothers to the infant test young for comparison with their responses to the entire range of stimuli offered at different ages by their own young. Our purpose was to discover if their responses to the test young followed a course that was markedly different from the course of their responses to their own young.

The test results with the 5- to 10-day-old pups are shown in Figure 5 for comparison with observations of maternal behavior in

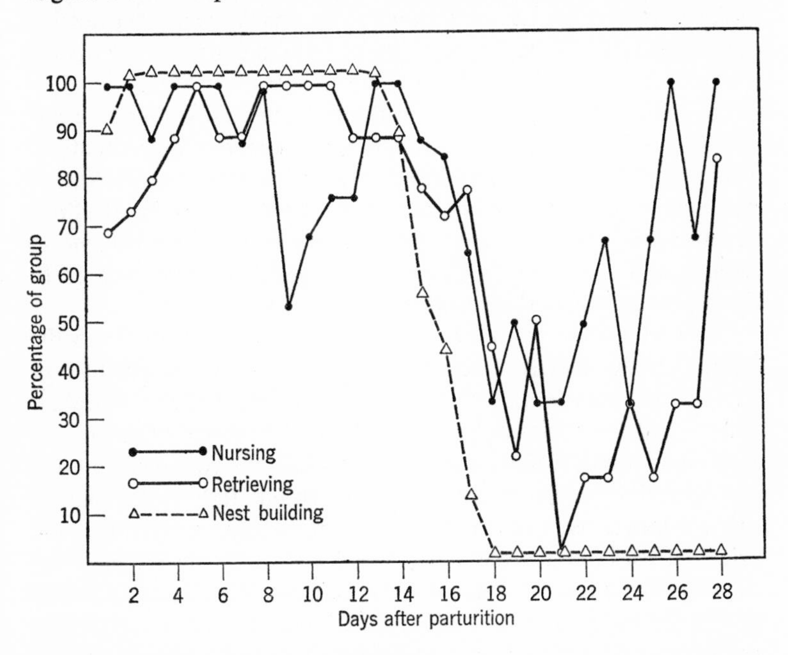

FIG. 5

The cycle of maternal behavior in the female rat rearing its own young from the 1*st to* 28*th day after parturition. Graph shows the percentage of the group of mothers that nursed and retrieved standard test young* (5 *to* 10 *days of age*) *and built nests each day* ($N=9$).

the litter situation shown in Figure 4. The cyclical character of maternal behavior in the tests follows within a day or two, a similar cycle of maternal behavior in the litter. Nestbuilding declined rapidly in both situations between the thirteenth and eighteenth day. Retrieving declined to below 70 per cent of the group after the fifteenth and sixteenth days in the litter situation compared with a similar decline after the seventeenth day in the test situation. The decline of nursing to below 40 per cent of the mothers in the test situation corresponded not so much to a decline of all nursing in the litter situation but rather to a decline of nursings initiated by the mother. After the fifteenth and sixteenth days, in the litter situation, the females less frequently entered the nest to initiate nursing; at about the same time nursing declined in the test situation and the decline was accelerated after the seventeenth day. With the decline of female-initiated nursing the offspring began to approach the mother outside the nest and initiate feeding sessions, a situation that was not possible for the 5- to 10-day-old pups used in the tests.

The maternal behavior cycle in the test situation is therefore not markedly different from that which appears in the litter situation. There are differences consisting of a short delay in the decline of nestbuilding and retrieving in the test situation compared to the litter situation, and those which arise from the more advanced behavioral capacities of the mother's offspring at 3 weeks of age compared to those of the 5- to 10-day-old pups used in the tests.

Our findings are contrary to the hypothesis stated earlier to the effect that the maternal behavior cycle was simply a product of stimulus changes in the young and the different effects of infant stimuli and later stimuli on the elicitation of maternal responses. Although stimuli from the 5- to 10-day-old pups elicit nestbuilding and retrieving from mothers for a short period after these responses can no longer be elicited by their own young, nevertheless the principal basis for the maternal behavior cycle lies in the *maternal condition* of the female. This condition changes as the lactation period progresses and towards the middle of the third week the mother is not only non-maternal to her own young, she also does not respond maternally to 5- to 10-day-old pups.

We have found that the conceptual distinction of the *maternal condition* and the *maternal behavior* of the female is a useful one in the analysis of the synchronous development of the mother-young relationship. It emphasizes, on the mother's part, the separate contribution of her psycho-physiological condition to the mother-young relationship, which on the part of the young is represented by behavioral changes and physical maturation.

Our findings indicate that for a large part of the cycle, maternal behavior in the litter situation fairly well represents the maternal condition of the mother as determined by her responses to the test pups. At the end of the cycle, however, the maternal responses in the litter diverge from the maternal condition indicated in the tests. In Figure 5 there is shown a rise in the percentage of mothers that began to nurse and retrieve the test pups during the fourth week. This revival of maternal behavior after it had already declined shortly before occurred only in the test situation and solely with respect to these maternal behaviors; no such revival was shown in the litter situation. The most we can say at present concerning this unusual revival of maternal behavior is that it was not due to the induction of pseudopregnancy by suckling since all of the females were undergoing regular estrous cycles by this time.

B. *Origin of the maternal behavior cycle*

What is the origin of the maternal behavior cycle? We have approached this problem in two ways; the first approach is represented in the study described above in which we traced the course of the cycle in relation to the development of the offspring. There is no basis for assuming, however, that the maternal behavior cycle or the maternal condition underlying it follows in detail the development of the young. The female's maternal condition may develop before the young are born, that is, during pregnancy; since the young are not yet present to elicit the various components of maternal behavior, the mother may give no evidence of the fact that she is maternally responsive. Our next experiment therefore examined the female's responsiveness to young during pregnancy in an attempt to determine the beginning of the maternal behavior cycle.

Our second approach to the origin of the maternal behavior cycle was to study the conditions under which the cycle appeared. The general hypothesis guiding our work led us to study first the relationship between the mother and the young. By interfering either with the development or the maintenance of this relationship, we hoped to discover the degree to which the maternal behavior cycle is dependent upon stimulation that the mother receives from her offspring. In this section we shall describe several studies which pursued this idea.

The beginning of the maternal behavior cycle was studied by testing seventeen pregnant females for their maternal responses to 5- to 10-day-old young. Females were tested on alternate days starting at the eleventh day before parturition. Tests were made on alternate days for each half of the group in order not to unduly influence the course of pregnancy by the test procedure.

The results of testing females during pregnancy are shown in Figure 6. They show that nursing and retrieving cannot be elicited

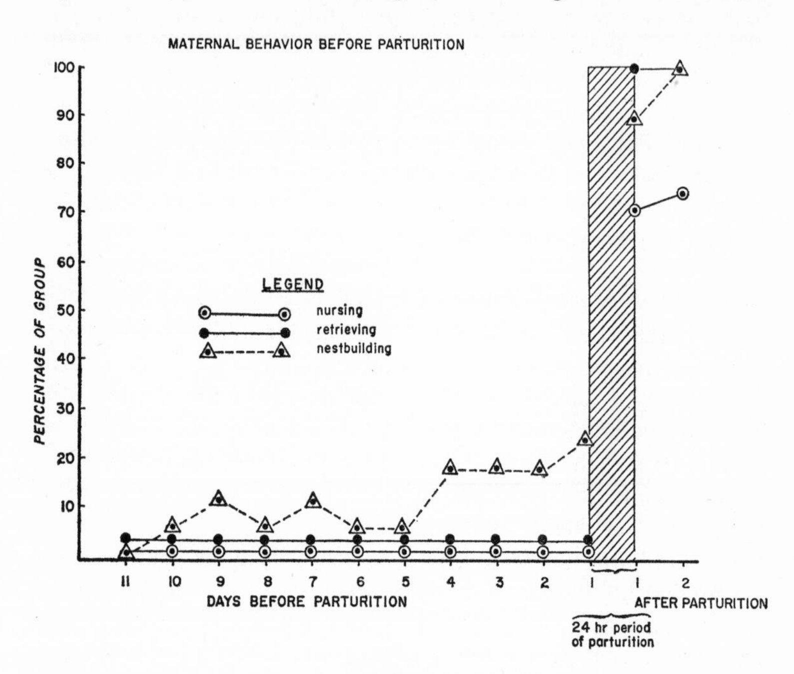

FIG. 6

Maternal behavior before parturition. Graphs show the percentage of a group of seventeen pregnant females that nursed and retrieved test young and built nests during the eleven days before parturition and the first two days after parturition.

from females before parturition: neither component of maternal behavior appeared in more than 100 tests between the eleventh day prepartum and delivery of the young. Shortly after parturition, however, both behaviors appeared in nearly all of the females. Nest-building was exhibited by an occasional female before parturition but for the most part nests were not built until parturition had begun or was completed.

The beginning of the maternal behavior cycle therefore coincides with the appearance of the young. This is not to say, however, that the young initiate the cycle by stimulating the female during parturition. At present we do not know if this is the case, or whether the process of parturition itself produces physiological changes and involves behavioral events which initiate the cycle. I might say that we have begun studies on this problem.

In view of these findings that the maternal behavior cycle begins during and immediately after the delivery of the young it seemed worth while to determine whether or not the further development of the cycle in the female is dependent upon continued contact with the young.

Six females were observed during parturition and their pups were removed after the mother had cleaned them, severed the umbilical cord and eaten the placenta. Nursing was not allowed. The mothers remained alone in their cages for a week then were given their first tests of nursing, retrieving and nestbuilding, using our usual test stimuli – 5- to 10-day-old young. Until the end of the fourth week, these tests were repeated at weekly intervals. As controls, mothers whose litters remained with them were tested at the same intervals.

The solid lines in Figure 7 show the results for the mothers without young and the broken lines present the results for the females that were allowed to rear their young. Estimates of nestbuilding could be made daily since it required only that the condition of the nest be scored each morning.

The group of mothers without young was clearly less maternal than the control group. Fewer of these mothers nursed or retrieved the test young at the first testing on the sixth day and on every testing thereafter. Nestbuilding also declined rapidly when the young were removed at parturition. The performance of the control group, tested once a week was similar to that of mothers tested daily (see Figure 5) for the corresponding days of the maternal behavior cycle.

An important condition for the appearance of the maternal behavior cycle therefore is contact between the mother and her young. Preventing the mother from receiving stimulation from the young prevents the cycle from developing. We can see now that in our initial study the mother's responsiveness to the test young (i.e. 5- to 10-day-old pups) was a product of the stimulation she received from her own pups in the litter situation. At this point we can say the maternal behavior cycle is not the product of processes unfolding endogenously in sequence; maternal processes in the mother are dependent upon stimulation from the offspring from an early period of the cycle.

This experiment stimulated our interest to study the onset of the maternal behavior cycle in greater detail for two reasons. First the greater part of the effect on the mother of removing the pups at parturition was already completed by the end of the first week. The effect may have been gradual, however, and if so, it would indicate that, while the offspring are necessary to maintain maternal behavior over a long period, over a short period the female may remain maternal without receiving stimulation from her pups.

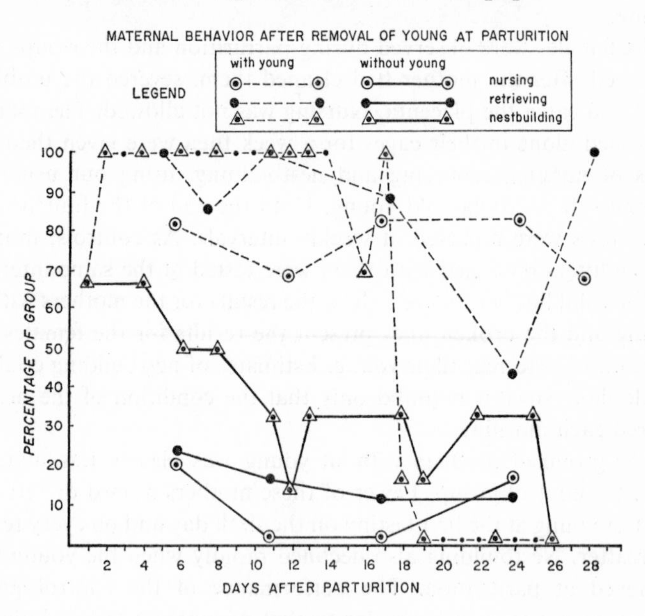

FIG. 7

Maternal responsiveness to standard test young of mothers whose young were removed at birth compared with that of mothers whose young remained with them. Nursing and retrieving were tested weekly; nestbuilding was tested approximately daily (N=6 per group).

Our second reason supports the first. Studies have shown that mothers delivered by Caesarean section, having no contact with their offspring during parturition, are nevertheless maternal towards the pups almost immediately (Wiesner & Sheard, 1933; Labriola, 1953). This would indicate that contact with the young during parturition is not crucial for the development of maternal behavior. According to this view maternal behavior arises from the physiological changes accompanying parturition. If this is true, then removal of the young at parturition does not interfere with the onset of maternal behavior and the maternal condition underlying it, but it prevents this condition from being maintained and developing further. We should therefore be able to trace the decline of the maternal condition established during parturition in females whose young are removed at parturition.

The procedure was to remove pups from mothers during parturition, as in the previous study. One group of nine mothers was given test pups for the first time after two days postpartum (i.e. 60 hours postpartum) and a second group of eight mothers had pups returned to them for the first time after four days (i.e. 108 hours postpartum). The mothers were tested for nursing, retrieving, and nestbuilding behavior, then a litter of five test pups was left with each mother to see if the mother could rear them. A control group consisted of nine mothers rearing their offspring starting at parturition.

As we had anticipated, maternal behavior did not disappear immediately after removal of the young at parturition. As Figure 8 shows, after two days without young, on the morning of the third day, one-third of the mothers adopted a nursing posture over the test pups, a smaller percentage retrieved the young, and about 40 per cent built nests. Compared to the mothers that were rearing their pups, nearly all of which exhibited all three components of maternal behavior in the tests, in the mothers without young for sixty hours starting at parturition a significant decline in maternal responsiveness had occurred. After four days without young, none of the mothers nursed or retrieved the test young; nestbuilding, however, remained at about 40 per cent of the group, as in the first group of mothers.

We cannot say that maternal behavior arises endogenously at parturition since the mothers were permitted to clean the pups and eat the placentas during delivery. But, allowing for this amount and kind of contact, the maternal condition that was produced waned slowly over the following days. The decline in maternal behavior was undoubtedly due to the absence of stimulation from pups. We can say, therefore, that however maternal behavior arises at parturition, its further maintenance is dependent upon stimulation from the offspring.

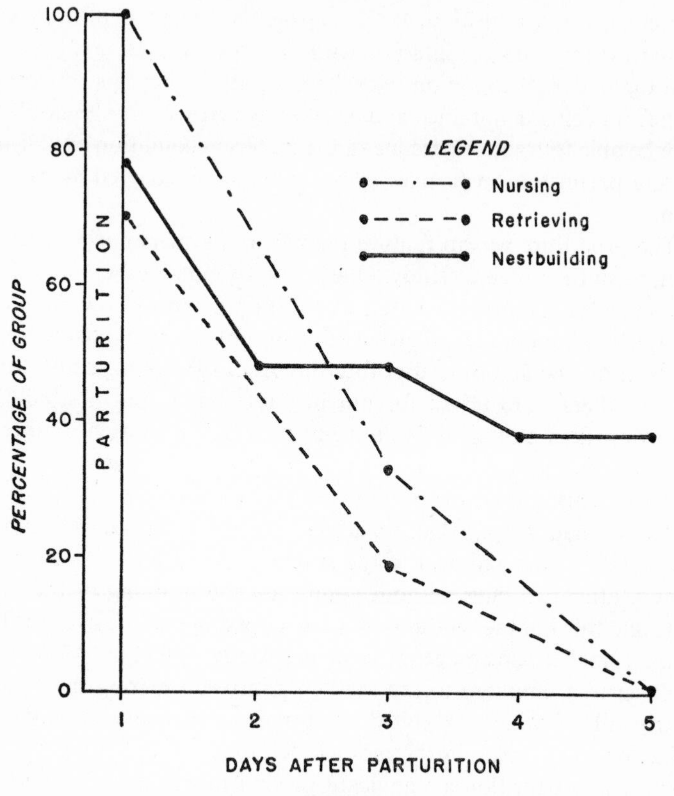

FIG. 8

Maternal responses to test young of two groups of mothers whose young were removed at parturition. Graph shows the percentage of each group that nursed and retrieved test young and built nests. One group was tested 60 *hrs. and the other* 108 *hrs. after parturition* ($N=9$ *and* 8).

It will be recalled that in addition to tests of maternal behavior the mothers whose litters were removed at parturition were given litters to rear, consisting of five pups, 5 to 10 days of age. They were tested for maternal behavior again after twenty-four hours and thereafter they were observed periodically for evidence of maternal care. The condition of the pups was watched carefully and the mothers were observed for the reappearance of estrous cycles. The premature resumption of estrous cycling under these conditions is an indication that no nursing is occurring and that the female has returned to a non-maternal condition.

The results of this part of the study will be summarized briefly. Among the mothers that had been without young for two days following parturition, those who had exhibited maternal behavior in the first test were joined by several others that had been stimulated to maternal behavior by their adopted litters, and a total of 50 to 65 per cent of the group exhibited maternal behavior within four days of receiving the litters. The adopted litters were entirely responsible for the appearance of nursing and retrieving behavior in 40 per cent and nestbuilding in 60 per cent of the mothers that had been without young for the first four postpartum days.

In both groups, however, the maternal behavior induced by the adopted litters was not maintained. After four days, mothers of the first group (two days without young) began to decline in maternal behavior and by the eighth day after receiving young, only two mothers were still showing maternal behavior. These two mothers reared their litters through the suckling period. The decline of maternal behavior was more rapid in the second group, beginning two days after the mothers received litters. By the fifth day these mothers were no longer maternal and all the litters had died.

We are not in a position to say what would have happened had the adopted litters been replaced with fresh pups each day. As it was, only two mothers began to lactate as a result of suckling by the pups, and the pups of all the other litters gradually grew weak and died. A large proportion of the mothers resumed estrous cycling while tending the adopted litters, and others began cycling shortly after the litters died.

The effects of the two- or four-day initial period without young was not overcome by giving litters to mothers at the end of these periods. This raises an important point since normally the appearance of pups at parturition and the beginning of suckling is sufficient to maintain the female's maternal condition. At parturition the mother is not only highly responsive to the eliciting stimuli provided by the young, in response to which she nurses, retrieves, nestbuilds and performs other maternal activities, she is also maximally receptive with respect to the effect of the young on her maternal condition. Delaying the beginning of contact with young by two or four days produced changes that reduced the female's responsiveness to the young and also lowered her receptivity to them.

This dual expression of effects produced by removing young at parturition, which may in fact have been a single change in the mother exhibited in two different ways, started us thinking whether these effects were particularly related to removal of young at parturition. Would similar changes occur if young were removed from mothers for four days at other times during the maternal behavior cycle? The following study was undertaken to answer this question.

Three groups of five or six mothers each were allowed to rear their young to 3, 9, or 14 days of age. Then the young were removed and the mothers were left alone for a period of four days corresponding to the interval that the mothers whose young were removed at parturition were left without their offspring. At the end of this period the mothers were tested for nursing, retrieving, and nestbuilding with 5- to 10-day-old pups and were given a litter of five of these pups to rear.

When the separation occurred at parturition, as we have already seen, none of the mothers displayed nursing or retrieving and only a small percentage built nests on the morning of the fifth day (Figure 9, *a*). When the litters were removed on the third, ninth, or fourteenth day, four days later nursing was shown by 60 to 75 per cent of the mothers and retrieving responses by 40 to 75 per cent (Figure 9, *b*, *c*, *d*). In all four groups, however, nestbuilding declined to equally low levels.

In addition to the greater retention of maternal responsiveness over the four-day period without young, the mothers whose litters had been removed later in the litter period, also showed greater receptivity to the effects of the young. Maternal behavior was restored to its previous level in all the mothers and the mothers resumed maternal care of their adopted litters. The maternal behavior cycle went on to completion and all of the pups were carried through to weaning successfully.

The effects on maternal behavior of a four-day period without young starting at parturition are much greater than the effects of a similar period without young starting later in the maternal behavior cycle. Interference with the onset of maternal behavior produces changes in the mother which apparently are irreversible while interference with a well-established maternal condition produces changes from which the mother can recover. Maternal behavior is fully restored after the young are returned.

It will be recalled that we set out to study the origin of the maternal behavior cycle in the sense of when does it begin, and what are the conditions necessary for the cycle to appear. The cycle begins at parturition; very likely both the physiological changes and the behavioral events of parturition contribute to the development of the female's maternal condition. Once this condition is established, however, it rapidly wanes if the young are removed. The mother is dependent upon the young for the maintenance and further development of her maternal condition. She is much more affected by the removal of her young at parturition than at later periods of the cycle when maternal behavior is well established. We are led to conclude that the processes involved in the development of maternal behavior at parturition and immediately afterwards are different from those involved in its maintenance at a later time. Since both are dependent upon the female's maternal condition, this indicates that different processes are involved at various times during the maternal behavior cycle.

C. *The decline of maternal behavior*

What can we say about the decline of maternal behavior? In our studies as well as under natural conditions (Calhoun, 1963), maternal behavior declines while the young are still with the mother. The decline occurs with respect to 5- to 10-day-old pups as well as 3-week-old pups, therefore it cannot be attributed solely to the stimulus characteristics of the pups. Furthermore, although we implied earlier that the entire maternal behavior cycle arose from the effects of the pups upon the mother, this conclusion could not validly be drawn from studies on the effects of permanent removal of young at parturition. Since removal of the newly born pups prevented development of early phases of the maternal behavior cycle, later phases were naturally precluded from appearing.

Our next study was undertaken to determine whether a decline in maternal behavior could be produced by removing the litter. Previous studies (Wiesner & Sheard, 1933; Bruce, 1961) showing that the decline of maternal behavior may be *prevented* by replacing grown litters with pups less than a week old led us to believe that the declining phase of maternal behavior, like the onset and to a lesser extent the maintenance phase, is in some way dependent upon the offspring.

Two groups of ten mothers each were allowed to rear their young until the ninth and fourteenth day. The litters were then permanently

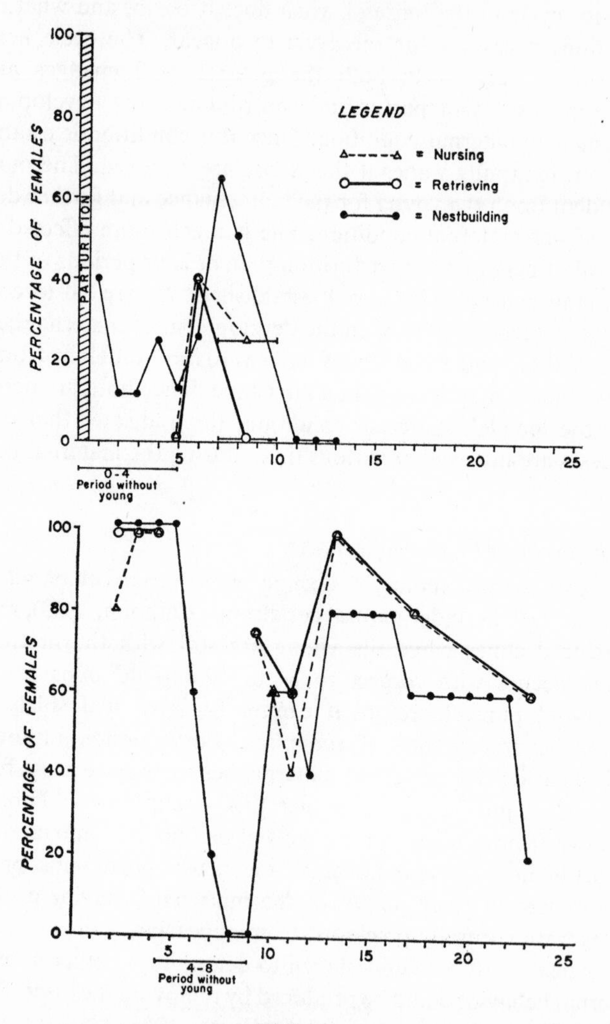

FIG. 9

Maternal responses to test young of mothers whose litters were removed for four days at various times during the four-week litter period: upper left; litter removed at birth; lower left, litter removed on the 4th day; post partum; upper right, litter removed on the 10*th day post-*

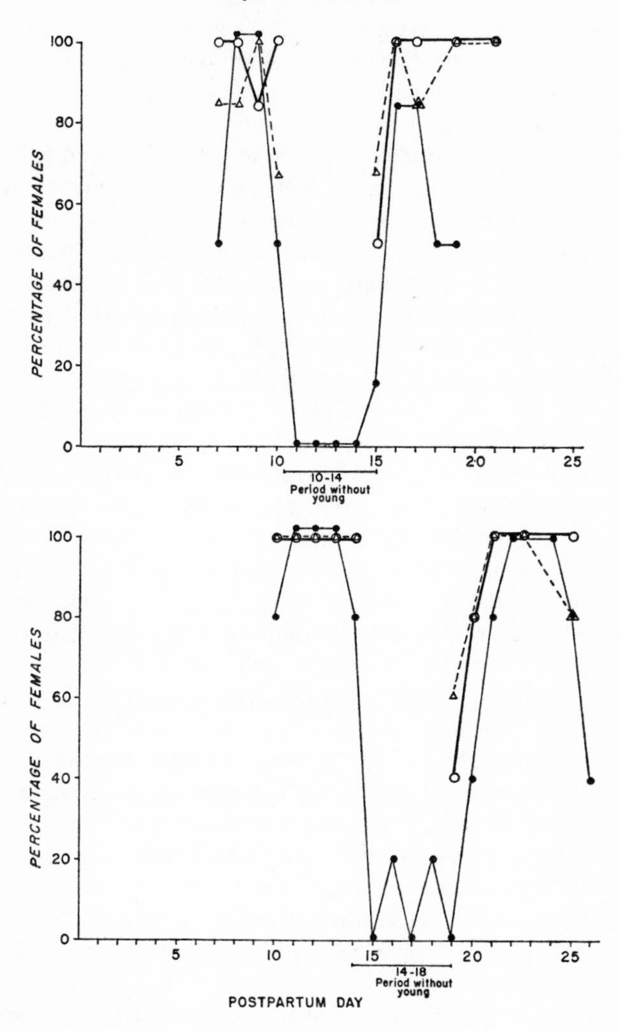

FIG. 9 (*continued*)

partum; lower right, litter removed on the 14*th day postpartum. Litters of* 5- *to* 10-*day old pups were returned to mothers at the end of four days.* (*N*=5 *to* 8 *mothers*).

removed and the mothers were tested for their maternal responses to 5- to 10-day-old pups. Each group of ten mothers was divided into two groups of five and tested on alternate days in order to minimize the effects of the tests.

The results of this study are shown in Figure 10 *a* and *b*. The test performances of mothers whose litters were permanently removed on the ninth and fourteenth days are compared with those of mothers whose litters remained with them until weaning. The effect of removing litters on the ninth day was to produce an immediate decline in the number of mothers that nursed and retrieved the test young and built nests (Figure 10, *a*). By the tenth day nestbuilding had already declined to a low level that was only reached by mothers with young by seventeenth and eighteenth days. By the fifteenth and sixteenth days nursing had declined to a level that was characteristic of mothers with young on their seventeenth and eighteenth day. Retrieving declined almost immediately to a level that was not reached by the mothers with young until the nineteenth and twentieth days. Removal of the litters on the ninth day, therefore, had the effect of speeding up the decline of maternal behavior by about one week compared to the rate at which maternal behavior declined when the young were present. It is quite clear then that the decline of maternal behavior is related to removal of the litter; removal on the ninth day precipitates a premature decline of maternal behavior.

The permanent removal of the litters on the fourteenth day had the same general effect of producing a decline of maternal behavior (Figure 10, *b*). However, since there is a general decline in maternal behavior at this time among mothers with litters we are able to compare the effects of permanently removing litters with the natural decline which occurs when litters are present. Removal speeded up the decline of nestbuilding but had little effect in accelerating the decline in nursing.

What is most interesting is that the decline of retrieving behavior was slowed by removing the litters on the fourteenth day. The initial decline in retrieving, following litter removal, did not continue. After the initial effect of litter removal there appears to have been stabilization of retrieving among the mothers without litters, while, among mothers with young, retrieving continued to decline to the low level shown on the twenty-second and twenty-third days.

One prevalent theory is that maternal behavior declines as a result of the gradual disappearance from the young of stimuli which elicit

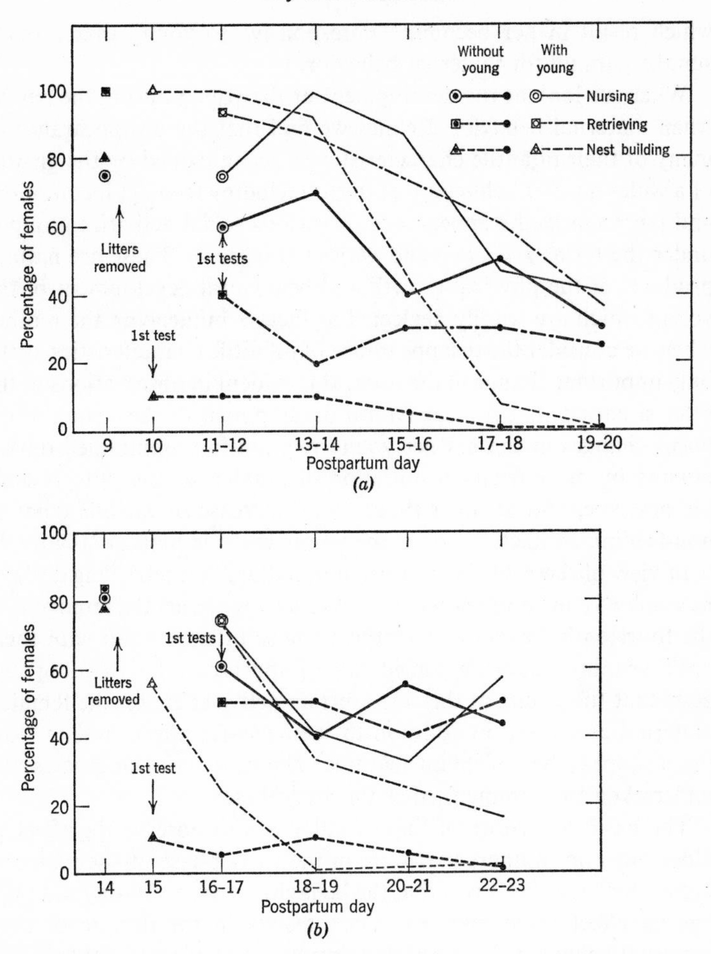

FIG. 10

Decline of maternal responsiveness to standard stimulus pups after permanent removal of the mother's litter compared with decline of maternal responsiveness in mothers kept with their young. Upper graph: litters removed at 9th day postpartum; lower graph: litters removed at 14th day postpartum (N = 10 per group).

maternal responses from the mother. While this theory might account for the failure of 3-week-old young to elicit maternal behavior it cannot account for the failure of the mother to respond to our test young. The issue then is what produces the changes in the mother which result in her becoming unresponsive to young that provide suitable stimuli for maternal behavior.

When we look at the development of the young during the period when maternal behavior declines we find that the disappearance of many of their infantile characteristics is accompanied by the growth of a wide range of behavioral patterns including feeding, locomotion, and particularly the appearance of various social activities grouped under the terms *grooming* and *playing* (Figure 4). These are natural products of the physical growth and behavioral development of the young which are wholly neglected as factors influencing the mother when we consider the disappearance of infantile characteristics as the only important change in the litter. It is evident in observations of the litter situation that the behavioral development of the young introduces changes in the mother-young relationship exemplified during nursing by more frequent initiation of nursing by the pups outside the nest site, and at other times by an increase in various types of non-feeding contacts between the young and the mother (Figure 4).

In view of these considerations, our finding, that retrieving declines more slowly in mothers whose litters are permanently removed on the fourteenth day than in mothers whose litters remain with them until weaning, takes on considerable importance. This finding suggests that the young at this age exert an active effect on the female's maternal condition, in addition to their passive effect, arising from the disappearance of infant features. The next series of studies was undertaken to examine further this hypotheses.

The basic procedure of these studies was to observe the effect of older pups on mothers that were in the early phase of the maternal cycle. Our hypothesis was that the behavior of 14- to 19-day-old pups has an effect upon mothers which results in the decline of their maternal behavior. As in previous studies tests of maternal behavior were made using 5- to 10-day-old pups.

In our first study litters of 11-day-old pups were given to six mothers that were in their third day postpartum in place of the mothers' own litters. Our intention was to allow the mother and adopted pups three days to adjust to one another before the pups, then 14 days of age, would begin to exert the effects which we anticipated. The mother would then be in her seventh postpartum day and if the effects of the older pups' required several days to appear, the mothers would begin to show a decline in maternal behavior around the tenth day which would be well in advance of the time when mothers rearing their own litters begin to show a decline in maternal behavior.

Contrary to our expectations, the older pups caused only a slight and even questionable acceleration in the decline of maternal behavior of their foster mothers. Nestbuilding declined two days earlier than usual (Figure 11) but nursing and retrieving reactions declined at the usual time.

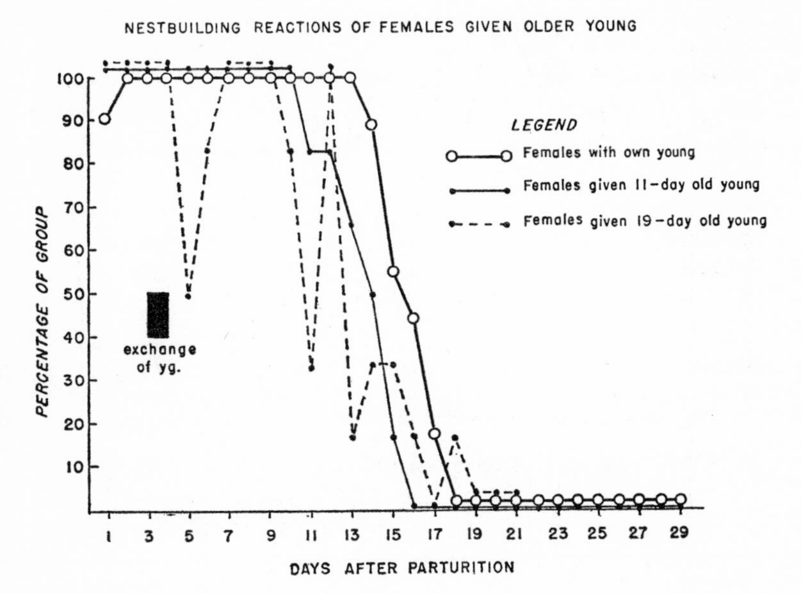

FIG. 11

Decline in nestbuilding in mothers given older young in exchange for their own litters on the 3rd or 4th day post-partum compared with decline in nestbuilding in mothers kept with their own young. (*N*=6 *to* 9 *per group*).

What we had neglected to take into account was the effect of the mothers upon the development of the 11-day-old pups. When they were first placed with the mothers these pups were beginning to crawl out of the nest, but the foster mothers, unlike their own mothers, retrieved them back to the nest each time they left it. This situation continued for the next few days until the pups either did not leave the nest or upon leaving it, ran back to it each time the mother approached. At 16 and 17 days of age when pups normally wander freely around the cage, these pups remained huddled at the nest site and only rarely exhibited normal behavior for their age. In effect, the foster mothers had so influenced the development of the adopted pups that the mothers in turn were not receiving stimulation typical of 2½-week-old pups.

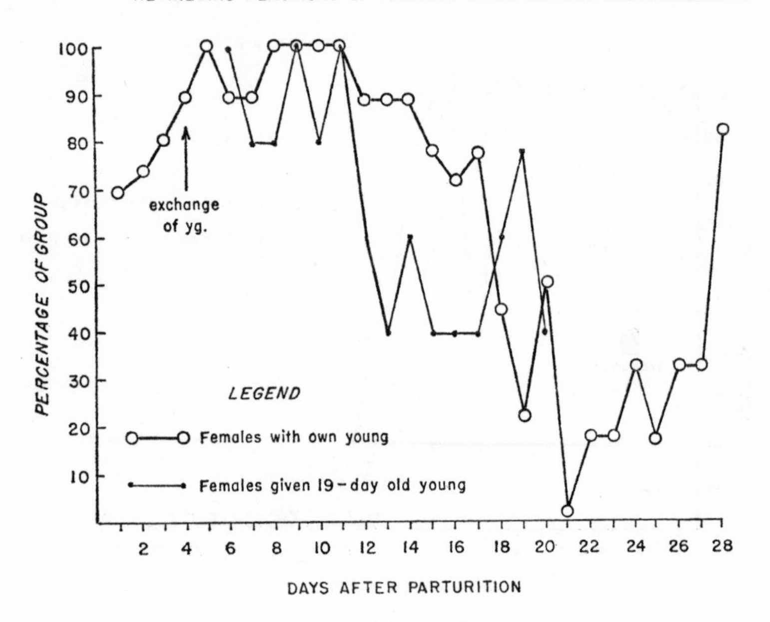

FIG. 12

Decline of retrieving responses to test young in mothers given older young in exchange for their own young on the 4th day postpartum compared with decline of retrieving responses in mothers kept with their own young (N=6 to 9 per group).

To avoid a repetition of this situation 19-day-old pups were used in the second study. The mothers' own litters were removed on the fourth day and replaced by the older pups. Tests of maternal behavior using 5- to 10-day-old pups were made each day.

In view of the age of the adopted pups, the decline of maternal behavior which we sought should have occurred shortly after the exchange of the older pups for the mothers' own pups. This was not the case, however. Nursing responses to the test young were unaffected and the effect on retrieving and nestbuilding was somewhat ambiguous. Nestbuilding was erratic from day to day but it showed a general decline after the ninth postpartum day (Figure 11). Retrieving declined in 40 to 60 per cent of the mothers after the eleventh day postpartum, however the remaining animals continued to retrieve the test pups for as long as did the mothers that were rearing their own young (Figure 12).

The results of these two studies are in no way conclusive. At best they are suggestive that age-conditioned changes in the behavior of pups influence the decline of maternal behavior. The influence of the older pups on the mother in our studies was very likely attenuated by two factors: changes in pup behavior resulting from the maternal behavior of the foster mother which differed from that of their own mother and, secondly, the importance of the period that had elapsed since parturition, on the maternal condition of the mother.

Discussion

Our studies indicate that synchrony in the behavioral interaction between the mother and offspring arises from the effects of the young, at different ages, on the *maternal condition* of the female. The evidence for and significance of this conclusion will be discussed in this section.

A. *Onset and maintenance of mother-young interaction*

Our studies have shown that when the litter is removed during parturition the rat mother does not undergo the maternal behavior cycle. Moreover, maternal behavior declines rapidly and the female's maternal condition, developed during pregnancy and parturition, wanes. Four days after the removal of the litter maternal responses to 5- to 10-day-old pups have disappeared and waning of the maternal condition has progressed to the point where it cannot be restored, except temporarily in a few animals, by giving new litters to the mothers.

The studies indicate, therefore, that during the initial contacts between the mother and offspring, immediately after parturition, the young begin to exert an influence upon the mother, initiating the pattern of synchronized changes that is maintained until after weaning.

In describing the mother's contribution to the maternal-young relationship as based upon her maternal condition we mean to imply a condition in the female which, on the one hand has a basis in a special physiological state and on the other hand, gives rise to a motivational condition summarized by the phrase - readiness to respond maternally to pups. The hormonal basis of maternal behavior in birds and mammals in general has recently been reviewed by Lehrman (1961) and in the rat specifically by Rosenblatt & Lehrman (1963).

The endocrine basis of maternal behavior has not yet been established for any mammal. However, the many parallels that exist between maternal behavior and lactation have led to the belief that maternal behavior is an effect of prolactin, the hormone of the anterior pituitary gland which also stimulates milk production (e.g. Darling, 1937). To mention a few of these parallels, the onset of lactation and maternal behavior occur at parturition; both develop during the late stages of pregnancy. Lactation declines, as does the maternal condition, if the young are removed shortly after parturition. There is a striking similarity between the involutional changes in the mammary glands and the decline of maternal behavior in mothers whose young have been removed on the day of parturition (Cowie & Foley, 1961).

More specifically, the non-suckled mammary gland of the rat shows an initial period of reduction in vascularization of the alveoli, and unresponsiveness to intravenous injection of oxytocin up to the end of the third day, followed by further changes after this time. These further changes include collapse of the alveoli, the secretory structures of the mammary gland, which precludes restoration of lactation by suckling applied after the 110th hour following removal of the young (Silver, 1956).

As we have shown maternal behavior also declines in mothers whose young have been removed (see Figure 8) shortly after delivery. After 60 hours, 20 to 40 per cent of the mothers still nurse and retrieve pups, and maternal behavior can be restored temporarily in 50 to 65 per cent of the animals. A longer interval without young produces a greater decline in maternal behavior: after 108 hours, none of the mothers display nursing or retrieving. However, when they are given litters nursing and retrieving are restored, for a brief period, in about half the animals.

Paralleling the lactation study, the restoration of maternal behavior lasts longer in mothers that have been without young for two days than for four days; two mothers of the former group were able to rear their adopted litters through the weaning period.

A reasonable interpretation of these parallels between lactation and maternal behaviour is that suckling, by causing the release of prolactin, has the two effects of promoting lactation and maintaining the maternal condition of the mother. Removing the suckling stimulus leads to involutional changes in the mammary gland and waning of the maternal condition, both being the effects of prolactin withdrawal. To explain the fact that after 108 hours suckling restores maternal behavior in some mothers while it fails to restore lactation in any of them, we might suppose that the neural substrate of the maternal condition, unlike the glandular substrate of lactation, does not undergo structural changes when prolactin is withdrawn. When prolactin secretion is stimulated by the renewal of suckling, waning of the maternal condition is partially reversed in some mothers; involution of the mammary gland on the other hand has so altered the structure that prolactin no longer can reverse the process and lactation cannot be restored.

At the time the studies described in this report were presented there was no *direct* evidence that prolactin was involved in the maternal behavior of the rat. Recent attempts to *induce* maternal behavior in estrous cycling females by injections of prolactin, progesterone, estrogen or combinations of these hormones have resulted in failure (Beach & Wilson, 1963; Lott, 1962; Lott & Fuchs, 1962) despite earlier reports of success (Riddle, Lahr & Bates, 1942).

In studies we have conducted since that time, we have been able to *maintain* the maternal condition of mothers whose young were removed on the first day postpartum by injecting them with prolactin and oxytocin in doses similar to those previously used to maintain lactation under similar conditions. At the end of ten days of injections, mothers that were treated with these hormones, in 90 per cent of the cases, responded within twenty-four hours by displaying nursing behavior, retrieving and nestbuilding, although contrary to our expectations, lactation was not maintained. Mothers that were not treated with hormones during the ten-day period without young responded maternally in only 20 to 30 per cent of the cases. The study indicates that the treatment with prolactin and oxytocin prevented waning of the maternal condition.

Another problem in characterizing the factors which enter into the female's maternal condition is raised by the markedly different effects on this condition of a four-day period without young inserted immediately after parturition compared to one inserted three, nine or fourteen days after parturition. When litter removal occurred several days after parturition, the maternal condition waned less rapidly and could be restored more fully than when it occurred immediately after parturition. Therefore at parturition maintenance of the maternal condition is more dependent upon stimulation from young than at any time later in the maternal behavior cycle. We are led to consider what is different about the female's maternal condition in the beginning as compared with later in the maternal behavior cycle.

B. *Developmental approach versus the 'critical period' theory*

By focussing our attention on the female's maternal condition in the *early* postpartum period we run the risk of contributing to the current tendency to conceptualize any examination of early development in terms of the 'critical period' theory of Scott (1958, 1962). We have had the previous experience of having to extricate our work from the framework of this theory, with which we disagree (Schneirla & Rosenblatt, 1963), and for this reason we feel some remarks are necessary beforehand.

Our principal objection to the critical period theory is that it isolates one period of development from those which have preceded it and thus, rather than illuminating developmental processes, it either ignores them or deals with them solely in terms of maturational processes or gains (Scott, 1958, 1962). Further, because developments during the critical period are isolated from those during earlier periods by use of the concept of 'critical period' these developments cannot be properly understood. Although some regard is given to the role of experience, in the last analysis maturational processes are viewed as the principal basis for developmental gains. Thus neither experiential and maturational contributions to behavioral development nor developmental processes themselves are illuminated by this theory.

We can understand why investigators studying a variety of developmental phenomena such as early social attachment, neonatal emotionality, early learning, etc., have adopted the term 'critical period' as a descriptive one referring to the special effects that can occur during one period of development as against other periods. As an introductory concept it serves to focus attention on a 'sensitive' period (Hinde, 1962) in development and in this sense the concept can serve the heuristic value of suggesting an area of special research effort. Unfortunately, except with respect to a few areas, the use of the concept has often suggested that we already know what is the basis of the special sensitivity to influence during this period, namely, maturational changes, and this has served to discourage further study.

It is undoubtedly true that the series of events occurring at parturition and shortly after are critical for the development of the female's maternal condition, and on this basis, for the formation of the relationship between the mother and offspring. In recognition of this fact, we have previously referred to parturition as a *nodal* or *pivotal event* in the maternal behavior cycle (Rosenblatt & Lehrman, 1963). Physiologically parturition involves a shift in the regulation of maternal endocrine secretions from largely endogenous processes and a self-stimulative basis to regulation by external sources of stimulation (Rosenblatt & Lehrman, 1963; Young, 1961; Everett, 1961). During pregnancy ovarian hormones and pituitary gonadotrophins are secreted by the placenta, an organ that is relatively independent of regulation by the pituitary gland, and therefore of external stimuli. After parturition, with the loss of the placental source of hormones, the pituitary gland resumes regulation of gonadotrophin and ovarian secretion. Hypothalamic regulation of the pituitary gland allows external stimuli (e.g. from suckling) to play a role in the control of pituitary and ovarian endocrine activity.

Accompanying the physiological changes of parturition and the shift in regulation of endocrine activity is the onset of the female's maternal condition – the beginning of her readiness to respond to the pups. What is crucial about the early postparturitive period therefore is based upon these two processes – the shift in regulation of hormonal secretion from placental to pituitary gland control and development of the mother's responsiveness to pups.

On the basis of her initial responsiveness to the pups the mother makes contact with them during and immediately after parturition. In the course of contact, which involves licking the pups, crouching over them, mouthing them, carrying them to the nest (i.e. retrieving), and above all, nursing them, stimuli are provided which in turn regulate the secretory activity of the pituitary gland. Rothchild (1960) has shown that suckling has a dual effect on the hypothalamus and therefore on the pituitary gland. On the one hand it stimulates the secretion of prolactin, thereby promoting lactation and maintenance of corpora lutea, the progesterone-secreting structures of the ovary. On the other hand it prevents estrous cycling by maintaining the estrogen secreting structures of the ovary in a quiescent condition. As we have seen, prolactin secretion very likely forms the hormonal basis of the female's maternal condition; thus the initial maternal responsiveness of the postparturient female by bringing her into contact with the young, produces a feed-back effect, augmenting her maternal condition.

The crucial nature of stimulation from the litter immediately after parturition is directly related to the maintenance and development in the mother of the processes described above. Withholding this stimulation by removing the litter for a period of four days after parturition, returning them on the beginning of the fifth day, leads to changes which indicate a failure to maintain the mother's hormonal and behavioral condition. At the beginning of the fifth day the mother is initially unresponsive to the pups and estrous cycling is resumed or in the process of resuming (Rothchild, 1960). Pups left with the mother stimulate an increase in maternal responsiveness in some females, but there is a delay in the appearance of items of maternal behavior, and with the absence of lactation, contact between mother and adopted young is irregular and not sustained, lacking the trophallactic basis that nursing and suckling provide. Without feeding, the young begin to weaken and provide less than optimal stimulation to the mother. The final result is that after a brief rise in maternal behavior, within a few days there is a waning of the maternal condition and invariably the young die.

If they are viewed in terms of the 'critical period' theory the first four days after parturition are seen as a 'special' period; once it has passed it cannot be replaced by the following period. Viewed in terms of development it is precisely the changes in the mother occurring during the four-day period without young that diminish the effectiveness of the mother-young interaction on the fifth and following days compared to the interaction following immediately after parturition. Notwithstanding changes in the mother, it must be noted that failure of mother-young interaction to develop under the altered conditions is a result of the nature of the interaction on the fifth and succeeding days.

In a previous paper (Rosenblatt & Lehrman, 1963) we have traced some of the behavioral changes during pregnancy that contribute to the effectiveness of initial contacts with the young in establishing a bond between the mother and her offspring. The changes resulting in maternal nestbuilding are related to thermoregulatory mechanisms and to hormonal effects on contact sensitivity (Lehrman, 1961). The living space begins to be differentiated [or is further differentiated in wild rats (Calhoun, 1953)] into regions of greater or lesser disturbance to the pregnant female, the proximity of nesting material and food, and in accordance with environmental features that offer support for a nest, such as a corner, etc. Considerable progress towards the building of a nest occurs before parturition as shown by the female's construction of a resting mat late in pregnancy; the final stages in development of nestbuilding are dependent upon stimulation from the young (Sturman-Hulbe & Stone, 1929; Kinder, 1927; Riess, 1950, 1954; Eibl-Eibesfeldt, 1955).

Change in the female's orientation to her own body during pregnancy also contributes to her reactions when the young appear. In a study conducted by Lorraine L. Roth in our laboratory, we have found changes in the self-licking behavior of pregnant females during the last half of pregnancy (see Figure 13). As term approaches, the pregnant female begins to lick her nipple lines, anogenital and pelvic regions for longer periods and other regions of the body for shorter periods (Roth & Rosenblatt, 1964). After parturition there is a sharp drop in self-licking and in its place the female's licking activity is directed towards the pups, principally the pup's genital region.

Birch (1956) has suggested that self-licking of the genital region by the pregnant female provides the experiential basis for the initial actions of the mother towards the newly born fetuses. By raising females from weaning to the beginning of delivery in collars designed to prevent self-licking of the body, Birch was able to interfere with the female's parturitive behavior of licking and gathering pups to her mammary region. As a consequence of interfering with the mother's cleaning of the young and other parturitive care the offspring died in nearly all cases; the few that survived delivery did not live beyond the second week. These findings have not been confirmed by Coomans (cited by Eibl-Eibesfeldt, 1958). Differences in the collaring technique used in these two studies and also in a recent study by Wagman, Christoferson & Friedlich (1964) unfortunately make it impossible to compare the separate studies.

We have been concerned with the effect of self-licking of the

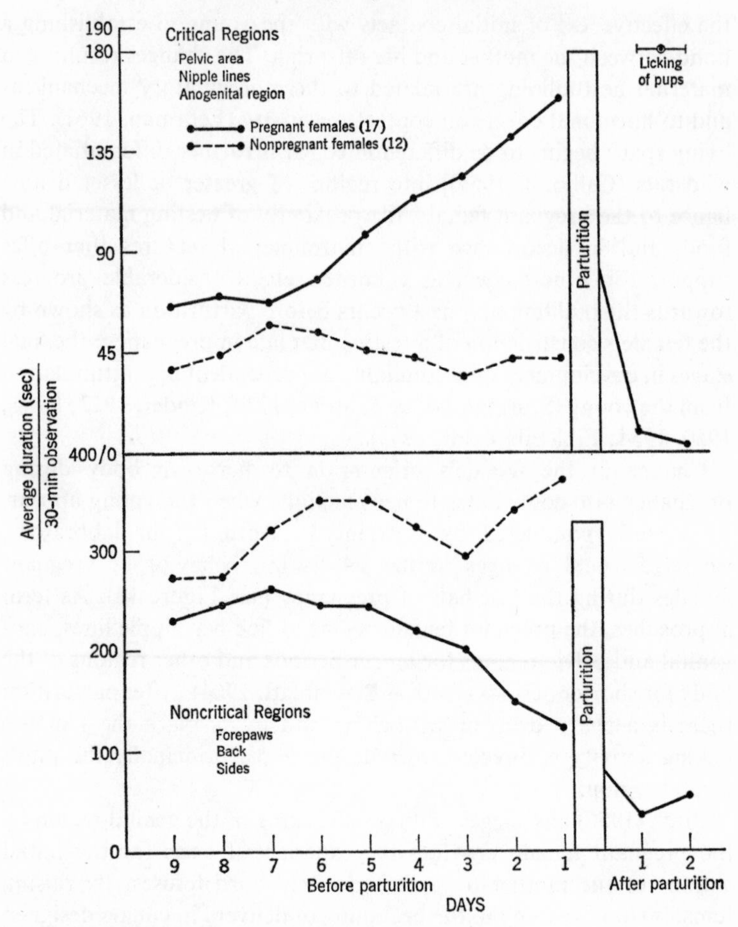

FIG. 13

Comparison of changes in distribution of self-licking in pregnant females and in nonpregnant (control) females observed for an equivalent period. The curves are smoothed by using three-day moving averages; each point represents the mean score for that day, the preceding day, and the following day (if any) (Roth and Rosenblatt, 1964).

mammary region on mammary gland development and lactation and, through this, on maternal behavior. Mrs Roth has recently completed a preliminary study in which females were prevented from licking the mammary region during pregnancy by collars similar to those used by Birch. On the twenty-second day of pregnancy, just prior to parturition, the females were sacrificed and their mammary glands were examined grossly and histologically for comparison with the mammary glands of females allowed to lick themselves without restriction during pregnancy. The mammary glands of females prevented from licking their body during pregnancy were noticeably underdeveloped with regard to overall size of the secretory portion of the gland, the amount of milk found in the alveoli and the size of the alveolar secretory cells.

Female self-licking in response to stimuli from the mammary region, therefore has an effect on mammary gland development in addition to whatever effect it has on maternal behavior during delivery of the fetuses. The likelihood is that licking the nipples stimulates the secretion of prolactin and this in turn has two effects: it augments milk-formation and mammary growth and it contributes to the development of the female's maternal condition. Since suckling by the pups plays a similar role in milk production and in maintenance of maternal behavior after parturition, the preparturitive behavior of the female provides a self-stimulative precursor that may in fact be operative in the formation of the mother-young relationship.

It must not be forgotten that internal stimulation in the pregnant female arising from various sources including uterine distention, movement of the fetuses, and swelling of the mammary glands also affects her physiological and behavioral condition. Some of these effects have already been noted, but others are exerted directly upon the nervous system and alter the female's condition. Nemtsova, Morachevskaia, & Andreyeva (1958) recorded one effect during their attempts to condition late pregnant rats. They indicate that these internal stimuli introduce a lability into the functioning of the higher nervous centers that interferes with the establishment of conditioned differentiation of external stimuli. The increasing prominence of internal stimuli, reflected in their relative dominance over higher neural centers, may serve to explain the frequently reported observation that late pregnant females seek out secluded nest sites where they can remain undisturbed by external stimuli. It has also been noted that as term approaches the female appears to be very responsive to movement of the fetuses within her and many of her postural changes are prompted by these stimuli.

In our laboratory Dr Dale Lott has been studying the effect of

Caesarean delivery of young, at various times during pregnancy, upon the appearance of maternal behavior. Emptying the uterus as early as ten days before the usual delivery date appears to set in motion changes which stimulate the appearance of maternal behavior shortly afterward. If these preliminary results are confirmed in later studies, then we must consider uterine emptying as contributing in an important way to development of the maternal condition at parturition. The loss of placental hormones offers one likely means by which this effect is produced as shown in studies on the rabbit in which various techniques for terminating pregnancy before normal parturition (e.g. Caesarean delivery, inducing abortion) resulted in the induction of maternal nestbuilding behavior (Zarrow, Sawin, Ross & Denenberg, 1962). However, uterine regulation of hormone secretion by the ovary cannot be excluded as a possible mechanism (Everett, 1961).

While we are just beginning to study the preparturitional background of the development of the maternal condition and the appearance of maternal behavior toward newly born young, it is apparent even from the few lines of evidence that are now available that knowing this background will enable us to understand the importance of the early postparturitional period for the establishment of the maternal-young relationship. Events at parturition and during the first few days postpartum period will be seen in relation to the earlier developmental period and the need for viewing them in isolation as forming a 'critical period' will then have lost even its heurisitc value.

C. *The decline of maternal behavior*

The decline of maternal behavior is a natural part of the maternal behavior cycle; in the relationship between the mother and young it corresponds to the period when the young attain independent functioning. Some evidence we have cited suggests that it also contributes to this attainment by the young.

Studies have shown that the decline of maternal behavior may be prevented by replacing grown litters by younger pups. Wiesner & Sheard (1933) were able to reverse the decline of maternal behavior repeatedly by replacing 3-week-old pups by newborn, less than a week old. There was often a delay of several hours or even one or two days between the replacement of the older pups by the younger ones and the reappearance of maternal behavior. On occasion maternal responses appeared immediately after the young pups were introduced. Where there was a delay, however, it is suggested that the presence of the young gradually restored the maternal condition of the mother, enabling the female to respond to the pups with a display of maternal behavior. By this method these investigators were able to maintain maternal behavior for as long as nine months in several mothers and more than a year in one mother.

Wiesner and Sheard were unable to maintain lactation for as long as they were able to maintain maternal behavior, but more recently several investigators have reported the maintenance of lactation for periods up to a year using essentially the same method (Nicoll & Meites, 1959; Bruce, 1961).

We were concerned with the question of the decline of maternal behavior and therefore our procedure emphasized the use of grown pups in place of the female's own, younger pups, as a means of inducing premature decline of maternal behavior. Our results are not conclusive; further studies are needed along the lines indicated previously. In so far as our hypothesis has been supported with respect to retrieving and nestbuilding behavior, it is suggested that the final phase of the maternal behavior cycle, like the earlier phases, is the consequence of the interaction between the mother and her offspring.

In conclusion, therefore, we may say that the basis of synchrony in the behavioral interaction between the mother and her offspring lies in the effects of the offspring at different ages on the maternal condition of the mother. At an early age stimuli from the young promote the development and maintenance of the female's maternal condition thus ensuring maternal care necessary for their survival and development. Later the young have an opposite effect upon the mother. The waning of maternal behavior, however, corresponds to the period when the young gradually become fully capable of functioning on their own.

Discussion following Dr Rosenblatt's Paper

KAUFMAN *What did you do with all these young that were removed from their mothers?*

ROSENBLATT *Unfortunately we were not able to study the effects of separation from the mother on the young as you have done. In some instances 3- and 4-day-old young were given to mothers on the eighteenth day postpartum and we were able to duplicate earlier reports of prolongation of maternal behaviour.*

AMBROSE *When you did separate the young from the mother, would they not show distress cries or distress reactions?*

ROSENBLATT *Although we took some precautions to minimize disturbance of the litter by keeping them together in a warm environment, and in fact we found that they fell asleep soon after they were removed from the mother, nevertheless you are correct in pointing out that they must have produced cries of distress which did reach the mother. It will be recalled, however, that the mother was given one hour to settle down following removal of the litter and it is likely that by this time the disturbance had become minimal.*

BOWLBY *I wonder how much difficulty there is with rats in that some mothers might be distressed to lose their own young and find themselves confronted with strangers?*

ROSENBLATT *As I have indicated in the paper, we found no evidence of disturbance to the mother of testing her with alien pups* 5 *to* 10 *days of age, despite the fact that Beach & Jaynes* (1956a) *have shown that at this age mothers recognize their own young. When the mother's own litter was* 5 *to* 10 *days of age we could compare the effect of the test young with the mother's own young – their ages now being equal – and we have found no difference in the main measures of retrieving. Mothers are sometimes disturbed by pups that are older than their own pups as for example the mothers that were given* 11- *or* 19-*day-old pups in place of their own* 3- *or* 4-*day-old pups. This was an individual matter, however, appearing only in a few mothers and then disappearing after a day or two. We rarely lost a pup as a result of attack by the mother.*

BOWLBY *What about the removal of young of, say,* 3 *days and substitution of young of* 7 *or* 8 *days?*

ROSENBLATT *Mothers are not disturbed by being given pups whose age is only four or five days greater than their own pups during this period–we have done this often in the course of testing. Pups at these two ages do not differ markedly in physical or behavioural characteristics. If the alien young are much older and are very different in appearance and behaviour then some mothers will be disturbed by them.*

BOWLBY *I take it that there's no recognition of individual offspring when they are so young?*

ROSENBLATT *As I have indicated, the mother does recognize her young by around the sixth day but this does not prevent her from retrieving alien young. She may hesitate before retrieving them or she may retrieve her own young before picking up the alien pups, but she does retrieve all young of appropriate age.*

FOSS *Because the mothers will retrieve almost anything, such as the young of different species, one wonders whether you could have used an even more standard stimulus, such as some sort of moving model.*

ROSENBLATT *This would be possible of course, and is indicated if a study of the stimuli eliciting retrieving was being done* (see Beach & Jaynes, 1956b). *We were more interested in how the mother's behaviour varies in her response to the characteristics of the young and how this responsiveness varies with developmental changes in these characteristics.*

KAUFMAN *Why didn't you use the mother's own litters as the test animals?*

ROSENBLATT *You understand, of course, the point about having constant stimulus young for the entire period of four weeks during which the mothers were tested. As a matter of fact we did begin our studies using the mother's own litter, but after the twelfth day test results were so ambiguous with regard to the mother's behaviour that we abandoned that method. In many of our studies we have records of tests using the constant age pups and two groups of variable age pups – the mother's own litter and an alien litter of exactly the same age. We have not reported the results as yet but the mother's responses to these two kinds of young were identical. Finally, I see the point you are making in another way. If we had used 2- to 4-day-old stimulus young or 12- to 14-day young, for example, would our results be different? We have in mind to do this at some later date.*

ROWELL *Your rats seem to stop being maternal very soon. Is it possible that you have a rather unmaternal strain as compared with some used in earlier experiments, when even virgin rats behaved maternally?*

ROSENBLATT *I'm sure that a question of strain differences is involved in the number of females that are maternal while still virgin in the different studies you mentioned. But there are also differences in techniques of eliciting maternal behaviour and generally speaking virgin females were permitted longer periods of contact with young – a so-called 'period of sensitization' – in these earlier studies. Using our technique of simply testing females without giving them a prior period of exposure to young, we have found about* 10 *per cent of a group of thirteen virgins retrieve young. Using primiparous females several months after they have weaned their young, we have found that one or two out of six may retrieve young occasionally, but not regularly.*

KAUFMAN *Could I jump to the question of critical periods? Were you saying that Scott considers physiological readiness to be initiated from within the nervous system, and you say from outside?*

ROSENBLATT *No, the difference is more basic than that. Scott's view, despite the context in which it arose, is not a developmental approach since, as I have indicated, it tends to isolate the 'critical period' from developments during earlier periods. Because of this the theory is forced to attribute the changes in behaviour during the critical period to maturational processes and those referred to are related to the central nervous system. There is a serious question in my mind whether, with this approach, even the changes of the critical period can be understood. Our view (Schneirla & Rosenblatt,* 1963) *is not that maturational processes are unimportant for behavioural change but that their importance can only be understood in terms of their contribution to ongoing behavioural development, analysed with respect to earlier effects of experience and maturation. Scott, for example, claimed, on the basis of studies in his laboratory, that puppies are incapable of learning simple conditioned responses until the middle of the third week. We had already found that kittens began to learn simple discriminations and orientated movements during the first few days after birth. I would say that the difference in our work (apart from species differences in our subjects) arose from our different viewpoints. We felt that learning, if it occurred at an early age, would appear in the responses of kittens to the mother, littermates and the home environment – that is the life situation of the kitten at that developmental stage. Recent studies with puppies have also shown that learning appears quite early in the puppy's life provided the observer looks for it in situations that are relevant to the early adjustments of the puppy – that is for example in suckling behaviour (Cornwell & Fuller,* 1961*; Stanely, Cornwell, Poggiani & Trattner,* 1963).

I should like to point out something not mentioned in the paper, that although our studies bear on the problem of synchrony between the mother and offspring in the rat, I have also been interested in similar phenomena in humans. I have noticed, for instance, that the mother – my wife – has a much closer 'synchrony' with our children than I do – I am usually about two weeks behind her in knowing what they can do – not that I have not seen them for two weeks – but I cannot always catch subtle changes which indicate that a behaviour is changing from an accidental expression of the baby's condition to the baby's purposeful use of the behaviour in play. Another familiar phenomenon is that mothers are often surprised (and fathers too) at the discrepancy between their memory of the baby's appearance and behaviour months earlier, and the reality as seen in a picture or report. It is almost as though the mother must constantly forget the younger baby to remain in contact with the present baby. Mothers may in fact differ in their sensitivity to changes in their babies, one being more sensitive than the other. They may differ in the aspects of the baby to which they are most sensitive, etc. A mother's preference for one type of child or one stage of her infant's behavioural development may also enter into determining her sensitivity to the infant and to the kind of synchrony that is established between mother and infant. I was interested in the different kinds of mother-infant patterns of interaction shown by David and Appell from this point of view. In my mind the studies on the rat can be useful mainly as a general background from which ideas for studies on humans may arise.

On Observational Methodology and Preliminary Studies of Mother-Infant Interaction in Monkeys[1]

GORDON D. JENSEN and RUTH A. BOBBITT

As a pediatrician and as a clinician I have always had a special interest in the processes underlying normal growth and development, and particularly in the clinical problems created by separations of mothers and infants and by maternal deprivation of infants. While looking around for a feasible scientific way to study such problems of the mother-child relationship I became inspired by Dr Harry Harlow's work with monkeys.

Our initial approach in studies with monkeys was through observations of normal mother-infant development and separation studies (Jensen, 1961; Jensen & Tolman, 1962 a and b). Observing the mother-infant relationship, I soon came to realize that behavior exists only in a context of interaction – not only that, but constantly changing interaction; particularly one that develops. I felt that a study of these multiple changing factors of interaction would yield insight into the processes of development and provide measures to get at the variables in which I was interested.

The problem of methodology presented itself foremost. We chose to approach this problem utilizing a simplified and highly controlled environment with only the mother-infant pair. I will keep the technical details of our observational technique and method (Bobbitt *et al.*, 1964) to a minimum, but will be glad to give as much detail as you like. Instead, I will give examples of some of the findings from pilot studies which will illustrate our methodology.

A major principle of our observational method is that it is based

[1] This research was supported by a PHS Research Grant No. MH-05241-02 from the National Institute of Mental Health, Public Health Service and PHS FR-00166 from the Division of Research Facilities and Resources, National Institutes of Health, Public Health Service.

upon discrete coding of behavioral units (Figure 14). Our 'behavioral event' is illustrated diagramatically with the clearly defined behavioral act or unit surrounded by three referents. So at each moment in

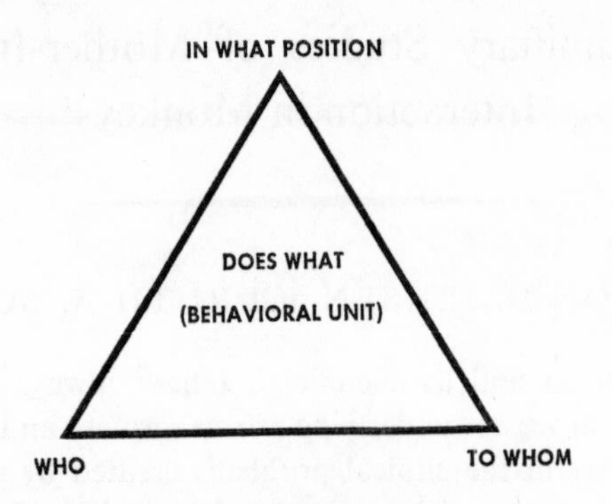

FIG. 14

The behavioral unit and the three referents constitute a behavioral event.

time as the behavior is observed the observer records in what relative position, who does what to whom. This can be accomplished with speed and high reliability since each behavioral unit or act and the referents are given simple verbal codes that are spoken into a tape recorder. An automatic time signal indicates three-second intervals during the daily ten-minute observation period. Because we desire to obtain maximal detail of behavior we have a catalogue of approximately thirty-five behavioral units that can occur in various referential contexts.[1] When all the units and referents are combined in various possible combinations of behavioral events that could be coded, it gives some idea of the flexibility of the basic coding structure. Of course, we are interested not only in individual events but in sequences of behavioral events. Our method of *process* or *pattern analysis* is designed to handle these data meaningfully as I will soon illustrate.

As is true with many persons who watch human babies or infant monkeys grow up, we are especially interested in how the little ones come to be emancipated from their mothers; how it comes about that they change from almost entirely dependent, clinging infants into

[1] Copies of our catalogue of behavioral units are available on request.

romping, climbing, agile juveniles. The data, of course, told us that they not only become emancipated from their mothers but that their mothers also become emancipated from them. We ask, what is the nature of her role and what role does the infant have in this emancipation process? I would like to illustrate now how our interaction development approach may shed light on this question.

Although I use the terms 'independence' and 'emancipation' I do so advisedly and will not try to define them. I will deal, instead, with what we see the animals do. We see them interact in a very close relationship and at distances farther away from each other. When I say 'independence' I mean it in quotation marks and in fact it means that the animals are separated in space. I will get to the details of this separation later.

In the pilot study we analyzed the data from two pairs of animals from birth through 70 days (Bobbitt *et al.*, 1964). They were pigtailed monkeys, one infant a male and one a female. I am going to present a series of trends that all cover the same period of time (birth to 70 days). In the graphs a straight line indicates that the linear component of the trend was statistically significant at the ·01 to ·05 level and a similarly significant quadratic component is shown by a curved line. The nature of the trends is indicated by regression lines which have been fitted by graphic methods and not intended to imply exact slopes (Guilford, 1954). The ranges covered by the ordinates vary with each measure so that the trends will be more apparent in the limited space available.

First let us look at a very general measure (Figure 15). The infant's increasingly active behavior with progressive development is indicated by the upward slope, which is a ratio of the infant's total behaviors to the mother's total behaviors. Infants are initially less active than their mothers. Their activity level rises sharply following birth, passes the mother's near the end of the first month and remains higher than hers on into the third month. A separate analysis shows that the mother's absolute activity remains stable during this period so that the increase illustrated here is entirely due to a rapid increase in the infant's activity.

As a first step in reducing the data, we found it useful to classify all behaviors within five major classes or dimensions, as we call them (Figure 16). The dimensional profile of one mother-infant pair is presented here. It was not combined with the other pair because of the individual differences of the two mothers, but the profile relationships are very similar for each pair. It is interesting to note that the mother's profile of dimensions shows an even distribution as to quantities of behavior in each dimension and this pattern does not differ over the five blocks, from birth to 70 days. The infant, on the

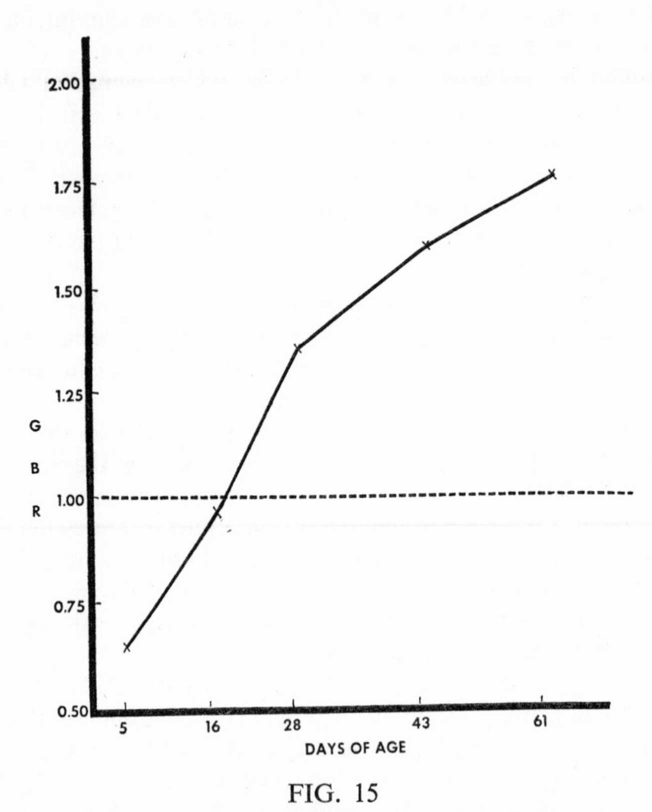

FIG. 15

The general behavior ratio—(GBR)—total infant behaviors divided by total mother behaviors.

other hand, shows marked differences in profile between block one and block five. Note in block one the high proportion of his total behavior that is in the dimension of physical contact. By the last block or the end of the 70 days the infant's profile looks much more like its mother's.

Now we will make a finer breakdown of the data from the two pair. We will confine our attention to the contact dimension, one which I am sure most will agree is among the most important for the mother-infant relationship.

First we look at two aspects of the infant's interactive development in his contact with his mother (Figure 17). The infant contacts the mother relatively less and less frequently over time. (The frequency of

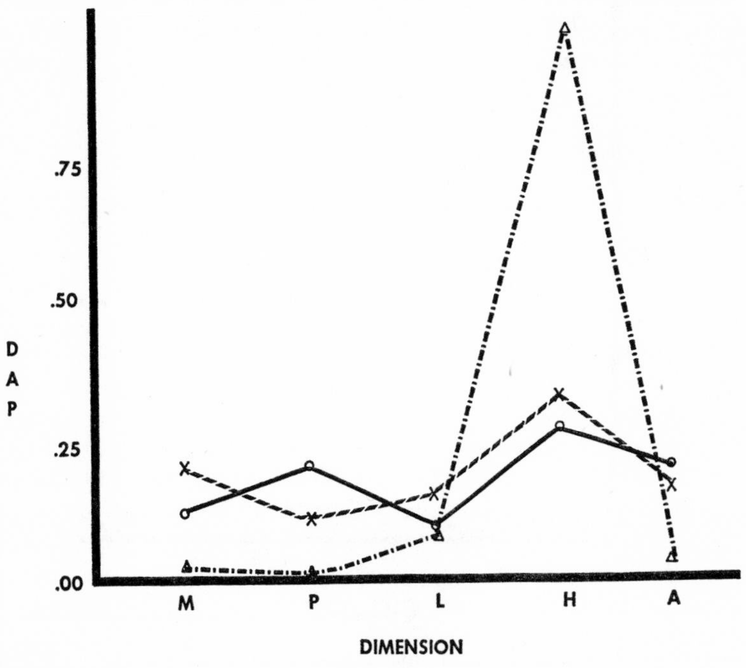

FIG. 16

Dimensional activity profiles (*DAP*). *Dimensions: locomotion* (*M*), *posture* (*P*), *visual* (*L*), *physical contact* (*H*), *self-oriented* (*A*). *Solid line: mother, overall* 5 *blocks. Dot-dash: infant, block I*, (1-14 *days*). *Broken line: infant, block V* (56-70 *days*).

absolute contact is increased.) This is a more detailed illustration of the change in the infant's dimensional profile of the previous figure. Now note that while the relative frequency of contact behavior by the infant decreases (line, A) the relative frequency of total contact behavior that is active in character (line B), increases until, at 70 days of age, 90 per cent of all contacts are active. Thus while the infant's contact with the mother is less a part of his total behavior picture, most of his contacts are active. As these two graphs are

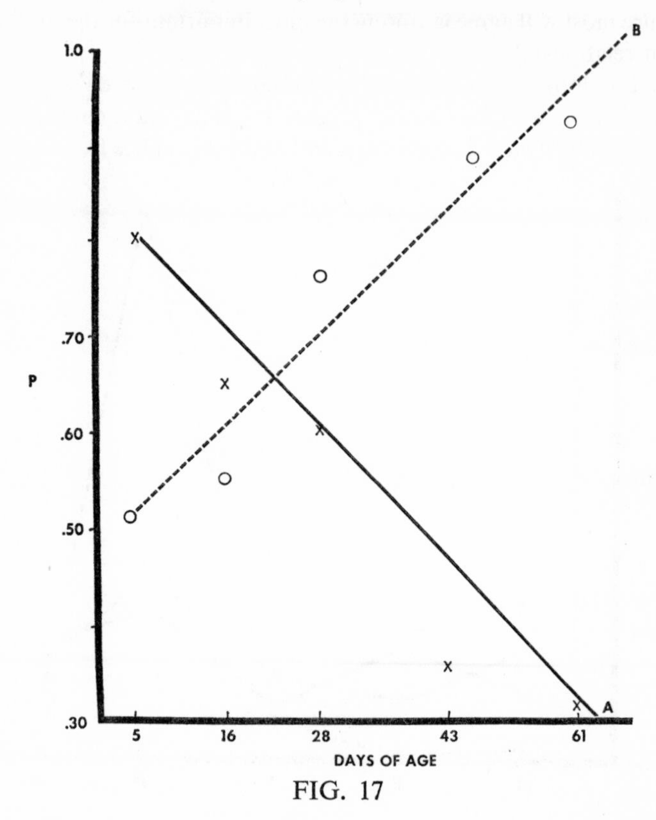

FIG. 17

(A) Relative frequency of infant's contacts with mother. (B) Relative frequency of infant's active physical contact with mother.

superimposed you have the first example of the types of trends we deal with in this kind of analysis. These are simultaneous, antithetical, yet undoubtedly related and concordant trends.

Turning to several aspects of the mother's contact of her infant, we find that the mother is retaining less frequently (Figure 18, A). Retaining behaviors are those which tend to keep the infant close to the mother, such as cradling, retrieving and following with the hand. At the same time we see that the mother is punishing more (Figure 18, B). Punishing behaviors include hitting, biting and vigorous manipulation or pushing the infant away. In summary, in these four curves, the two negative ones relate to maintaining closeness and the two positive ones relate to activity.

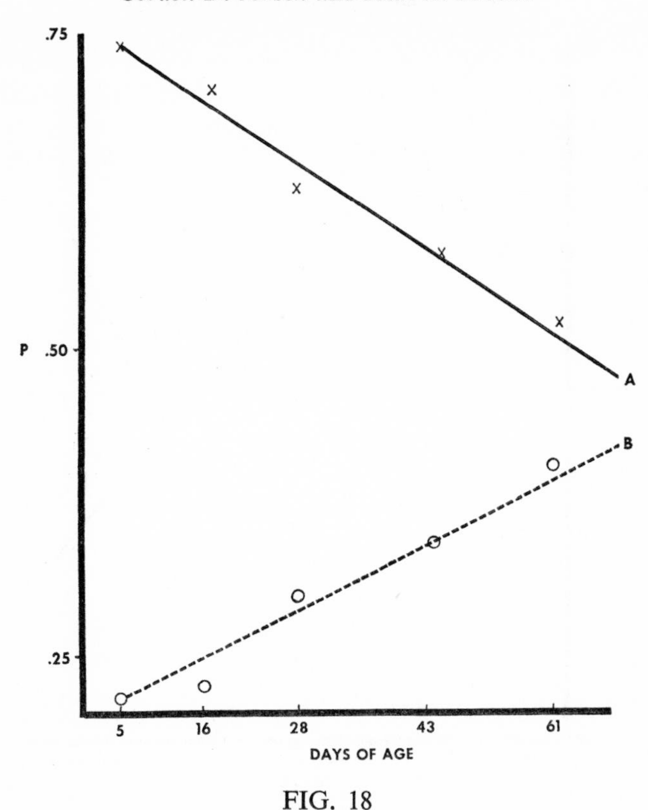

FIG. 18

(*A*) *Proportion of mother's retaining of infant.* (*B*) *Proportion of mother's punishing of infant.*

Let us now look at the amount of time the mother-infant pair actually spends (Figure 19) in various relative positions. First, in the On-Position the slope A declines sharply. In the Near-Position (defined as the infant being out of the mother's lap but adjacent to her body and touching her in one way or another, at least frequently if not constantly) the curve is positively accelerated (Figure 19, B). Time in the Separated-Position (at least one foot distance between the two animals) appears to increase, but during the period covered by this study the increase is not statistically significant.

So far we have looked at an analysis of either individual codes or sums of individual behavioral events in terms of relative frequency or duration. We can learn more about the interaction development

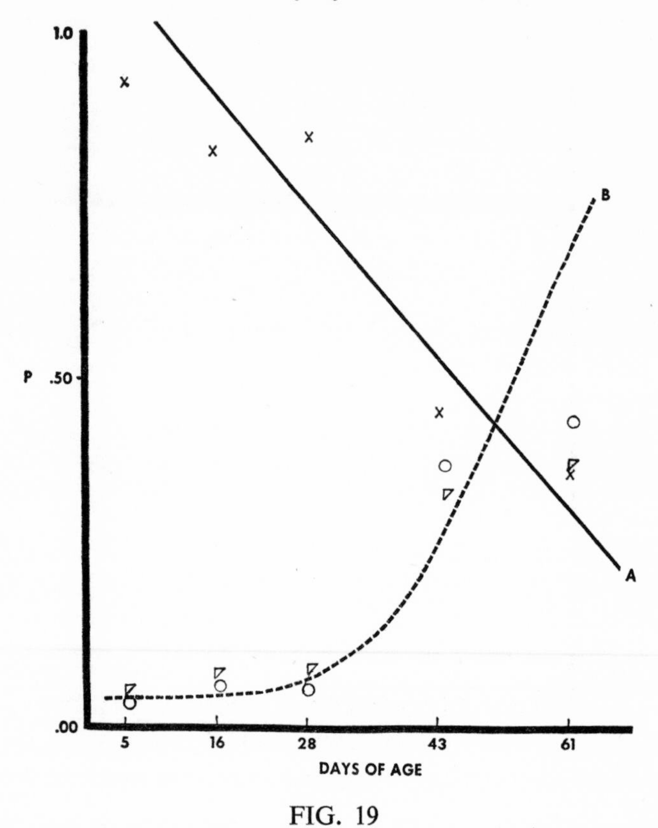

FIG. 19

Time spent in relative positions: (A) on position; (B) near position; data for separated position indicated by triangles.

process by studying the various patterns of behavioral events. At this point I would like to amplify and clarify our interactive pattern concept. We define a pattern as any behavioral event or any naturally meaningful combination of behavioral events that occur in a temporally related sequence. Here we use our judgment although in our present studies programmed for computer analysis we will be able to form patterns on an empirical basis. Now these patterns may be individual or interactive. In the case of an individual pattern you might say that the animal can interact with himself, in that one event follows or occurs with another in a particular way. However, what we think of as individual patterns may really be interactive patterns.

Let us say the infant is sitting in the corner of the cage grooming himself. This appears to be an individual pattern and unrelated to interaction with the mother. However, we might also find that particular maternal behavior tends to occur or is related to the infant's grooming himself in this position away from the mother. It would then have to be regarded as an interactive pattern. A good example of an interactive pattern would be the infant clinging to the mother's abdomen and nursing while the mother cradles the infant. Several things are happening here at the same time on the part of and to both animals. Note that in our concept of behavioral events and patterns it is not necessary that only one thing happen at a time, as is true of some models for analysis of social interaction such as Altmann's (1962).

We group patterns of a similar sort into groups and call them *pattern groups*. A good example is the quiet-on pattern group which includes all kinds of patterns that involve mother-infant interaction where the infant is essentially quiet and in close contact with the mother. A comparable pattern group is infant active-on the mother. After combining the patterns into pattern groups, we then divide each pattern group into *variants* which are breakdowns in the organization of patterns in the group that we find occurring regularly or in which we have a particular interest. An example of the latter would be 'infant quiet-on, mother-punishing'. It doesn't happen often, but we are interested. Occurring often, however, are maternal behavioral events classified as punitive while the infant is active-on the mother. These fall under the pattern group variant of 'infant active-on, mother-punishing'.

Let us look first at a simultaneous series of trends in infant interactive patterns (Figure 20). Starting with the active-on pattern group (A) we see that in the first two blocks the infant's behavior that is active-on the mother is increasing. It reaches a peak in the third block and thereafter decreases. This is a duration measure and represents the amount of time spent in the active-on position relative to the total amount of time in the block. Several other trends are relevant to this type of curve for this pattern and to our question of developing mutual independence. Now look at the general pattern of 'infant approach' and 'depart from' mother (Figure 20, B); the infant is increasingly often departing from the mother. He is also increasingly often approaching his mother (Figure 20, C). Next an interactive sequence (line D): we see that when the mother is indifferent to

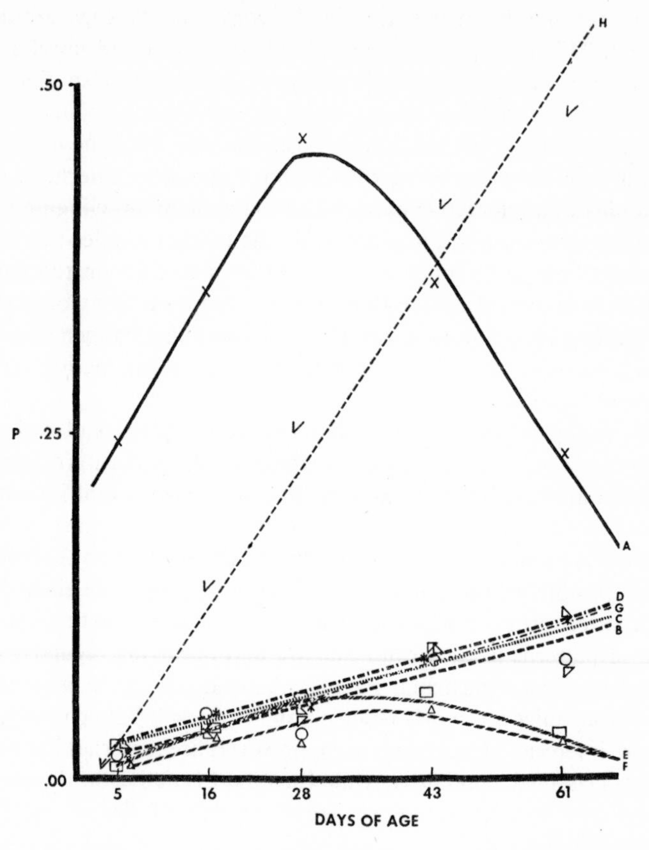

FIG. 20

Infant interactive patterns: (A) active on; (B) departs from mother; (C) approaches mother; (D) when mother is indifferent, infant moves from on to near position; (E) active-on to near position; (F) infant moving from separated to on position; (G) infant leaving from near to go farther away; (H) infant approaching mother from separated position.

the infant who is actively playing on her, the infant moves to the near position with increasing frequency. In other words, when mother neither restrains nor punishes the active-on infant he increasingly often moves off of her to be active near her rather than on her or completely separated from her. Curve E shows the trend for the infant who is active on the mother and progresses to the near position. Again we see the dome-shaped curve that peaks in the third block reminiscent of the active-on curve. In Curve F we see a similar trend for the pattern of infant in a separated position from the mother and coming back on her. Line G shows the upward linear trend of the infant leaving from the near position to go farther away from the mother and a similar trend for the infant approaching toward the mother but moving from a separated position to the near rather than on position (Figure 20, H).

In summary, putting these trends together we can see the following: While we saw earlier that the infant spends less total time on the mother, he spends increasingly more time being active on her though this behavior peaks toward the end of the first month. He is moving away more frequently and increasingly moving farther away. At the height of his active-on behavior he is in the habit of coming back often from the separated position to touch home base (Figure 20, E). On the tail of the decline of the active-on curve he is playing away from the mother more although still in a yo-yo movement (i.e. moving away, coming back close but not on and moving away again). Thus we can picture three phases in his role in emancipation from his mother: (1) the earliest period of life in the first block when the infant is spending almost all his time on the mother, and much of it quietly; (2) the middle of the seventy-day period when he is moving away increasingly frequently but often coming back to the mother to touch or play on her and leave again; and (3) the end of the seventy-day period when he is pretty much playing away from the mother.

We should now ask for more information on what the mother is doing meanwhile (Figure 21). We see (line A) that she is departing from the infant an increasing amount (remember that he is doing likewise but she is *not* also approaching him more) and that she is carrying the infant less and less (line B). But more specifically (line C) the mother is increasingly completely separating herself from the infant who leaves her to play actively but still near her. In other words, when the infant is active and leaves her to play near by, the mother gets up and walks completely away from the infant. This is the point at which she often shows a facial gesture and look which I will discuss later. The next question is, what is the mother doing to the active-on infant? We can imagine he becomes an incredible pest, climbing all over her head, jumping from her head to the cage and back again while swinging from her ears. Recall that when she was indifferent the infant left her to return to the larger environment. Figure 22, A shows the trend for the frequency with which the mother retains the active-on infant. In comparison, the mother retains the infant about twice as often when he is quiet as when he is active on her; she retains the quiet infant 70 per cent of the time even at the end of the seventy-day period. Although the

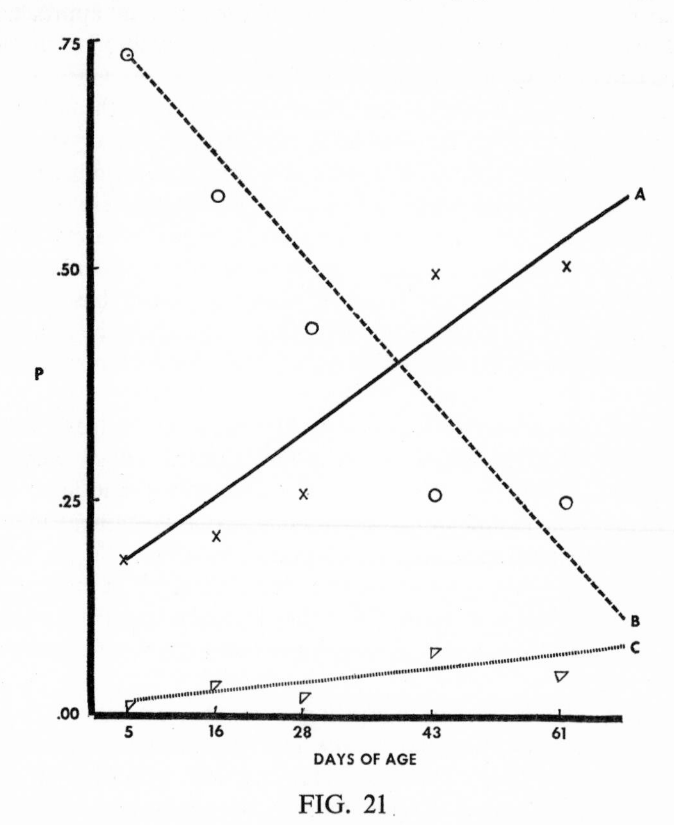

FIG. 21

Maternal Patterns: (A) departing from infant; (B) carrying infant; (C) mother leaves infant after her infant gets off of her to be nearby.

mother often retains the active-on infant we see in Figure 22, B an antithetical response in the same situation. The mother rejects or punishes the active-on infant with increasing frequency. Note the increasing amount of punishment she gives to her active-on infant. These three measures are as close as I can come to portraying what appears to be an intense ambivalence of the mother. In comparing this with what she does with the quiet-on infant we find an opposite trend for the punishment she gives to a quiet infant; she punishes the quiet-on infant less and less.

From these data I think you can begin to see how each participant has a role in this mutual emancipation process. At different times and

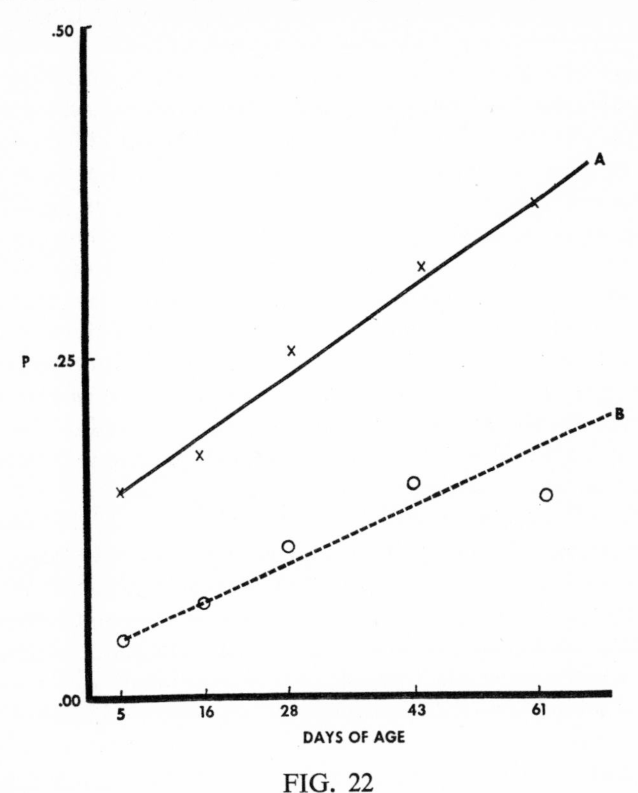

FIG. 22

Maternal Patterns: (A) retains her infant; (B) punishes the active-on infant.

in different ways, different animals of the pair carried parts of the burden. At times the mother took a more active role by leaving, punishing or retaining. At times she was just indifferent and let the infant go. At other times but often simultaneously the infant took a more active role by leaving the mother to explore his environment, playing on the mother, or playing away from her. These data support the notion that independence appears to be a function of the mother letting the increasingly active infant go, and in the first seventy days they further indicate that the mother 'pushes her baby out of the nest'. We feel that the various interactive variables we have looked at here should be put to definitive tests.

There are a number of factors and variables to consider in a process as general as this one we have talked about. Important is individual differences in a group study of developmental trends. This is always a problem for almost all behavioral research utilizing small samples. However, our pilot study showed few significant subject variances and fewer subject × block interactions. Individual differences are not, however, a detriment to study of developmental process. With the baseline and interactive pattern concepts, there is provided a bridge from the usual statistical approach to the individual case approach of the clinician. One can analyze the trend of individual interactive patterns in terms of the subject's own baseline. Say for example we introduce (or have operating) a condition which influences the baseline in one direction which is consistent with our hypothesis. In another pair of animals with a different baseline, if we introduce (or have operating) the same condition, we may predict a reverse effect in the measures. Then the general hypothesis receives substantiation from each case.

Another important variable to consider is the sex of the animals. Males appear to be more active, for example, than are females. If males are more active-on the mother we would predict from our hypothesis that they provoke more punishment. Indeed, this appears to be so in our studies underway. The environment undoubtedly plays an important role. Our studies of mother-infant pairs raised in a most severely restricted environment (one of social and manipulative privation except for the animal pair) indicate that there is a great deal more interaction between mother and infant when the infant has nothing else to play on or with; he is more active-on his mother and apparently uses her as a play object. Accordingly, we would predict more punishment. Our current studies indicate that after several months she does in fact punish a great deal and sometimes to the extent that she looks like a severely 'rejecting' mother. Of course, the social group that the monkeys live in would have an effect including the dominance relationships and rank of the mother. Physical maturation of the infant could be an important factor because of size alone. The sex cycle of the mother could also enter into this process.

We are attempting to unravel some of these interactive variables beginning with our mother-infant pairs in a strictly controlled setting, and to test hypotheses about the effect on them of specific enrichments of the environment. The variables of greatest interest can be subjected to specific experimental tests when ingenious enough experimental designs are developed.

Now I would like to turn to the sequence analysis of a gesture that pigtails commonly make, one of their communication systems no doubt. We call it a 'len', which stands for the major components of the gesture; movement of the lips, ears and neck (Figure 23). We

FIG. 23

Left: usual face of M. nemestrina. *Right: the "len," a species specific facial gesture.*

differentiate this facial gesture from a silly grin, an open-mouthed look, the lip smack and yawn. We are trying to see if this gesture has a specific function for the monkeys. These pilots are from three pairs of animals for the first seventy days of life.

We were interested in seeing what behaviors preceded the len and what behaviors followed it. When we tabulated the frequency of all behavioral events that occurred in such sequences we found so many of them that it was necessary to analyze the data by pattern groups and their variants. Therefore, we took ten pattern groups such as the moving away pattern group and the approaching pattern group. We made a matrix and tabulated the pattern groups occurring immediately before and immediately after the len event. We found that in one-third of the instances of all the lens, some form of moving away preceded the len and that in 80 per cent of the instances the moving away was done by the mother. Now, since lens in general decline in frequency in the first seventy days we must assume that this moving away is mostly done early in life, a time when actually moving away behavior is a small proportion of the total behavior. Looking at the patterns that occurred immediately after the len, we find that when the mother did move away and lenned immediately afterwards, in 76 per cent of these instances the infant immediately approached. Now you may say that only a one-third incidence isn't very convincing for an understanding of the functional significance of mother moving away behavior for the len and that 76 per cent return of the infant after these lens isn't very significant, if this is the function of the len. But if we look at all of the behavior patterns preceding the len we find that in 92 per cent of the instances the len was preceded immediately by some kind of separated behavior. When you realize that in this same age-period the animals were separated only 35 per cent of the time the 92 per cent figure is of tremendous significance. Looking at other patterns following the len we found, for example, that sometimes the mother moved away, lenned and then moved away again and lenned again. It appeared as though the mother were training the infant. These instances were scored as failures in terms of bringing the infant to the mother. Therefore we looked at the second, third and fourth patterns after the len (occurring within 45 seconds following the len) and found that 71 per cent of *all* the lens are followed by an approach to the mother or a closer relationship of the pair.

In our current studies we will have a finer breakdown of behavioral events in the len sequences plus developmental trends. Our observations tell us that mother lens a lot in the beginning of the infant's life, and it either occurs when the animals are already close or it is not very effective in bringing the infant. Later on it is quite effective and still later lenning appears to drop out. By getting at the details of the developmental sequences, week by week, one can learn the process of len communication.

If we look at the len according to learning theory we would say 'why yes, the len is followed by the animals being closer together and being close together is a reinforcement'. Suppose, then, we look at the data of the variant of the mother cradling the infant following the len. We wonder if, when they do get closer together following the len, she does cradle more often. Bear in mind that ordinarily when the pair is close together she gives a cradling response an average of 75 per cent of the time. But after a len when they do get closer together she cradles 90 per cent of the time. That's quite a significant difference and I think you would agree a real reinforcement at least for the infant.

In summary, I have presented a methodology which we have developed and tested and which quantitatively and reliably measures the development of social interaction. A concept of interactive patterns enables analysis of the process of development and the dynamics of interaction (i.e. how the behavior changes with respect to multiple interactions). The interactive pattern concept and baseline measures also provide a bridge from the purely group statistical approach to the analysis of individual changes in the interactive pattern variables in a single case under different conditions.

Data from our pilot study showed how we will proceed to obtain baseline data of interactive patterns or significant interactive variables of the mother-infant relationship. By knowing the history of the behavioral sequences and patterns, both immediate and developmental, we will have empirical grounds for hunches about the independent variables that operate to control the interactive behavior.

Discussion following Professor Jensen's Paper

ROWELL *I think this is a beautiful study, but I disagree with some of your interpretation. For instance, the gesture you describe as a len has all the components of a mild threat, and you haven't said anything which would make me think it was more than that. In your film it appeared with other threat behaviour, sometimes leading to direct attack. Also the len appears less when the animals are physically distant from each other. You said the mothers cuddled their babies more after a len, and this is what I would expect after they had been threatened. Even looking at a monkey straight in the eyes, without the jaw thrusting, is threatening.*

FREEDMAN *Is that always the case?*

ROWELL *Yes, particularly in baboons. They never look at another baboon in the face except as a threat. It works if a human does it, and between them it is a mild threat.*

JENSEN *I agree with that, but why does the mother monkey len to her infant?*

ROWELL *If the mother threatens the baby, it makes the baby fearful, and if it's fearful, the one thing it does is run to its mother, regardless of the origin of the frightening stimulus.*

HALL *Normally, of course, if a larger animal threatens a smaller one, the smaller one runs away. There are also other features of the len which suggest that it may in this species function as something other than threat. Van Hooff (personal communication) has observed that lenning in the mother-infant situation occurs at a much higher rate than threat displays in an ordinary agonistic situation; and in adults, it frequently precedes or accompanies copulation. Van Hooff's* (1962) *conclusion is that the len or 'Flehmen' face has the same function in the pig-tailed monkey as lip-smacking in other species.*

JENSEN *I do not know on what evidence we could consider the len a threat gesture. All we can say is that when mothers len, babies come. True, infants do look soulfully, directly and, perhaps, naïvely into their mother's eyes; it appears that mothers len in this situation. However, the infants do not then leave as one might expect from a threat. Furthermore, for mothers to threaten and then to fondly embrace their infant is a behaviour sequence difficult for me to reconcile.*

KAUFMAN *We're quite familiar with the len. We call it a jaw-thrust, and we see it in a variety of contexts. When it's done to the infant, the infant comes to the mother, as Gordon Jensen says; it is used by males prior to copulation, and will frequently lead to the female presenting; and it's also produced by staring into the eyes, as you say. But it doesn't seem to me to help if you call it a threat. Sometimes it appears with other threatening behaviour, but not always, and I think it would be difficult to define threat so as to cover all instances.*

FREEDMAN *When the mother does it to the infant, the frequency of occurrence is so much higher that perhaps that particular len should be classified separately from the others? High-speed photography might in fact show it to be different.*

RHEINGOLD *I suggest that the len is a kind of efficient retrieving behaviour, and functions in the same way as what Harlow calls 'the affectional present'. The mother presents to the infant, and this results in the infant coming to her, so it has a retrieving function. But of course presenting has other functions too.*

HINDE *I think the issue is being confused because sometimes we are talking about the function of the len and sometimes about its causation. Also I would disagree with the argument that because the len is not followed by an attack, this must mean that it is not aggressive. There is plenty of evidence that a tendency to behave aggressively, or sexually, may be present in a movement even when that movement is never followed by overt aggressive or sexual behaviour.*

KAUFMAN *I still would like to know the evidence for saying that it functions as a threat, or that it is caused in the same way as a threat is.*

FOSS *Perhaps, as has already been suggested, the len has many functions. The only other primate facial expression I can think of which occurs with such high frequency is the human smile. Now that has a great many functions, some of which, as it happens, are closely connected with aggression – especially the placatory smile. Another kind of smile is also used a lot between mothers and infants. And yet other smiles, and even more so laughs, occur in conflict situations, and it's my impression that the len often seems to appear in situations of increased conflict.*

AMBROSE *My interpretation is that the first smiles of the infant are low intensity laughing, and laughing is essentially an ambivalent response. So that I would say that there may sometimes be a negative component in smiling.*

GEWIRTZ *Another similarity between the len and the smile that has occurred to me is that both may sometimes occur as forms of the* startle *response. Aside from that point, I have difficulty going along with the idea that ambivalence need be involved.*

FOSS *Of course, in adult humans, the various ways in which smiling is used depend on the particular social setting. If the len is similar, in that it has come to serve several different functions as a means of communication, would one expect to find it functioning differently in different monkey colonies? Perhaps this is a source of disagreement.*

JENSEN *It could be. So far, our analysis of the len is a crude one. A more complete study of the len patterns should give a clearer indication of its functions. The study would include observation of the actual sequences of behaviour, the antecedents and consequences of the len, and a similar analysis of other facial gestures such as open mouth threats.*

Rhesus Monkey Aunts

R. A. HINDE

The fact of the far-reaching importance of maternal influence on a young primate is now beyond question. We are trying to analyse the ways in which this influence is exerted in the rhesus monkey.[1] In the course of our work the importance of two other influences on the young monkey has become apparent. One of these – that of the infant's peers, with whom it spends much time in rough-and-tumble and approach-withdrawal play, has already been studied elsewhere (Harlow, 1962). The second, that exerted by the females in the group other than the infant's own mother, is the subject of this chapter. These females, which we refer to as 'aunts' with no implication of blood relationship, influence the infants in two ways – by direct interaction with them, and by affecting the relationship between the infant and its mother.

Most of our animals live in small social groups, each consisting of a male, three or four females, and their young. The present data were obtained from seven infants living in three such social groups, and from three infants living alone with their mothers. The pens were described in Hinde & Rowell (1962).

The interaction between aunts and infants is difficult to describe. In the first place, the aunts show a rapid succession of different patterns of behaviour, belonging to diverse functional categories, so that their behaviour appears to be markedly ambivalent: secondly, the mother is always ready to interfere, so that the aunts' responses are mostly tentative and incomplete. Functionally, most of their behaviour could be classified within the categories of maternal, sexual, aggressive, grooming and play responses. Descriptively, we found the following categories useful:

[1] This chapter is based on work carried out jointly – earlier with Dr Thelma Rowell and currently with Miss Y. Spencer-Booth. It summarizes data presented in more detail in the papers to which reference is made.

(i) Tentative approaches. The aunt approached the baby, which might be on or off its mother, examining it closely and reaching out as if to take it. This was most common during the first three weeks, and was not seen after the infants were *c*. 4 months old. (The time relations given here refer to five of the infants. The aunt-infant relations in the other two cases differed markedly, and are discussed later.)

(ii) Touching. Sometimes the aunt actually touched the baby. This was most common in weeks three to ten, and became rare later.

(iii) Grooming. Grooming of infants by aunts became fairly frequent after the fifth week, and was more common when the infants were between 15 and 30 weeks old than at any other time in the first year.

(iv) Carrying/cuddling. Sometimes, while an infant was away from its mother, an aunt would approach it, and then walk along beside it or crouch over it and even attempt to pick it up and carry it. While crouching over it, the aunt might show incipient male copulatory behaviour, with pelvic thrusts. If she picked it up, the infant usually did not cling and tried to struggle clear. Such behaviour increased up to the time when the babies were 7-8 weeks old and then declined, though similar patterns appeared later in play.

(v) Play. Sometimes aunts would play with the infants, using patterns similar to those used in infant-infant play. This reached a peak in the third month.

(vi) Aggression. Although the aunts were usually tolerant of the infants' activities, they would sometimes show aggression towards them. Aggression towards infants by aunts without young of their own became common when the infants were *c*. 3 months old. Aggression by aunts with infants of their own was mostly directed towards infants 1-2 months old, but this may have been related to the age of their own babies.

Aunts showed a number of other types of behaviour to the babies, but these were difficult to treat quantitatively. For instance, the interest and visual examination which they showed towards the young babies merged with tentative approaches; and as the babies became more independent of their mothers, aunts would occasionally hover near them as if in a protective role. Furthermore aunts used a number of the adult communication patterns, such as lip-smacking and presenting, to infants: one noise, the cough-grunt, seemed to be confined to situations in which an aunt was watching an infant crawling near or on its mother (Rowell & Hinde, 1962). Further data on the aunts' behaviour are given by Rowell, Hinde & Spencer-Booth (1964).

As indicated above, the frequency with which these various types of aunt-infant interaction occurred varied with the age of the infant. Very young babies were so closely protected by their mothers that tentative approaches and touching only were possible. As the babies' locomotor skills improved and they started to make longer excursions from their mothers, they became more available for carry/cuddling. They also started to elicit aggressive responses from aunts – either because they became a nuisance to them in their play or because they played roughly with the aunts' own infants.

Grooming by aunts increased when the infants were about 4 months old: it is at about this age that the rhesus loses its baby coat and assumes a more adult appearance. It also makes adult-type grooming invitation postures. Play behaviour by aunts became common only after the babies were 5-6 weeks old and thus fairly mobile. All these types of aunt-infant interaction decreased towards the end of the first year.

Frequency of aunt-infant interaction also varied with the age and status of the aunt. Aunts with infants of their own were more likely to be aggressive to infants than were childless females, but tentative approaches, play and grooming were more common from the latter. All patterns were more likely to be shown by the more dominant aunts than by the subordinate ones.

The relationship of the mother with the aunt was also an important issue. Some mothers habitually left their infants in the company of some aunts, but never left them with others. The aunts who were permitted most often to carry or cuddle five of the infants were all subordinate to the mother, who tolerated their attentions secure in her ability to retrieve the infant at any time.

Two of the infants, however, interacted most with an aunt who was dominant to their mothers. These two, Nik and Andy, lived in a group which also contained an adolescent female, Eliane, who was the male's favourite. Eliane was dominant to the mothers of Nik and Andy, and was able to interact with them freely. On many occasions when the mothers attempted to retrieve their infants, the male interfered on the side of Eliane. Unlike any of the other aunts, Eliane sometimes carried one of these babies around for an hour or more at a time. At such times it often seemed as if she would have preferred not actually to carry them, but the babies would cling even more tightly to her when she attempted to push them off. Such separations had a marked effect on one of the mothers, who was in ill health throughout nearly the whole period of Eliane's attentions, and was especially likely to show increased symptoms of weakness and muscular incoordination during the hours following a period in which Eliane had had her baby.

Eliane's behaviour also had a marked effect on the relations of these mothers with their infants, for the mothers became very restrictive, and rarely let their infants go beyond arms' reach throughout their first twenty weeks. In this respect they differed markedly from mothers living in groups where less aunt-infant interaction occurred (Hinde, Rowell & Spencer-Booth, 1964), and differed even more markedly from mothers living alone with their infants in similar cages (Spencer-Booth & Hinde, in preparation). Some representative figures which exemplify this are shown in Table 1: they were taken

TABLE 1

Comparison of data from (a) Nik and Andy, born into a group containing the assertive aunt Eliane, (b) five infants living in groups in which there was less aunt-infant interaction, (c) three infants living with their mothers but without aunts. The figures refer to (i) the proportion of half-minute periods in the routine watches in which the infant was more than two feet from the mother for the whole period, and (ii) the proportion of the half-minute periods in which the infant was off the mother in which it went more than 2 feet from her.

	Age of Infant	(*a*) Nik and Andy	(*b*) 5 'Normal' Infants	(*c*) 3 'Isolate' Infants
(i) % of total periods throughout which infant was more than 2 feet from mother	7–8 weeks	Range 0–0 Mean 0	7–15 10·3	7–19 13·7
	13–14 weeks	Range 0–2·9 Mean 1·5	12–37 35·8	11–40 26·0
(ii) % of periods off mother in which infant went more than 2 feet from mother	7–8 weeks	Range 0–2 Mean 1	21–55 37	47–70 59·4
	13–14 weeks	Range 0–22 Mean 11	53–68 64	58–82 72·7

from data obtained in our routine watches. As a result of the restrictiveness induced in their mothers by Eliane's behaviour, the various types of aunt-infant interaction reached their peak frequencies rather later with Nik and Andy than with the other infants.

The restrictiveness of these mothers had marked effects on the locomotor achievements of Nik and Andy. For instance, we recorded the ages at which we first observed each infant to climb 4 feet up the netting: these were 106 and 152 days for Nik and Andy as compared with means of 25 days (range 17-40) for the other group-reared infants and 31 days (range 24-41 days) for the infants isolated with their mothers.

It is thus clear that the attentions of aunts may profoundly affect the environment of a young rhesus not only directly, but also by influencing the degree of permissiveness shown by the infants' own mother. What long-term effect this may have on the infants' development remains to be seen: a series of tests given at the age of about one year indicated that Nik and Andy were less disturbed by strange objects or by being moved to a new pen than were the other, group-reared, infants.

Of course, these observations on captive monkeys tell us little about the importance of aunt-infant interaction in wild rhesus. The fact that, on the death of the mother, one of our infants was taken over at 8 months and cared for by an aunt suggests that aunt-infant interaction may be of survival value, though such interaction seems to be less frequent in rhesus than in langur monkeys (Jay, 1962). From our point of view, however, it is likely to be a useful experimental tool: we hope to exploit it further in order to vary the degree of permissiveness shown by mothers and the richness of the environment available to the infants, and to assess the influence which these have on their development.

Discussion following Professor Hinde's Paper

ROSENBLATT *Are you suggesting that the 'aunts' are behaving maternally, even though no appropriate physiological condition exists.*

HINDE *It was certainly true in the one case we have where the mother died. Eliane was 32 weeks old when Lois died, and one of the aunts, Rosie, immediately adopted her, and showed all the maternal responses except secreting milk. But Harlow has had examples of female rhesus monkeys that did actually produce milk under these circumstances. Of course, aunts do not show only maternal behaviour – they may be aggressive and so on too.*

ROWELL *Though the infants Harlow's monkeys were given to adopt were a good deal younger than Eliane.*

BOWLBY *What happens in other mammals?*

ROSENBLATT *You find maternal behaviour in females that have not been pregnant, very often among mice and hamsters, but very rarely among cats and rats.*

HINDE *Our monkey aunts would behave more maternally still if it were not for the intervention of the mother. The mothers of Nik and Andy were especially restrictive and kept their babies close to them because Eliane was always trying to steal them.*

AMBROSE *Do you think the babies were unresponsive to strange objects because they were always close to the mother?*

HINDE *It's possible that restrictive mothers make anxious babies, but the reverse could also be true. The trouble with doing personality tests on baby monkeys is that you cannot instruct the mother not to take part. And if you try to separate the baby from the mother it's a quite different animal. So what we have done is to make a baby filter of the type that Harry Harlow has used. We have attached a six-foot long cage on to the main cage, with a filter between so that the baby can get through and the mother can't, and we let the babies go through into this smaller cage and get used to it, and then put the strange object or the mirror or whatever it is that we are using for the test in this smaller cage. These experiments are now in progress.*

BOWLBY *When the babies are brought up with mothers in isolation, are they in that circumstance from the birth of the baby?*

HINDE *From at least two or three weeks before the birth of the baby.*

BOWLBY *What effect does that have on the mother?*

HINDE *Well she can see other monkeys, she communicates with them.*

HALL *Have you had any babies and mothers in visual isolation?*

HINDE *No, we haven't.*

HALL *Because I imagine that would make a big difference to the mothers?*

HINDE *I think it would.*

OPPÉ *Do you have any information on the behaviour of monkeys which never had a chance to be aunts when they were childless? This is a speculation on the human situation now; we get a lot of young girls becoming mothers who never had a chance to know much about babies, to deal with babies.*

HINDE *You mean, are the monkeys less competent? We have suspected this, but I know of no good data on it. We don't know the history of all our animals in sufficient detail to see this. We get them from zoos and other places.*

OPPÉ *Would it be possible to do this some time in the future?*

HINDE *Oh yes. Is there a difference in the human mothers that you can see?*

OPPÉ *I would say that there's a clinical impression that there is a difference, but I wouldn't put it more strongly than that.*

GUNTHER *I have had many mothers who have not known how to feed. It's unusual now for any woman coming into our hospital to have seen other babies fed, particularly from the breast. They haven't a clue how to do it. A thing which I see all the time is that many of the young women who have never had young siblings to practise on don't have the urge to look after their own baby. I don't know whether they feel they won't be competent at it, or whether the actual aunt kind of behaviour may not have been aroused in them.*

KAUFMAN *I have the case of a monkey which was very much involved in the care of a newborn infant, had subsequently the opportunity to witness three more births and three more babies, and yet when she herself became pregnant, was so frightfully naïve in the birth process that her baby died as a consequence. So this is evidence in the other direction.*

ROSENBLATT *I don't know very much about the maternal cycle in the monkey. Can the aunt have an indirect effect upon the development of the young? For instance, because Eliane was trying to steal the young, did this have any effect upon how long they suckled from the mother?*

HINDE *There are two issues; one is how long the baby spent on the nipple, and the other is how long he went on getting milk. It is very difficult for us to see when they are actively sucking and when they are just attached.*

ROSENBLATT *What I'm trying to say is that because Eliane, the aunt, caused the mother to be over-protective, this might have a secondary effect through the prolongation of maternal behaviour. I have the impression that among rats and cats at least, maternal behaviour finally declines because normally the young leave the mother. But in this case they are prevented from doing so.*

HINDE *I think the mothers play a more active part in terminating maternal behaviour. Active weaning starts at least as early as* 10 *weeks, and she frequently rejects the infant after that time.*

AMBROSE *Can you tell at what age the young can distinguish between the mother and the aunt?*

HINDE *Almost as soon as they are off their mothers, a matter of a few days. But we can't really say what is the basis for this discrimination.*

BOWLBY *I gather that fostering isn't so difficult with monkeys; and that they seem to take to any mother figure. But what happens if the aunt is unfamiliar to the infant?*

JENSEN *They will certainly cling to fairly unfamiliar adults. In the Santiago colony, as I recall, there were one or two males which acted as aunts. They took infants for periods of time and carried them around just as a mother would.*

HINDE *I remember seeing, in a film of the Santiago colony, rhesus infants being carried on the back. We rarely saw this in our monkeys until we kept some mothers in relative isolation, and then they did it. I'm wondering if it depends on not having a lot of other monkeys too close.*

KAUFMAN *We've never seen them being carried on the back, but ours are kept close to each other.*

FOSS *Could there be fashions in this sort of thing? I mean, is it possible that different colonies have different traditions?*

ROWELL *This has been suggested by several people working on rhesus monkeys. Basically they do the same things, though the emphasis is different, in different colonies. One colony I knew would never, or very rarely, use one communicatory gesture and another gesture was unusually common. Incidentally, on carrying babies on the back, even baboons don't do it in my cage in Kampala. I think it's because of short distances and low doors.*

RHEINGOLD *Some of the Japanese workers with Japanese monkeys have found differences from one colony to another, for example in paternal care. It is more common in one group of monkeys than in another; some have learned what's called the candy-opening technique. Others haven't learned it and do nothing with a candy wrapped in paper.*

HINDE *This has been shown very nicely by Weiskrantz & Cowey* (1963) *in Cambridge for the responses of monkeys to new foods. They have found that if an animal is kept in a cage where it could see another animal drinking Ribena, it would readily accept Ribena; whereas an animal which had not seen another individual ever having this new food, took weeks and weeks to accept it.*

ROWELL *This happens in the wild too, in baboons, when a group suddenly picks up a new behaviour pattern. I know of some baboons which had to be exterminated because they took to killing goats, which is not normal baboon behaviour.*

AMBROSE *Could I go back to the mother's handling of the infant? When she was holding them to protect them from the aunt, I presume that there was a good deal of anxiety on the part of the mother and that this would be an anxious holding as opposed to other mothers who would hold their babies much less anxiously but would just let them cling. Did this have any noticeable effect on these two infants?*

HINDE *This is one of the things that we didn't look at sufficiently at the time, and we now have adjusted our recording technique to try to get a line on it. We do know that on the first day or so of life some mothers seem to hold their babies too tight and too high for them to reach the nipple, and they can't reach the nipple until the mother relaxes and allows them to. If the baby's held right up he can't turn his head to find the nipple. Now we are finding out whether, when the baby goes on to the nipple, the mother puts her arm round it or doesn't and so on. But I can't give the information yet.*

ROSENBLATT *Can you really say that the aunt, Eliane, was the cause of the heightened maternal behaviour? Couldn't it be a personality difference in the mother?*

HINDE *Well, it happens that these two babies were statistically outside the range of all the other babies on general behaviour measures, and the one thing they had in common was that their mothers were pestered by Eliane.*

ROSENBLATT *And you'd say that the other mothers would have reacted to Eliane in the same way, if they'd been in the group?*

ROWELL *If the male hadn't been there, the answer is probably no. With a group of animals like this you can't change any one animal without affecting the whole group. So that Eliane's behaviour, and the way the mother reacted to it, and the consequences for the infants, may all be, to some extent, functions of the structure of this particular group of animals.*

HINDE *Nevertheless, we have very consistent data showing that the permissiveness or restrictiveness of the mother depends on dominance reactions of the females.*

Some Observations on a Hand-reared Baboon

THELMA ROWELL

A monkey is relatively helpless at birth; for many weeks it needs milk, transport, warmth and protection. Normally it derives all these from one source, the body of its mother, and it is born with a set of responses which can form one-half of the complex interaction with her by which these needs can be fulfilled. Mother-infant behaviour is so well integrated that it is impossible by observation alone to separate the different maternal functions. When the infant is reared artificially, however, it must make its responses to a bizarre set of stimuli often very unlike the equivalent from its natural mother, and not all collected into one complex 'mother object'. The way in which it adapts to this situation can throw light on the normal behaviour. This technique was first used by Harlow (1958), who separated the sources of food and contact for artificially reared Rhesus monkeys and showed that the 'mother' providing contact was the one with which the infant spent most time.

I hand-reared a baby baboon while working on the behaviour of adult baboons, including some mothers with babies, and have interpreted his responses on the basis of communications between these animals. Observations were made in an ordinary domestic environment, not under exactly controlled conditions, but they could be reliably and repeatedly reproduced: except where stated all descriptions are based on observations made nearly every day for six weeks.

The baboon was about 5 weeks old when I received him, and had then been in captivity "about four weeks". He had been fed on bananas for the first three weeks and probably suffered from malnutrition. For the next week, and when I had him, he was fed on cow's milk four times a day from a baby's bottle; he also sampled all food he saw me eat, but at first this was mostly eliminated undigested. For much of the day he was carried about in the pocket of an apron. During the night he slept in a box with a piece of cloth. At all times he had a child's dummy teat available.

Sucking

When the baboon was first obtained he fretted and was restless unless allowed to suck at one's fingers or clothes. A dummy was provided (which was of course a much better shape for sucking). Rejected at first, within half an hour it was accepted to such an extent that its removal caused stress and active searching behaviour, and there was no further attempt to suck fingers or clothes, unless the dummy was not there when he was under stress. He kept the dummy in his mouth night and day, and while awake was usually making very small, shallow sucking movements on it (Plate 1). When playing or exploring he sometimes dropped it, but then whenever he passed it he would stop and mouth it briefly. In the wild, a baby baboon frequently goes back to its mother during play and takes the nipple briefly in its mouth.

When hungry he would reach and grab wildly for the bottle when he saw it, spitting out the dummy as he did so (Plate 2). He reacted in this way to the bottle itself, empty or full, or to the teat alone, as well as to the fully prepared feed. If his feed was broken off and he was offered the dummy, he took it and sucked it with deep strong movements as if it was the bottle, but given the choice he chose the bottle. As soon as he was satiated (when the big jaw movements used to get milk turned to little shallow movements, or stopped) he chose the dummy when offered dummy and bottle simultaneously (Plate 3). Once he had the dummy in his mouth he would play with the bottle with his hands, but made no attempt to take it in his mouth (Plate 4). This choice behaviour was tested 'formally' two or three times a week, at all times of day, with the same result. Feeding always took place on my lap, so the tests were also done there. While exploring or playing, the dummy was carried or repeatedly returned to, but the bottle, though occasionally mouthed, seemed to have no more interest than any other object of comparable size to the satiated baboon.

Alarm and making Contact

A baby monkey clings to its mother when it finds itself in a frightening situation, or when gestures from the mother indicate her alarm. During the first weeks the mother always accepts her baby and cuddles and suckles it when it comes to her. Later she sometimes rejects it by fending it off or pushing it away, which has been described as weaning behaviour (e.g. by DeVore, 1963). The baby characteristically reacts to this with 'weaning tantrums' — screaming, geckering, calling, and throwing itself about.

Since I was unwilling to provide twenty-four-hour mothering to the infant baboon it was necessary to 'reject' him frequently. Plates 5-10 show a 'weaning tantrum' caused by putting him down suddenly on the floor and breaking contact. His response to this sort of situation and to being frightened by outside sources had many components in common, and will be discussed together. The pattern of his behaviour changed during the three weeks, and can be divided into three phases:

Phase 1

When alarmed by a loud noise or a sudden movement he ran to me and clung desperately hard to my leg; if the dummy was placed in his mouth then, he at once relaxed his grip to normal strength. If only slightly alarmed he might go to the dummy lying on the floor and take it in his mouth, and on two occasions he went to the bottle when neither dummy nor I were available. Presence of strangers did not produce these responses, but they were usually avoided. My putting a hand under him always caused him to cling at once but he did not respond to this invitation from other people. He would cling to be carried by members of the household, but tried to struggle free from strangers and return to me. (In the wild, baby baboons never meet strangers; they do cling to and are carried by other members of the troop for short distances before returning to their mothers.)

When I put him down he would have a 'tantrum' (Plate 5). Providing he was not hungry, this response was much reduced if he was given his dummy, and if he was also placed on the carrying apron the change was usually accepted and he would play there while I was out of sight. (When hungry he was insistent in maintaining contact and screamed continually if left.) Repeated rejection or punishment again produced a tantrum, which abated when he found an object to cling to. From there he would look across at me and make contact calls, then after a few seconds run to me screaming and try to cling again (Plates 6-10).

For the first ten days the pattern was this – recognizing me as primary caretaker, distinguishing familiar people, but content to stay with inanimate parts of his 'caretaker complex' if not hungry. He never, even at this stage, showed any positive responses to the box and cloth with which he spent at least half his life. At the end of this period he began to lipsmack to me when I came back into the room where he had been playing alone. This response was only seen during the few days before the onset of phase 2.

Phase 2

He no longer allowed me out of his sight, and refused to accept dummy or apron, but clung the more fiercely. If he saw me move or even caught my eye he would drop the dummy and run to me. Once on my lap he would begin to search for the dummy, usually at first with lateral swings of the head rubbing muzzle against me, without looking; if he didn't make contact with it in this way he then started looking, and if necessary then climbed down to the floor, get the dummy, and bring it back to my lap to suck. When rejected he tried much longer to get back and cling, and would finally go and hide his head under something and 'cry' – make mixed contact calls and geckers.

At this time he was taken on a stroll with a group of naturalists, whose movements were not dissimilar to those of a troop of foraging baboons, and it was noticeable how similar the baboon's behaviour was to that of babies in the wild. Most of the time he slept while being carried. When the whole group stopped, but not if I stopped alone, he tried to get down and explore. When the other people began to move he ran to me and clung and called before I had made any move. Thus though he made no direct responses to the other people, his movements in relation to me were much affected by them.

Phase 3

The highly dependent phase lasted about ten days, and then he began again to be willing to leave me and play, unless I made a sudden move, when he screamed and clung as before. He was becoming able to climb furniture then, so perhaps he was just more confident of being able to regain contact himself. He would now cling briefly to the feet of strangers, but ran to me if they tried to pick him up. The dummy continued to be important, but it was left for longer periods while playing, and was mainly required while being carried or sleeping.

It is impossible to house-train a monkey, since they have no innate tendency to eliminate in special places, unlike animals which mark a territory or keep a den clean. At this time, however, we realized that the baboon no longer urinated and defecated just anywhere, but he

1*a*. The baby baboon sucked the dummy almost all the time. Here he explored with it in his mouth.

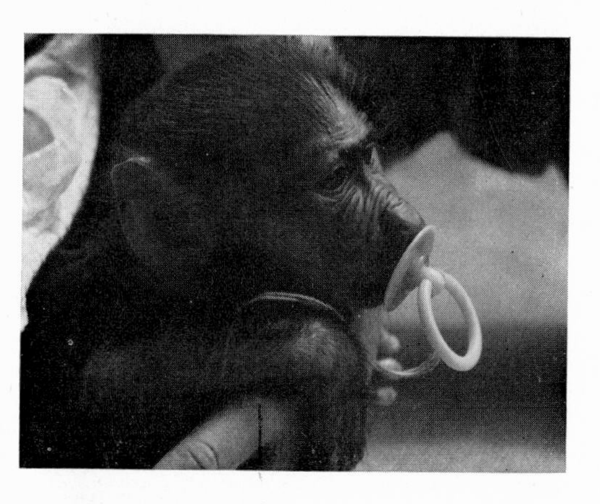

1*b*. At a meal time, before the bottle is shown. Sucks dummy quietly, with small shallow movements. (Note relaxed position of hands).

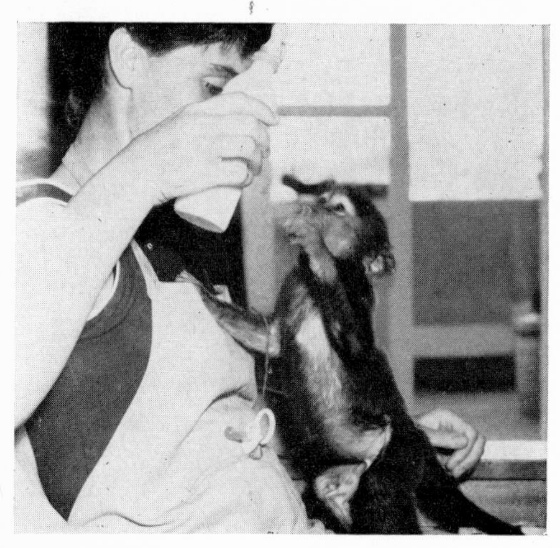

2. When he was hungry and saw the bottle, he grabbed for it, spitting the dummy out.

3. As soon as he was satiated, he chose the dummy if the bottle were taken away and then a choice of bottle and dummy offered. Before he was satiated, he chose the bottle.

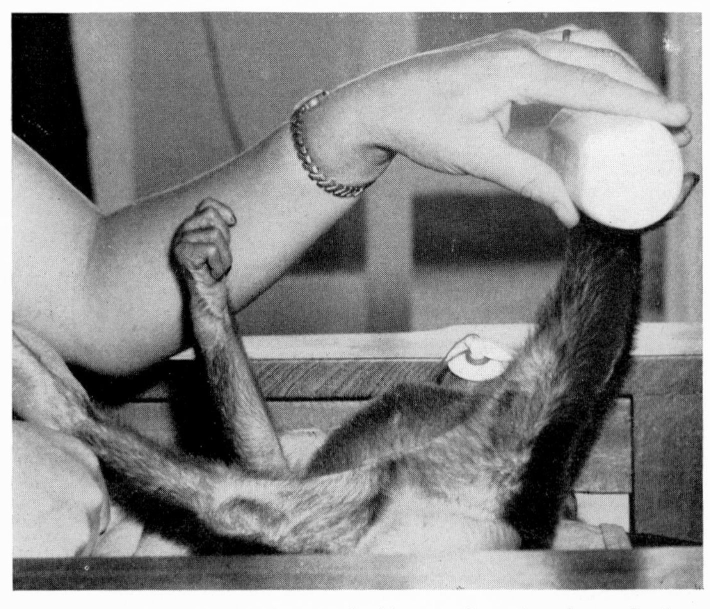

4. When he had the dummy in his mouth again after a feed he would play with the bottle with his hands, but made no attempt to mouth it.

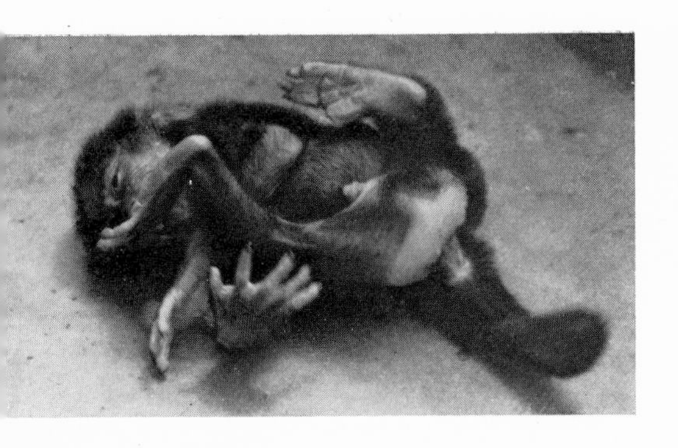

5. A 'weaning tantrum' on being put down. Violent uncoordinated activity, including grasping movements and screaming.

6. The tantrum abates slightly when he achieves some measure of 'contact' by clutching his own limbs.

7. The tantrum continues: he runs to the nearest object, clings to it, then turns and contact calls to the caretaker.

8. From the cushion, after calling, he runs screaming to the caretaker.

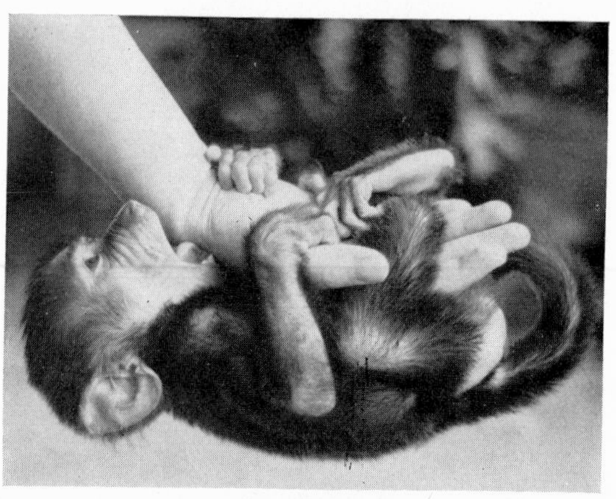

9. Contact regained. He clings frantically and tries to make oral contact too.

10. This position is still unsatisfactory; he looks at the caretaker's face and contact-calls again. He was satisfied when given the dummy and cuddled.

would come to my lap in the midst of play to eliminate, and go away again as soon as he had finished. This seemed to be the result of my having taken evasive action, so that the process became associated with an alarming sequence of being pushed away, followed by cleaning, etc.; so he made the usual response to an alarming situation when about to urinate or defecate by making contact with 'mother' – and thus reinforced the pattern. This behaviour died away when for several days he was given almost continuous contact and attention on a car journey.

Grooming, and Interactions with Baboons

The baboon showed passive acceptance of being handled by me, like that typical of mother-infant reactions in monkeys. He would also make 'grooming postures' in response to being gently scratched, but they were never extreme, and never held for long. His response to the grooming attempts of other baboons, in contrast, was very intense, and he would maintain a posture, head back, eyes shut, for as long as they would groom him through the wire of the cage. But he had been captured before he was old enough to have developed grooming postures, or to be groomed by baboons other than his mother. He was, however, anxious not to be left behind with them, and would leave them and cling to me as soon as I made any move to go.

After the six weeks, when he could feed himself, he was put in the cage with the others, and adopted by them, the adolescent female which had groomed him most becoming his foster mother, protecting, carrying and grooming him. He continues to make contact calls to me and touch me when he can even though for several months I have provided little or no reinforcement and have been absent for long periods.

Discussion

The importance to the baby monkey of having something to suck is shown by the very large part of the time spent sucking, by the hand-reared animal and by babies with their own mothers. Sucking seems to be an essential prerequisite for relaxed behaviour in the young babies; if a stressful situation arises one of the main responses is to try and suck, and if the baby can suck the symptoms of stress disappear. Sucking to get milk seems to be served by a different system of nervous control. The movements used are not the same, and where, as in this case, the objects provided for the two purposes were different, there was very little overlap in the uses to which they were put – the food provider had very little value as a security provider, The dummy, but not the bottle, was the object of some of Harlow's 'affectional responses'.

The different parts of the new caretaker complex were extremely quickly learned when I adopted the baboon, but at first were not markedly preferred one against the other. It was not for ten days that an individual attachment to the human carrier/handler developed which was stronger than the attachment to inanimate parts of the system, and which has continued when no longer reinforced. It was not surprising that this differentiation took place, if only because of the much more complex stimulus provided by me than by the dummy.

The young monkey's only response to alarm or stress is to cling to its mother and suck. When the mother rejects or causes alarm itself, the baby has no adequate organized response. Instead it goes into violent uncoordinated activity, throwing itself about and screaming and grasping randomly, which would appear to be non-adaptive (a mother monkey ignores it). Such a 'tantrum' only abates when something is found to cling to, which may be another monkey, or for the hand-reared animal a cushion, or even his own legs. From that position another attempt is made to contact the mother. The hand-reared baboon showed this behaviour at a much earlier age than babies whose own mothers do not reject them until they are weaning.

The baby baboon was captured before he was old enough to have much active interaction with baboons other than its mother, and after that all social responses were made to people or substitute objects. Yet only baboons could provide the correct stimuli for grooming postures, and adoption by baboons was not difficult. Social integration in this case was a flexible process.

Discussion following Dr Thelma Rowell's Paper

OPPÉ *The way in which the baboon preferred the dummy* (*or pacifier*) *to the bottle is very striking. Did the two have similar teats?*

ROWELL *They were both rubber but of different shapes, and neither was like a baboon teat.*

BOWLBY *And he was introduced to the bottle before the dummy?*

ROWELL *Yes. He was fed from a bottle for several days before I had him.*

KAUFMAN *Do you deduce anything from this comparison of the bottle with the pacifier or dummy?*

ROWELL *I concluded that what reinforcement the milk gave had no effect outside the feeding situation. I had expected that when he had finished feeding I would have to take away the bottle, but he always gave it up himself and went to the dummy.*

FOSS *Perhaps he could manipulate the dummy more easily?*

ROWELL *He made the same choice even when I was holding the dummy, so that he couldn't manipulate it.*

THOMAS *Some human infants put their thumb in along with the mother's teat, as though they had a need for something firmer to suck.*

BOWLBY *Yes, isn't it the case that dummies are firmer than bottle teats?*

ROWELL *They varied, but they were usually pretty soggy by the time I changed them for a new one.*

GUNTHER *I was struck by the two kinds of mouth and jaw movement during sucking. You said that only the larger movements were associated with feeding. Something like this happens with humans, but with them the smaller movements seem to function to call up the draft of milk, and then give place to larger movements. When they've finished feeding they do not make any more sucking movements, in fact they reject the teat by shutting the mouth firmly, or putting the tongue out.*

ROWELL *But doesn't a human baby often fall asleep on the nipple?*

GUNTHER *Yes, it often retains the nipple.*

FREEDMAN *Did the baboon usually close his eyes while feeding? In some of the pictures he seems to look up at you imploringly.*

ROWELL *He closes his eyes, and usually goes off to sleep, but opens them if he wants more milk or to look for the dummy. He usually didn't look at my face while actually feeding. At most the eyes were open a crack, as human babies do. Of course, if the bottle were removed, he would open his eyes immediately.*

FREEDMAN *When does eye-to-eye contact most often happen?*

ROWELL *It's commoner with older monkeys, especially when they want to play.*

GUNTHER *The human infant has his eyes on the mother at the beginning of the feed, but not usually afterwards.*

HALL *You seem to have a lot of trouble toilet-training the infant. How does the baboon mother avoid getting messed up?*

ROWELL *The infant's backside hangs clear of the mother when she's sitting on a branch, and all is well.*

AINSWORTH *What I found fascinating is that Ganda mothers behave exactly as you did, holding the infant out and letting it dribble on the floor – at least until they start systematic training.*

GEWIRTZ *When you visited baboons together with your baboon infant, did they respond to you as they would to a baboon mother?*

ROWELL *While I had the baboon, and for a short time afterwards, the baboons often presented to me for grooming and would sit close to me. When the baby went too close to what they regarded as dangers they would look to me to rescue him and grunt when I picked him up, as they do to baboon mothers; and when they tried to touch him through the wire they kept glancing at me to see my response, and jumped away if I moved.*

PART II

Human Studies

Transport of the Human Young

HARRIET L. RHEINGOLD and
GERALDINE C. KEENE

Transport of the young by the parent has been described for many animals, but transport of the human young, in contrast, has received little attention. Yet, in humans, transport of the young is not only common but open for inspection; its very obviousness undoubtedly has obscured it as a topic of interest. Salk (1960) did report that more mothers in a hospital held their newborn young on the left side than on the right. The child's contribution to transport has been discussed under the heading of clinging by Bowlby (1958). Viewing clinging more generally, and not specifically during transport, he proposed that clinging is one of several instinctual responses of the human infant which later becomes integrated into attachment behavior. Ainsworth (1963) also listed clinging as an attachment response.

Transport is one form of contact between parent and young and thus is of interest in the study of parent-child relationships. It is a simple and straightforward form; its charting is therefore easy and its relevance clear. Furthermore, since the young, human and animal, may assume some or all of the initiative – by clinging – a study of transport yields information on the contribution of the young to maintaining contact with the parent and thus to parent-infant interaction.

Four main problems appear to be important in the study of transport. Once it has been established for any species that transport does occur, the first problem is discovering the contribution of each member of the pair to the activity. In some species it is the adult who picks up, holds, and carries the more or less passive young. In others, the young clings to the adult with only acquiescence from the adult; that is, the adult permits the young to attach itself. In still other species, both adult and young contribute to the transport. Furthermore, in many species, the activity of each member of the pair changes as the young grow older.

The second problem is establishing the identity of the individual which transports the young. In most species this is not only a female but the mother; in others, fathers, males, and even juveniles may transport the young.

The third problem is describing the mode of transport. What organs of prehension does the animal employ? What are the bodily adjustments of the partner? The means employed for transport by adults and young vary considerably among the orders of animals and even among families within an order. Obviously, the structure of the animal and the capabilities of the young are determining factors.

The last problem is discovering the compass of transport. In some species, the adult transports the young only to the nest. Transport of this nature has been studied in the laboratory as 'retrieving'. In other species the young are transported more extensively, often as the adult pursues its usual round of daily activities.

The purpose of this paper is twofold. First, part of the literature on transport of the young in animals is summarized; the survey is illustrative and not complete, and the ordering of species is ours and not necessarily that of systematic zoology. Second, transport in the human will be described, based on a study of 546 adult-child pairs. The parts form separate studies, but the survey of transport in animals is intended as background against which transport in humans can be viewed.

Transport in Infra-mammalian Animals

Young, in larval or immature forms, as distinguished from eggs only, are transported by many non-mammalian species (Buchsbaum, 1948; Cloudsley-Thompson, 1960). With the common jellyfish, *Aurelia aurita*,[1] the larvae remain attached to the underside of the female. The larvae of the six-armed starfish, *Leptasterias*, are sheltered in a brood chamber on the lower side of the female and emerge as little starfish. In the wolf spider, *Tarantula inquilina*, newly hatched young are closely packed on the female's abdomen and disperse only if disturbed. The female scorpion, on the other hand, carries young on her back; as many as twenty young may be transported in this manner. Certain arthropods of the class Crustacea, such as crayfish,

[1] The nomenclature used by the quoted author has been adopted in every instance.

lobsters, and some crabs, also carry embryos about with them. For example, the eggs of the crayfish develop while attached to the swimmerets; they hatch into young which look like miniature adults and cling for some time.

Transport of the young by the male occurs in the native pipefish; in *Syngnathus* and seahorses, the young are carried in brood pouches. Male participation is also found in mouthbreeding fish, such as *Arius falcarius*, and in the cichlids. In *Tilapia natalensis*, the hatched young at first spend the nights in the mouth of the male and slip back into it when in danger.

Transport of the young by flying non-mammalian animals is rare, if at all. In the social insects and birds, animals in which parental care is well developed, the young mature in stationary nurseries. That the young of swan and woodcock are transported on the backs of their parents has been reported by Burton (1957).

Transport in Mammals

Among mammals, in contrast to the other classes of animals, transport of the young is more often the rule, less often the exception (Bourlière, 1954; Causey & Waters, 1936). The ungulates form a conspicuous exception.

The young of the Spiny Echidna (*Tachyglossus aculeatus*) of the order Monotremata are carried in the female's pouch for several weeks (Cockrum, 1962). Females of the order Marsupialia possess well-developed marsupia, containing mammary glands, in which the young are carried for several months. The opossum, koala, and kangaroo are the best-known examples in this order; the opossum and the koala young also ride the mother's back for some time after they leave the pouch.

The young of the pouchless marsupial, *Marmosa cinera* (Plate 11), cling to their mothers throughout the first part of their lives by grasping her nipples with their mouths and her fur with their feet (Beach, 1939). In retrieving, the *Marmosa* pushes the young under her belly. There, the young rolls over on its back, seizes the ventral hair of the mother with its feet, and makes searching movements with its snout until the mouth fastens to a nipple.

The female flying lemur, *Cynocephalus volans*, the sole representative of the order Dermoptera, hangs upside down from a tree or in a den; her infant hangs across her abdomen, rear feet on one side, fore feet on the other (Wharton, 1950), with its head near the two nipples in the axilla of each forearm. It is sometimes left hanging alone while the mother is feeding.

From birth, the young of bats (order Chiroptera) clings to the ventral surface of the female with its clawed thumb and feet, as well as to the nipple with its mouth (Davis, Herreid & Short, 1962; Pearson, Koford & Pearson, 1952). Howell & Little (1924) described the young of the California bat (*Eptesicus fuscus fuscus*) as 'not clinging to the under surface of the female with feet and wings "spraddled out", but in such position beneath the membrane as to face the same direction as the dam, strongly reminding us of the attitude assumed by a human mother when walking with an arm and a portion of her cape over the shoulders of her child' (p. 261). Although the young of most species hang head downward, in the same direction as the mother's body, young horseshoe bats (*Rhinolophus*) hang head upwards (Hediger, 1955). According to Harms, as reported by Hediger (p. 75), the males of some bats carry the young alternately with the females. As the young usually do not accompany adults on their flying trips, transport in this order is limited.

The sloths, among the Edentata, carry their single young on their bellies – in their laps, so to speak – as they move among the branches with their dorsal surfaces parallel to the ground (Causey & Waters, 1936). Yet the giant ant-eater young of the same order rides its mother's back (Plate 12).

Transport in the Lagomorpha has not been observed (Ross, Denenberg, Frommer & Sawin, 1959).

In the order Rodentia, which includes mice, rats, hamsters, squirrels, chipmunks and beavers, in contrast, transport appears to be the rule; it not only has been frequently reported in naturalistic and laboratory studies but, as retrieving, has been extensively manipulated both for the stimuli eliciting it and for measures of maternal attentiveness (e.g. Beach & Jaynes, 1956; Causey & Waters, 1936; Lehrman, 1961; Rosenblatt & Lehrman, 1963; Rowell, 1960; Wiesner & Sheard, 1933).

Young mice are sometimes transported by their own efforts – by clinging to the female's nipples (reported for *Peromyscus nuttalli* by Goodpaster & Hoffmeister, 1954; for *Peromyscus maniculatus* by Huestis, 1933, and King, 1958; for *Peromyscus gossypinus* by Pournelle, 1952), often so tenaciously that it is difficult to remove them – and sometimes by the mother who grasps them in her mouth. In nature, the stimulus for the mother's retrieving seems to be some disturbance to the nest or the young's presence outside the nest during the early days of its life; it is to the nest, the old one or a new one, that she transports them.

In retrieving, the female grasps the young in her teeth, belly side up or, variably, by some other part, and then manipulates it with her front paws until the young is in a horizontal position with its ventral surface toward the mother (Curio, 1955; Goodpaster & Hoffmeister, 1954; Huestis, 1933). Older young, which cannot be so easily manipulated by the mother, are often transported by the nape of the neck or by the skin of its back (King, 1958).

Other members of the species, besides the mother, have been reported to transport young mice – males (Horner, 1947), virgin females, and even immature mice (Beniest-Noirot, 1958). Similarly, juvenile hamsters retrieve infant hamsters (Rowell, 1960).

Transport in the wood rat (*Neotoma albigula*) is achieved by the young's clinging to the nipple (Richardson, 1943). In the laboratory rat, transport appears to be limited to retrieving by the mother, and the mother alone (Causey & Waters, 1936). Although the female carries the young in her teeth and at times uses the front feet to shift the young in her mouth, no preference for any part of the young's anatomy is exhibited (Causey & Waters, 1936).

Squirrels and flying squirrels transport young in their mouths, grasping their ventral surfaces, the young apparently responding by curling its head and fore limbs on one side of the mother's head, its tail and hind limbs on the other (Hatt, 1927; Lang, 1925; Svihla, 1930). The thirteen-striped ground squirrel (*Citellus tridecemlineatus*) retrieves the infant at its belly, the older young at its shoulder, neck, or foot, and partly drags it back to the nest (Wade, 1927).

Retrieving by the chipmunks resembles that of the other rodents. The young of *Eutamias dorsalis dorsalis* is held belly-side up in its mother's mouth, with its tail, hind legs and fore paws curled around the mother's neck (Svihla & Svihla, 1930). Similarly, the muskrat (Warren, 1924) carries young in its mouth, holding it by the skin of the belly. Tevis (1950), during three months of careful observation, never saw a young beaver being transported, either by the mother's efforts or by the young's riding the mother's back.

Transport of the young by the dog, among the carnivores, is not common (Causey & Waters, 1936; Rheingold, 1963b), retrieving to the home place more often being accomplished by homing it in, nose to nose. But, the female wolf will move young born away from the den; she holds them in the mouth so that the head and tail project on each side of her head, although she may take them on occasion by the nape of the neck (Young & Goldman, 1944).

The sea otter (*Enhydra lutris nereis*), in contrast to the rodents and the Canidae, carries the infant on her chest, and holds it with her forepaws as she lies in the water or swims on her back (Barabash-Nikiforov, 1962; Fisher, 1940).

With the Felidae, one returns to a retrieving type of transport (Plate 13). The mother cat grasps the kitten with her teeth, most frequently at the nape of the neck (Leyhausen, 1956), although not always (Schneirla, 1963).

The suborder of Pinnepedia concludes the survey of the carnivores. Cows of the Alaska fur seal (*Callorhinus ursinus*) retrieve pups only in the hours immediately following parturition and only if the pups move or fall away from them. They carry the pups in the mouth for a few feet (Bartholomew, 1959). Scheffer (1945) observed two sea lions (*Eumentopias jubata*) carry their young at the approach of man, using their mouths: one animal was seized by the skinfolds of its neck, the other by its rump. A young sea lion was also seen trying to climb on its mother's back. Thus, also, a manatee young (order Sirenia, *Trichechus manatus latirostris*) was observed riding its mother's back, holding on with its flippers (Moore, 1957).

Transport in the Primates

Primates of all families carry the young on their bodies and for days and weeks the contact between young and parent is almost constant. In general, the young grasp the fur of the adult, using hands and feet, with little assistance from the adult. They cling to the ventral surface at first; later, many primate young cling to the back, and some eventually ride jockey style, sitting on the rump of the parent. (Plate 14 illustrates back clinging in the squirrel monkey.)

The young of lorises and lemurs cling transversally across the abdomens of their mothers (Hediger, 1955). The marmoset, on the other hand, clutches the fur of the father's back. The female takes the young to its ventral surface for nursing and cleaning and then 'transfers it back to the male immediately upon completion of these activities' (Stellar, 1960, p. 4).

The rhesus infant clings to its mother from birth (Tinklepaugh & Hartman, 1932). The infant orients itself toward her in the ventral-ventral position and holds the fur on either side of her body with both hands and feet. In the early days of its life, the head of the young is oriented upward toward the mother as she walks (personal observation of the colony at Santiago Island, Puerto Rico, in 1959). When he is a few weeks old, however, he twists his head and faces forward, that is, in the direction his mother is travelling. As the infant grows older, he may occasionally be seen on his mother's back, usually lying prone, head down, grasping her fur with hands and feet. Sometimes he rides close to her neck, at other times closer to her haunches. No instance of a mother's holding the infant in place was seen in a week of observation, although mothers sometimes drew infants to themselves preliminary to moving away.

The infant baboon clings to its mother within a few hours of birth (DeVore, 1963). During a long trek – the troop moves three miles a day – the mother may clasp a hand to the infant every twenty to twenty-five steps. After the second day of life even this assistance is rarely given. (Only the most dominant males occasionally carry infants on their bellies). The infant rides underneath the mother for the first month; thereafter, he rides her back more and more often. At first he lies across her back but by 4 to 6 months of age he sits up and rides jockey style. It is the infant who takes the initiative in most instances; the mother signals when she is about to move away from the infant; she clasps him to her only when startled. Until the infant is 7½ months old he rides the mother's back for a large part of each day. Weaning, between the eleventh and fifteenth month, involves, among other deprivations, not permitting the young to ride her back.

The langur also clings to its mother's belly at birth (Jay, 1963), but for several days it receives assistance when she walks or runs. During the first week of life the mother helps it into a riding position with a touch of the hand or a sweeping gesture of the arm. Other adult females, besides its mother, hold and carry it also. By the second month of life, the mother no longer signals when she is departing. Clinging to the ventral surface continues until weaning; riding the mother's back was not observed.

The newborn gorilla infant, in contrast to rhesus, langur and baboon infants, is continuously supported by the mother's arm (Schaller, 1963). The infant, in the ventral-ventral position and parallel to the long axis of the mother, grasps her fur but its hold is insecure and frequently a leg or arm slips off and waves in the air. The infant is a month old before it can cling without assistance long enough to permit the female to climb into trees. Infants may lack the strength to clasp securely, but it is also possible that the conformation of the mother's body may make grasping difficult: her chest is broad and sparsely haired and the abdomen is rounded. Her back, in contrast, is broad and flat, and the hair is long. Infants begin to ride their mother's backs at three months of age, and by a year are carried against the chest only when startled. The characteristic position on the back of a moving female is prostrate, with the head near her shoulders, hands grasping hair on each side, and legs spread. Retrieving by the gorilla mother is common; the infants are pulled back during the first four or five months when they venture more than ten feet away. Other members of the group, adult males and females, as well as juveniles, transport infants but only for short distances; over long distances the infants cling only to mothers.

The gibbon infant clings crosswise at the mother's thighs (Coolidge, 1933). When the mother climbs (about the cage), she draws up her hind legs and forms a pocket in which the infant lies with its head on one side of her body and its legs on the other.

The early position of the chimpanzee infant is on the lower surface of the mother's abdomen, in ventral-ventral contact, head uppermost, the limbs extending along her sides and the extremities grasping hair, skin, or both (Tomilin & Yerkes, 1935). During the fifth month, the infant shifts from clinging to the abdominal wall of the mother to riding her back. From personal observation at the Washington Zoo (during 1960), we know that by at least the sixth day the infant can cling unaided as the mother walks and climbs in her cage.

Transport in the Human

To obtain information on how the human child is transported, we set up a descriptive study and observed adults carrying children in public places in metropolitan Washington, D.C. People just holding children in laps or pushing children in baby carriages were not included in the survey; neither were children carrying children. And, to discover whether people carried children in the same way as they carried other objects, we also observed people carrying bags of groceries.

The items of behavior selected for recording in the study refer in part to how the adult carried the child and in part to how the child contributed or adjusted to being carried. For the adult the items were: *side of body* child was carried on, right, left, or middle; *transport location*, shoulder, chest, hip, back or neck (child sitting on shoulders of adult, straddling shoulders and neck); and *orientation* of the child's body to the adult's, toward, sideway, or away. For the child the items were: *activity of arms*, resting on the adult's body or 'free', and *activity of the hands*, closed on adult's clothing or body, resting on some part of adult's body, or 'free'. 'Free' was employed when the child's hand or arm was not in contact with the adult's body or clothing. Other items of interest were age and sex of child, sex and handedness of adult, and relation of child to the adult who was carrying him.

Method

To provide a set of standards for recording the items referring to posture during transport, sixteen mothers holding their infants were photographed in the laboratory. Every effort was made to catch their natural mode of carrying the child, but in any case they served only as examples and were not included in the survey. The infants ranged in age from 2·7 to 17·7 months. Front views were taken first, and then back views if the child's hands or arms were not visible in the front view. From this series Plates 15, 16, 17 and 18 were chosen to illustrate the major items.

In the summer of 1963, the observers visited public places where people carrying children were likely to be. The places included parks, fairs, airports, amusement parks, and shopping centers. Weekends were sampled as well as weekdays and, within a day, late afternoon and early evening were more frequently sampled than morning or early afternoon. The resulting sample, therefore, was a heterogeneous one, neither randomly nor systematically selected; it was, rather, a sample of people carrying children in the places, and at the times, we were observing.

On spotting an adult carrying a child, the observer approached until a clear view of adult and child was obtained, and the positions of the child in the adult's arms and of the child's hands and arms were fixed in mind. Only then did the observer address the adult, stating an interest in how people carry children and asking the child's age, the adult's relation to the child, and the adult's handedness (hand used to write with? cut with? etc.). The observations and the parent's responses were then recorded on a checklist. Most people reacted to the queries in positive and friendly fashion. Only two persons, both men, refused to respond; a few other men appeared somewhat reluctant. Women, in contrast, were more friendly, usually volunteered additional information and, if accompanying a man who hesitated, answered for him.

Subjects

Data were collected on 546 adult-child pairs. Of these, 475 (87 per cent) were white and 69 (13 per cent) Negro, as Table 2 shows. Women slightly outnumbered men as carriers of children, constituting 58·6 per cent of the sample. The most common relationship was parent and child; it was similar for both sexes, although the proportion of non-parent adults was greater in both Negro men and women.

TABLE 2

Sex and Color of Adult and Adult's Relation to Child

Sex and Relation	COLOR						Total
	White		Negro		Other		
	N	%	N	%	N	%	N
Male							
Parent	169	85·8	18	62·1	0	0·0	187
Other	28	14·2	11	37·9	0	0·0	39
Total	197	41·5	29	42·0	0	0·0	226
Female							
Parent	233	83·8	26	65·0	2	100·0	261
Other	45	16·2	14	35·0	0	0·0	59
Total	278	58·5	40	58·0	2	100·0	320
Total	475	87·0	69	12·8	2	0·004	546

The children ranged in age from 3 weeks to 8 years, with 89 per cent of them under 3 years of age (Table 3). After 3 years of age, the number of children being carried fell off sharply, although one 8-year-old girl was observed in her father's arms. The smaller number being carried under one year of age obviously tells little about the age at which the human child is most often carried; it suggests, rather, that infants under a year of age are not taken to the places sampled as often as children in the second year of life.

TABLE 3

Age of Child according to Sex of Adult and Child

Age of Child in Months	Adult Male			Adult Female			Total		
	Boys	Girls	Total	Boys	Girls	Total	Boys	Girls	Total
0– 11·9	16	22	38	54	57	111	70	79	149
12– 23·9	36	41	77	47	71	118	83	112	195
24– 35·9	48	30	78	29	36	65	77	66	143
36– 47·9	11	14	25	8	13	21	19	27	46
48– 59·9	1	4	5	2	1	3	3	5	8
60– 71·9	1	1	2	1	1	2	2	2	4
72– 83·9	0	0	0	0	0	0	0	0	0
84– 95·9	0	0	0	0	0	0	0	0	0
96–107·9	0	1	1	0	0	0	0	1	1
Total	113	113	226	141	179	320	254	292	546

Age of child and sex of adult appeared to be related (Table 3); the younger children were more often carried by women, the older children by men (chi square=24·12, P<·001, for a 2×2 table of sex of parent and age of child, divided into two categories: below and over 2 years of age). Age of child, however, appeared not to be related to sex of child. Sex of child and sex of adult were also not related: men carried boys and girls in equal proportion; women, in contrast, carried more girls than boys, but the difference was not significant.

Side of the body children carried on

Six of the children were carried in devices, one in a canvas sling and five in cradle boards (commercial name of device is often Infanseat). They ranged in age from 1·2 to 7 months; four of the adults were women, two were men, and all were white. These subjects are excluded from all subsequent tallies.

Table 4 (see row totals) shows that more men held children on their right side (46·9 per cent) than on their left (38·9 per cent); in contrast, more women held children on their left side (55·9 per cent) than on their right (37·8 per cent). The middle position, observed least often, was used by more of the men (14·2 per cent) than of the women

(6·2 per cent). Sex of adult and side therefore appear to be related; a test of significance over the three positions and the two sexes indicates that in fact sex and side in this sample are not independent (chi square = 19·3, $P < ·001$).

It should be noted that the percentage of women, right or left handed, carrying children on the left side departed markedly from Salk's (1960) report that 83 per cent of right-handed women and 78 per cent of left-handed women carried their infants on the left. Salk, however, observed mothers of newborn infants in a hospital, a sample different from ours.

What was the effect of handedness on side? The number of people reporting right, left and mixed handedness was similar for the sexes (Table 4). But no simple effect of handedness was apparent. Instead, it appeared that right-handed men behaved differently from right-handed women. Thus, right-handed men carried on the right or left in almost equal proportions (44·9 per cent and 40·9 per cent, respectively). Right-handed women, in contrast, showed proportions of 56·8 per cent for the left side and 36·5 per cent for the right. For right-handed persons, then, there is an interaction between side and sex (chi square = 14·69, $P < ·001$).

TABLE 4

Side of Body Child carried on according to Handedness and Sex of Adult

Handedness by Sex of Adult	SIDE CARRIED ON						Total	
	Right		Middle		Left			
	N	%	N	%	N	%	N	%
Male								
Right	89	44·9	28	14·1	81	40·9	198	87·6
Mixed	5	62·5	0	0·0	3	37·5	8	3·5
Left	12	60·0	4	20·0	4	20·0	20	8·8
Total	106	46·9	32	14·2	88	38·9	226	
Female								
Right	104	36·5	19	6·7	162	56·8	285	89·1
Mixed	1	16·7	0	0·0	5	83·3	6	1·9
Left	16	55·2	1	3·4	12	41·4	29	9·1
Total	121	37·8	20	6·2	179	55·9	320	

Left-handed men and women did resemble each other; the data suggest that more left-handed people carried the children on the right than on the left side. The number of cases was small, however, and the difference was not large. Similarly, mixed handedness occurred so infrequently that its effect upon side cannot be evaluated.

In summary, the data reveal no simple relationship between handedness and side. Sex of adult is at least one factor affecting the relationship; other factors, perhaps associated with early learning, may also be important.

Side of body groceries carried on

Are children and packages carried the same way? Does the nature of the object affect the side of the body on which it is held? How do handedness and side interact now? The observer, posted near the check-out counters of supermarkets, recorded the side on which large bags of groceries were held against the body. Data were obtained on 200 people, men and women as they came, who were asked only about their handedness.

As was true with the carrying of children, more records were made of women than of men carrying groceries (Table 5). More men *and*

TABLE 5

Transport of Groceries: Side carried on according to Handedness and Sex of Adult

Handedness by Sex of Adult	SIDE CARRIED ON						Total	
	Right		Middle		Left			
	N	%	N	%	N	%	N	%
Male								
Right	16	27·6	3	5·2	39	67·2	58	84·0
Mixed	2	33·33	0	0·0	4	66·7	6	8·7
Left	3	60·0	0	0·0	2	40·0	5	7·2
Total	21	30·4	3	4·3	45	65·2	69	
Female								
Right	50	41·7	11	9·2	59	49·2	120	91·6
Mixed	0	0·0	0	0·0	2	100·0	2	1·5
Left	4	44·4	1	11·1	4	44·4	9	6·9
Total	54	41·2	12	9·2	65	49·6	131	

women carried groceries on the left side than on the right (see totals for rows). The left side was favored, also, by right-handed men and women. In this respect, men carried children and groceries differently; women, not differently. The number of mixed- and left-handed persons of either sex in a sample of only 200 subjects unfortunately was too small for evaluation.

Transport location

The children were most often carried at the shoulder, less often at the chest, hip, back or neck (Table 6). More women than men carried children at the hip, and only men used the back or neck position. The chest was used more often for carrying the child under 1 year, the hip for older children. Thus, sex of adult and age of child appear to be related to the part of the body at which the child is held.

TABLE 6

Transport Location according to Sex of Adult and Age of Child (in percentages)

Part of Body	Age of Child in Months by Sex of Adult						Total	
	0–11·9		12–23·9		24+			
	Men	Women	Men	Women	Men	Women	Men	Women
Chest	36·1	26·2	19·5	10·2	11·7	12·1	18·3	16·1
Shoulder	50·0	56·1	51·9	40·7	45·0	36·3	48·2	44·6
Hip	11·1	17·8	23·4	49·2	30·6	51·6	25·0	39·2
Neck	2·8	0·0	5·2	0·0	10·8	0·0	7·6	0·0
Back	0·0	0·0	0·0	0·0	1·8	0·0	0·9	0·0

Orientation of child's body

Children were most often held with their bodies toward the parent, in ventral-ventral contact (Table 7). Both sideway and away orientation (child held so that his back was against the adult's body) were uncommon. An age trend was apparent: both the away and sideway positions were seen more often in the children under 1 year of age, whereas the toward position increased in frequency as age of child increased. On this variable, men and women were remarkably similar.

TABLE 7

Orientation of Child's Body to Adult's according to Sex of Adult and Age of Child (in percentages)

Orientation	Age of Child in Months by Sex of Adult						Total	
	0–11·9		12–23·9		24+			
	Men	Women	Men	Women	Men	Women	Men	Women
Toward	66·7	74·8	84·4	83·0	87·3	85·7	82·6	81·0
Away	19·4	7·5	7·8	5·1	4·5	4·4	8·0	5·7
Sideway	13·9	17·8	7·8	11·9	9·1	9·9	9·4	13·3

Activity of child's hands

The most characteristic position of the children's hands was free, that is, not resting or closed on the adults' bodies or clothing, not in any sense clinging. This was true for both sexes and at all ages (Table 8). Resting a hand on the adult (his clothing or body) was next in frequency. Holding the hand closed on the adult's clothing or body was an infrequent event, at no age accounting for more than 10 per cent of the observations. Aside from this main finding, inspection of the data reveals a few age and sex differences. The hands of children 2 years of age and older rested on the adult more frequently than was true of younger children, but even then this occurred in only about a third of the subjects. Similarly, frequency of having the hand not in contact with adult's body or clothing decreased in general with age; still at the oldest age (24 months and over) it was observed in more than half the subjects. As for sex differences, at each of the three ages more girls than boys closed their hands on the adult's body or clothing, more boys than girls rested their hands on the adult's body or clothing, more girls than boys held a hand free of the adult.

Since the hands of the children were predominantly free, neither resting on the adult nor closed on his clothing, it may be asked whether they were engaged in any other activity. The records show that the hands of only 4 of the 143 children under a year of age were engaged in some other activity: bringing a finger to mouth or holding a pacifier, his own clothing, or a balloon. For the 195 children between 1 and 2 years of age, there were 25 who had a finger in the mouth or held some other object; for the 202 children who were 2 years of age and older, there were 17 children holding something in their hands. The objects included toys, nursing bottles, and ice-cream cones. It must be concluded, therefore, that the great majority of the children were not only not holding on to the adults who carried them but were also not doing anything else with their hands. Their hands, instead, hung free, as Table 8 illustrates.

TABLE 8

Activity of Child's Hands by Age and Sex of Child
(*in percentages*)

Activity of Hands	Age in Months by Sex of Child						Total	
	0–11·9		12–23·9		24+			
	Boys	Girls	Boys	Girls	Boys	Girls	Boys	Girls
Closed on adult's body	2·9	0·7	1·0	2·2	2·5	7·4	2·2	3·6
Closed on adult's clothing	3·7	10·0	6·6	8·0	5·9	3·5	5·6	6·9
Resting on adult	25·7	8·7	19·3	10·3	37·1	32·7	28·2	17·7
Free	67·6	80·7	72·9	79·5	54·4	56·4	64·1	71·7
N of Children	68	75	83	112	101	101	252	288

Note. Activity of right and left hands were combined and averaged.

Position of child's arms

The children's arms, like their hands, were more often free than holding, or resting on, any part of the adult's body (Table 9). When they did have their arms on the adult, the adult's shoulders or arms were favored. No clear sex difference was apparent. Age brought a slight increase in arm on adult's shoulder, and a slight decrease in arm on adult's arm.

The data on the children's arm and hand activity indicate that, under the circumstances in which they were observed, the children in general did not hold on to their parents. Only 5 of the 546 records contain such terms as clinging, clutching or gripping. It was a sufficiently rare event to be worthy of note and would have been recorded. It must be concluded that the children in our sample contributed little to their own transport, if clinging is the criterion.

TABLE 9

Position of Child's Arms by Age and Sex of Child
(*in percentages*)

Position of Arms	Age of Child in Months by Sex of Child						Total	
	0–11·9		12–23·9		24+			
	Male	Female	Male	Female	Male	Female	Male	Female
On adult's neck	0·7	0·0	1·2	1·3	3·0	5·4	1·8	2·4
On adult's shoulder	11·0	9·3	16·3	12·9	26·2	26·7	18·8	16·8
On adult's arm	23·5	17·3	23·5	20·1	16·8	16·8	20·8	18·2
Free	64·7	73·3	59·0	65·6	54·0	51·0	58·5	62·5

Note. Activity of right and left arms were combined and averaged.

Effect of precarious balance

The few children who did cling were carried by adults who were leaning over or otherwise departing from their usual posture. In order to observe clinging produced by parental change in posture, seven mothers (from the original sixteen 'standard' subjects) returned to the laboratory for study. Each was asked, while holding her child, to pick up a small suitcase. The task did not produce clinging in five of the seven subjects (Plate 19 is illustrative). Of the two who did cling, Plate 20 is illustrative. The situation was contrived, to be sure. The mothers leaned over or bent their knees slowly and carefully; as a consequence, the balance of the children was probably never in peril. It seems likely that sudden movements or genuine loss of balance would elicit a clinging response. So, too, would a stranger's reaching for the child (Ainsworth, 1963).

Discussion

The results of the human survey showed that children were carried in public places by both men and women. They were most often carried by their parents, but sometimes by other members of the group, by aunts, uncles, grandparents and friends. The children ranged in age from 3 weeks to 8 years with most of them under 3 years. Men more often held children on the right side of their bodies, women more often on the left; the difference, however, was small. Handedness accounted only in small part for the side on which the child was carried. (Men tended to carry bags of groceries on the left, and thus differently from the side on which they carried children.) Children were most often carried at the shoulder, although younger ones were often held at the chest, older ones at the hip. In general, women favored the hip more than men, whereas only men were observed to carry children on their backs. The commonest orientation of child to adult for both men and women, regardless of the age of the child, was ventral-ventral contact. Children, it was found, seldom grasped the adults' bodies or clothing; rather, they tended not to have their arms, and especially not their hands, in contact with the adult.

The findings therefore suggest that in the human species the adult assumes the major responsibility for transporting the child. Under the conditions of observations in this study, the human child appeared to contribute little to his own support bymeans of her hands and arms.

Clinging to Immature Organisms

Clinging is defined (*Webster's Third International Dictionary*, 1961) as 'to hold on tightly or tenaciously (as with hands and feet) and to resist pressure to separate or dislodge'. The behavior of many immature mammals during transport, for example the bats, mice and rhesus, satisfies the definition; in ordinary everyday transport, the behavior of the human infant does not.

Early in life, the human child's organs of prehension are poorly developed. McGraw (1945) measured the length of time children could suspend themselves from a rod by their hands. At 4 days of age the duration was approximately 6 seconds; at 30 days it was 28 seconds. But thereafter it declined rapidly and did not again reach 28 seconds until the children were almost 5 years of age. Long before this, of course, children are walking and transporting themselves.

Although McGraw's findings offer some corroboration of the

11. Eight infant murine opossums (*Marmosa murina*) attached to mother's nipples (New York Zoological Society photo).

12. Giant anteater young (*Myrmecophage tridactyla*) riding on back of mother (New York Zoological Society photo).

13. Cat transporting 2 weeks old kitten.

14. Squirrel monkey (10 weeks old) riding mother's back (courtesy of D. W. Ploog).

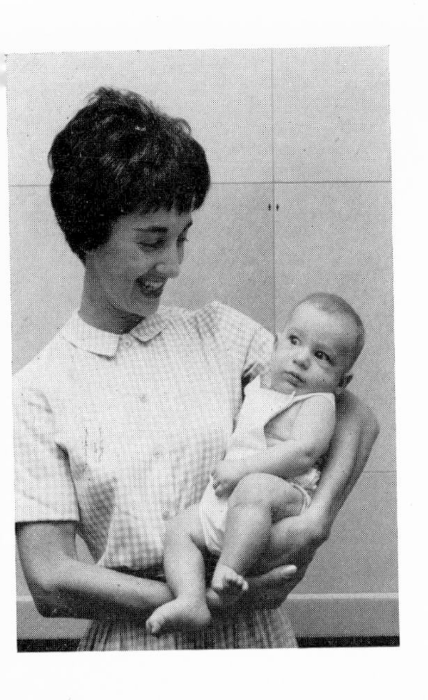

15. Infant (3 months old) held on left side, at chest, body oriented sideways; left hand and arm not in contact with mother's body or clothing.

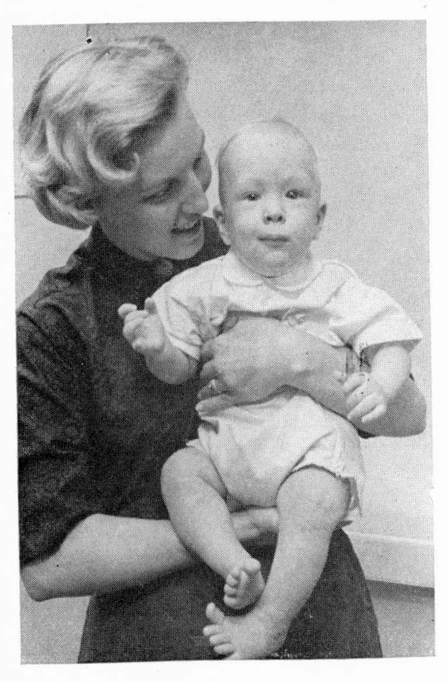

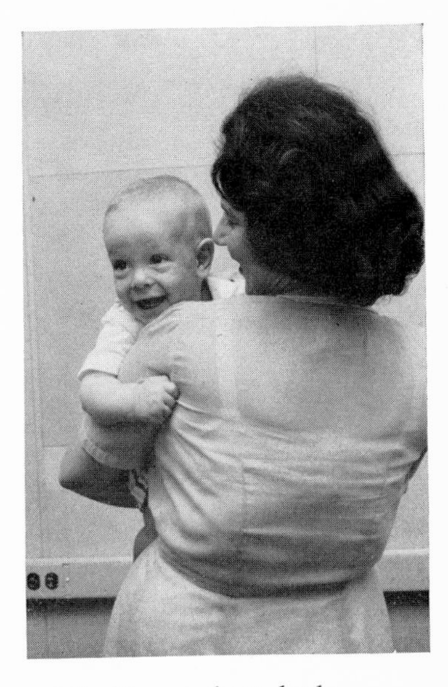

16. Infant (5 months old) held on left side, at chest, body oriented away; upper arms resting on mother, hands "free".

17. Infant (8 months old) held on left side, at the shoulder, oriented toward mother, left arm resting on mother's arm, right hand closed on mother's clothing.

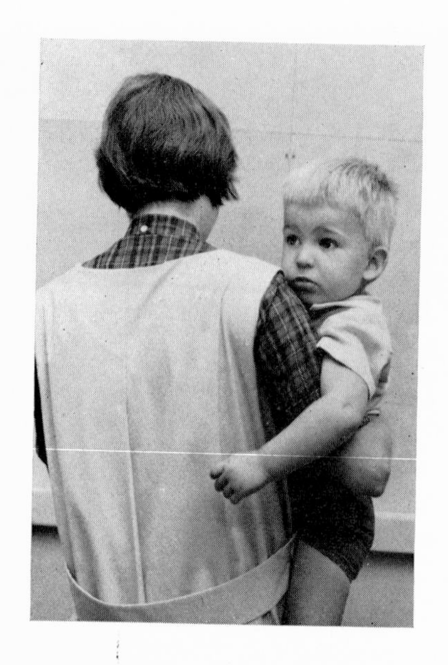

18. Child (18 months old) held on right side, at hip, oriented toward mother, left arm resting on mother's arm, left hand "free".

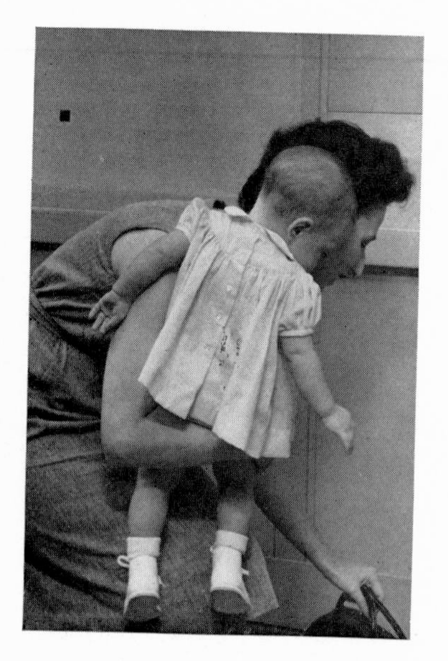

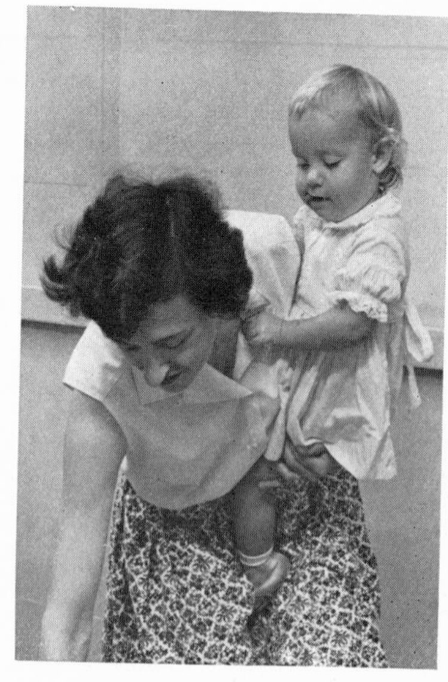

19. Child (11 months old) making no apparent adjustment to mother's leaning over.

20. Child (17 months old) grasping mother's blouse, tongue extended, while mother is leaning over.

findings, it is also clear that clinging to the parent may involve more than the ability to suspend one's body-weight by the hands alone. The arms, legs and trunk may also play some part. In our observations it was difficult to accurately assess the activity of the children's arms (although not of their hands). Although their arms appeared only to be resting on the parent, they may in fact have been exerting pressure. The activities of the children's legs, knees and feet were not charted; nevertheless they seemed not to play any important role in the child's contribution to transport. The contribution of the muscles of his trunk would be even more difficult to assess; but that they contributed to his transport seems likely. After all, even the young infant, and more so the older child, did not lie limp. Instead, he erected his head and maintained tonus in his back; he balanced himself; and in general he kept his hands free.

Some grasping with the hands did occur. Approximately 10 per cent of the children had their hands closed on some part of the adult's body or clothing. Some few, furthermore, were observed actively clutching the parent. The apparent cause was loss of balance. Fear of being removed from the mother would constitute another cause (Ainsworth, 1963; Bowlby, 1958). Nevertheless, there remains the general impression of a minimal contribution to transport. The aplomb with which the children, even infants under a year, rode in their parents' arms was impressive.

Implications for Further Study

The nature of the sample in which human transport was observed imposes certain limits on the conclusions. We feel, admittedly on an intuitive basis, that the sample was reasonably representative of the characteristics of transport in this limited segment of society. The major conclusions probably do not depart significantly from 'true' average values, defined on the basis of a probability sample of the entire population. Reservations are in order, however, concerning the generality of minor observations and comparisons; here chance fluctuations in proportional representation of ill-defined substrata of the population may have had an undue influence. For it is possible that the choices of times and places of observation affected some of the findings, especially those on the interaction of sex, age, color and behavior.

These reservations have special reference to the occasional use of statistical tests in the report. One can define a testable hypothesis, but to what population does the comparison refer? Furthermore, since some records were gathered under one condition (time, place), and others under another, the individual observations are not independent but have something of the nature of cluster samples.

The limitations of this survey, however, are not necessarily those of the study of transport. Populations can be defined and study designs drawn up based on probability samples. How and when infants are carried at home can be investigated. Repeated or extended observations of individual adults can test the assumption, implicit in this study, that each has a characteristic way of carrying children. The use of such conveyances as baby carriages, bicycle baskets, etc., could be included. More extensive and important topics are differences in transport among varied socio-economic, national, and cultural groups.

Conclusions

Within the limits of this survey, however, several broad conclusions can be drawn which serve to relate the findings to transport in other animals. First, although the human infant is undoubtedly retrieved to a safe place, as are, for example, the mouse, hamster and rat, unlike them he is often carried by his parent a considerable distance away from home. Unlike the primate infant, however, he usually has a home place to which he is returned. The behavior of nomadic people, however, might more closely resemble that of primates.

Second, the human infant is picked up and held by the adult's hands. Here too his transport resembles that of some primates, but also that of the sea otter. The mouth is not used. The young are usually held in ventral-ventral contact, although not entirely. When the child is carried on the back, it is usually the males who do so.

Third, the human child is often carried by other members of his group besides his mother – by his father, but also by other men and women, not all of whom are biologically related to him. He may also be carried by juveniles; their exclusion from our survey was arbitrary. Here he resembles many animals – to name a few, the woodmouse *Peromyscus*, the hamster, the langur, the gorilla.

Fourth, he is sometimes carried in devices. We included six subjects, one who used a sling and five who used cradleboards because these were held in the arms of the parents. But we know that human beings also use slings, carriages, bicycle baskets, cradleboards worn on the back, etc. In this respect they resemble no other animal.

Lastly, the human infant or child contributes less to his own transport than many other mammalian young. When very young he has few capabilities; when older his parent does so much and over so long a period of time. There is in him no counterpart of the rhesus which clings from birth by hands and feet with scarcely an assisting hand from the mother.

This paper, in summary, has described transport of the young, a class of behavior which occurs in many animals, including man. Although the forms it takes are varied, the behavior is intimately related to parent-child interaction. Transport of the young protects the young from the dangers of its world, it prolongs contact between parent and young, and it can also widen the experiences of the young. For many animals the details of transport have not yet been described. For man, there is much still to be learned. No simple classification of the behavior by zoological families or orders is yet apparent. Still, it is possible that knowledge about one class of behavior and its manifestations in different species can contribute to comparative psychology; at the same time knowledge about changes in the behavior as the young grow older can contribute to a developmental psychology.

Discussion following Professor Rheingold's Paper

FOSS *Did you ask people why they were carrying the child one way rather than another? Don't mothers change sides when one arm gets tired? Or perhaps, if they are shopping, they keep one hand free to get at their money?*

RHEINGOLD *I think people do not shift sides very much. But I didn't ask them because the answers would have been so variable, and their validity would have been questionable.*

AINSWORTH *I have asked Baltimore mothers about whether their children cling. They usually look blank, but often say something like, 'I can't remember, but there's a point at which they got heavier to carry, then all of a sudden they seemed to get lighter again'. After hearing your paper, I'm wondering how much of this is due to the infant learning to grip with its legs.*

RHEINGOLD *I think he also learns to coordinate his position with the mother's movements, and to hold his trunk upright.*

JOYCE ROBERTSON *It's very noticeable that some babies feel very much heavier than others, and it certainly seems to have something to do with their muscular adjustment.*

MICHELL *In the extreme case, the psychotic child seems very heavy because he doesn't learn to make this adjustment.*

OPPÉ *One of the most interesting things you have found is this absence of clinging. My impression is that most mothers actively discourage it. Clinging usually means clinging to the mother's clothing, and the mother doesn't approve of it, so the response gets extinguished.*

JOYCE ROBERTSON *Of course, babies cling to their own clothing a lot, and mothers will sometimes stop this too, because it crumples the clothes.*

RHEINGOLD *But that's one of the things we found surprisingly seldom; that is, the baby's hands being closed on its own clothing.*

AINSWORTH *There are all kinds of substitute things used for clinging, or at least for grasping – pillows, toys, the bottle and so on. One really wants a study of this along with the amount of clinging to the mother.*

JOYCE ROBERTSON *I have the impression that there is a lot of grasping during feeding, very often of the mother's clothes.*

JENSEN *I am interested in the way that breast-fed children seem to do more clinging to the mother's clothing during feeding.*

GUNTHER *The hands certainly seem to clench and unclench, but I don't think they offer any kind of support. The feet seem to behave in the same way, like some residual response. One could argue that these clinging responses during feeding are becoming vestigial.*

HALL *Or perhaps it's just that in the human infant they die out through lack of practice. In all the other Primates, where the infant has completely free access to the mother's body, the clinging response increases in strength from birth onwards and persists throughout infancy.*

RHEINGOLD *From the studies of the so-called grasp reflex, it looks as if the infant can't grasp long enough to support itself during feeding. But of course babies don't get much chance to practise. This is where it would be useful to have cross-cultural studies. The best I've been able to do is look at photographs, from all over the world, of babies being carried, and it's extremely rare to see the hands clutching.*

BOWLBY *I imagine that sometimes the clinging might be done with the legs?*

AINSWORTH *In African babies one way of being carried is in a sling on the back. The hands cannot cling, because they are inside the sling, and I should think the legs could not get much grip across the mother's back.*

RHEINGOLD *The human infant may be capable of clinging much more than we see him doing. Usually he doesn't need to because he is adequately supported otherwise.*

JAMES ROBERTSON *But it still comes out in certain situations, for instance if you try to take some babies away from the mother.*

RHEINGOLD *You are most likely to get clinging in situations giving rise to startle or fear.*

FREEDMAN *I would like to bring up the question of phases in the development of clinging. In humans there seem to be three of these – the first, automatic or grasp reflex phase, then a phase when the infant learns hand-eye coordinations and during which there is much less clinging, and finally a phase when the grasping and clinging looks voluntary, in the sense that the child first sees something, then stretches out to grasp it. I wonder if there is a sequence like this in other Primates?*

HALL *I think these things go simultaneously. The young Primates will grasp as a startle response, and hang on to the mother's hair, probably on a tactile basis rather than a visual one; but at the same time he may be reaching out with another hand – and he has four of them – to grasp something, relying on vision.*

AINSWORTH *Perhaps there is an antagonism between the two kinds of grasp, in that the reflex one may have to be inhibited before the voluntary one can occur. It's a question of learning to let go. Cathy Hayes described how her chimpanzee would climb a ladder and want to jump somewhere. She would launch herself into space with her hands free to grasp something, but forget to let go with her feet.*

ROWELL *In some Primates it is essential for the infant to cling because the mother uses all four limbs to move; but in others, including gorillas and humans, the mother supplies a lot of support, and it's not so necessary for clinging to be there – either innately or learned.*

HALL *On the theoretical question, the fact that gorillas and humans cling less does not mean that physical contact may not be very necessary in producing the attachment to the mother. The mechan-*

ism may be adjusted through the mother playing a larger part in maintaining contact.

BOWLBY *One thing which is clear to me is that there are clear phases, and it seems that clinging in the human is not so important in the middle of the first year. But I would say that it becomes important again in the second year, when the child has become mobile. At eighteen months he will cling a great deal, especially to the hand.*

AINSWORTH *But I think we should bear in mind that in fear situations you do get clinging, and especially is following and clinging evident when a child is returned to the mother after short separation. It is very persistent and remarkable, and I think one of the most important bits of evidence for John's hypothesis.*

PRECHTL *And I would remind you that the mother provides a very inadequate stimulus for clinging. If you try giving the infant your hair to grasp, you will see what I mean.*

BOWLBY *An experiment I long to propose is that a lady should bring up her child while dressed continuously in a fur coat.*

Mother-Infant Interaction from Birth to Twelve Months: Two Case Studies[1]

JOYCE ROBERTSON

Infants at birth are different from one another. Their potential, their birth experience, their physical health, and the intensity of their needs constitute some of these differences. For reasons of nature and nurture they develop into as many different personalities; but during the first year their development follows a common maturational path. They focus their eyes, smile, babble, grasp, find their limbs, distinguish the mothering figure, sit up, stand up and walk, search for lost toys, and so on. Nature and nurture combine to ensure that most infants develop along these lines and within weeks of a maturational time table. As students of child development we are concerned to evaluate the relative importance of environment and endowment.

In recent years the influence of environment has been increasingly understood. Many studies have shown that the inadequacies of institutional care can cause in all areas of development gross deviations which might appear to be constitutionally determined. But as yet little investigation has been made into the differences between children who are reared not in institutions but in ordinary families (Kris, 1962; Robertson, 1962; Sander, 1962).

I have the impression that, in accounting for the deviations and differences which occur in babies who are reared in their own families, undue weight is sometimes given to the concept of endowment and insufficient to the infant's earliest experience.

My work in a Well-Baby Clinic has led me to the belief that the quality of mothering, and of the interaction which develops between a mother and her infant in the earliest weeks of life, plays a substantial part in determining whether development in the first year follows

[1] My contact with these two mother-infant pairs originated in the Well-Baby Clinic of The Hampstead Child-Therapy Course and Clinic (Paediatrician Dr J. Stross). This Well-Baby Clinic, which is one of the Service Departments of the whole organization, is maintained by The Grant Foundation, Inc., New York.

closely on established maturational stages; and that the infant's status at twelve months is of prognostic importance. My belief derives from clinical experience and not from systematic study. I realize that this is a complex area in which definitive findings will require techniques which are outside my competence.

In an earlier paper (Robertson, 1962) which was based on a study of twenty-five mother-infant pairs, I instanced five extreme cases where the mother's lack of empathetic interaction with her infant, and her failure to protect him against potentially overwhelming experience, had resulted in deviant development. At 12 months the infants were poor in bodily tonus, in responsiveness both to the mother and to the wider environment, in ability to communicate and to express feeling. By 5 years of age four out of the five had been deemed in need of analytic treatment; the fate of the fifth was not known.

In this paper I take up another aspect by seeking to show that what might appear to be minor and transient disturbances occurring at an early stage in the mother-infant relationship can influence the course of an infant's development. The material is derived from my direct observation of two mother-infant pairs.

Summary

John and Peter were born in the same week, and each had a sibling of 2 years plus.

In the second month both families went through a crisis which caused each mother to become acutely anxious and to withdraw from her infant for a period of just under two weeks.

During her period of emotional withdrawal the first mother was able to maintain the physical comforts of her infant, including the feeding. On recovery from her upset she found him slower and quieter and less responsive than formerly. He demanded less and thenceforward she mothered him at this lower level.

The second mother was unable to maintain satisfactory physical care of her infant. He became desperate and had to struggle to find the perfunctorily offered breast. On recovery from her upset this mother found herself with a very alert, precocious infant. She responded to this with satisfaction and answered his new-found alertness with stimulation and reward.

At 12 months there was a marked disparity between these two

infants. John was slow, undemanding, placid, and lacking in outward investigatory behaviour. Peter was precociously forward, unrelaxed and relentless in his demands; he showed extreme mood swings, and was unusually aware of the sights and sounds of his environment.

I believe that these differences were substantially determined by the way in which each mother responded to the stressful event in the second month of her infant's life; and by the repercussions this had on the infant and on subsequent mother-infant interaction.

John

Mrs H was an immature young woman, rather unsure of herself but warm and sensitive and spontaneous in her relationships. She had a good relationship with her first child, Andrew, and his development was most satisfactory. When baby John was born, Andrew was a lively, intelligent and spontaneous child and a delight to his parents.

John was born normally at home, weight 6 lb. 6 oz. He was a healthy, hungry infant and four-hourly cows' milk feeds were started on the first day to tide him over until the breast milk came in on the third day.

Breast feeding was established easily and he gained a pound in his first week. The mother quickly became sensitively in contact with him – answering his needs without delay. She found pleasure in holding and looking at him.

At 10 days I watched them together after a feed. The baby lay on his mother's lap, wide awake, moving his head and eyes and mouth and sometimes his limbs. She was relaxed and happy as she caressed him, watched his movements, and spoke to him in a soft voice. Then after a while she reluctantly put him back into his cot, saying, 'I could sit all day with him'.

At 2 weeks she was adapting well to the rhythm of the new baby, fitting easily into his pattern of feeding and sleeping. When he looked with open steady eyes she tried to convince me that he was looking at her. He was 'a real baby', she said. By 3½ weeks she was becoming impatient for him to smile.

Her handling was warm and sensitive. He was peaceful, feeding well, putting on weight. His movements were gentle and flowing, and when one talked to him he listened and his gaze became steady. The mother was ready and waiting for the first sign that the infant was aware of her.

She tried to balance the needs of both children, but found it difficult to delay attending to the baby. If the baby cried when she was doing something for Andrew, she felt impelled to turn from Andrew and give immediate attention to the baby. She said, 'If he cries and no one comes he must feel deserted and unloved'; and added, 'He can't think, he can only feel'.

She realized, she said, that she felt at peace as long as she was able to follow the baby's rhythm, pick him up when he cried, feed him when hungry; but when conflicting demands were made on her her anxiety rose and she behaved in a confused way.

Her mood and that of her infant were closely interlocked. Every success in her mothering added to her contentment; every failure made her anxious.

At morning bathtime she usually contrived to have Andrew entertained downstairs by the daily help, so that she could play and talk freely with baby John. As I saw on a visit during the seventh week, this was a mutually satisfying time. John was active and responsive throughout the bath, babbled and exchanged smiles with his mother during the dressing, listened when she talked to him. He fed well. He looked peaceful, his skin was clear and delicately tinted, his chin rounded, his eyes clear and bright, and his limbs relaxed. The mother looked prettier and happier than at any other time over the four years I had known her.[1]

During this period the father supported and protected her, and she was able to accept his help. When, like many babies of this age, John did not settle after the 6 p.m. feed and needed extra comfort, they shared in his care – nursing him, giving him a dummy or an extra feed.

It looked as though the family was emerging satisfactorily from the adaptive period. The parents were pleased with their new son. They had re-allocated their affections to include baby John, and the family was settling in its new constellation. John was developing satisfactorily – feeding well and putting on weight, bodily active, lively and responsive. But a week later, when he was 8 weeks old, the serenity of his environment was suddenly disrupted.

[1] Applying my own criteria for assessing the adequacy of early mothering (1962), this mother was adequate because:

(*a*) she felt and expressed pleasure in the activities of mothering;
(*b*) she showed awareness of her baby's affective states and a willingness to respond to them;
(c) she used the heightened anxiety normal to this period in the service of her baby.

The father became ill and malignancy was suspected. On visiting the home next day, I found the mother shocked and confused. It was lunch-time but she was still in her dressing-gown. She could not eat, and had to be persuaded to have coffee. She was withdrawn and sat for long periods silently sighing. The baby was awake and a feed was due, but she could not decide whether or not to feed him. Throughout my visit, which stretched to four hours, she was slow, dreamy, indecisive, and near to tears.

The feed I then observed went peacefully, but in her withdrawn subdued state she fed the infant mechanically and without interaction. John remained wideawake throughout. Instead of finishing in his usual drowsy and sated state he was still alert when put into his pram.

During the next week the mother continued in a state of extreme anxiety and withdrawal from her baby. She managed to keep the breastfeeding going, and he suffered no physical neglect. But she was not in her former warm, responsive relationship with him.

Throughout a lengthy visit on the third day of the mother's upset I saw that he was not cuddled and talked to, kissed and caressed. His smiles and cooing failed to bring her answering voice and smile. Looking into her eyes did not bring him her answering look and touch. His limb movements were not answered by her caresses.

Within a week a marked setback to his development could be clearly observed. His bodily activity had decreased, and his smiles were fewer and harder to elicit – not only by the mother but by the father and me, to whom he had earlier reacted with animation.

A few days later a more hopeful statement about the father's prospects lessened the mother's anxiety; and when after another week it was confirmed that there was no malignancy, both parents gradually recovered much of their equilibrium. The mother was ready to resume her former relationship with John, but she complained that he was sombre and unresponsive.

At 10 weeks I watched her bathe and feed him. Her handling was as tender and intuitive as before, and she was eager to be playful with him. But although John listened and looked intently as she cuddled and kissed him, his responses were slower and his face serious and unsmiling. She shrugged off her disappointment and said in mock crossness 'Don't look so serious!' I saw that she was mirroring his serious expression, as two weeks earlier she had mirrored his smiling one.

This was an instance where a mother's readiness to interact with her infant was inhibited by the infant's lack of response. No longer withdrawn, she was ready to mother her infant sensitively as before; but John had not made the same spontaneous recovery. He now smiled only after much stimulation, more like a younger infant of 6 or 7 weeks. Recalling the lively interactions they had enjoyed only two weeks before, the mother complained 'Smile at your mother' – as if he had been deliberately withholding.

By the end of the third month most infants begin to discriminate between the mother and other people, and a phase of intense interaction develops between them in which the infant plays an increasingly active part in the mounting sequence of cues and responses which stimulate and draw them closer together.

In John the onset of discrimination was timely. By the thirteenth week he smiled more readily to his mother than to anyone else, and watched her as she moved about the room. But he did not develop outgoing actively seeking behaviour. They did not enter upon the sequence of intense and mounting interaction which is characteristic of the phase, and which I have little doubt would have occurred had not the mother's temporary withdrawal of affect inhibited his responses.

Throughout his third month John had recurrent bronchitis and was made miserable by the troublesome cough. During this illness, it was notable that when he was restless and fretful the mother responded adequately to meet his increased need of her. To comfort him she breast-fed him often and carried him around day and night. But when he recovered from the illness and reverted to his quiet, undemanding behaviour her attention subsided; she gave him no more than he demanded.

In the sense that she responded appropriately to the varying cues given by her son in health and sickness, this was an adequate mother who could not be faulted in her care. She met his needs at the level at which they were expressed. But I had no doubt that the level of interaction between them was too low to facilitate optimum development. At 4½ months his muscular development was not satisfactory. His back muscles were limp, his head not firmly held, and his limb movements few and poor. From this point I became increasingly uneasy about his general development, with its constellation of physical and emotional retardation.

As I saw it, the lowered interaction between them was an important causative factor. The mother had made a substantial recovery from her anxiety state, and had tried to resume the relationship with John at its former level. But John had not responded, and after meeting failure in her attempts to restore their lively interchange the mother's activity had dropped to the level that was no more than sufficient to meet his lessened demands. I therefore suggested to the mother that she should stimulate John beyond the extent called for by his meagre demands, that she should play and handle him more than she was doing.

I was surprised by the success of her efforts along these lines after only one week. He held his back and head more firmly, his movements were stronger, and he was generally more outgoing. He did not lie passively in his pram, but cried until taken on to his mother's knee where he watched the play of older children with lively interest.

But a week later this improvement had disappeared. John was again passive, limp and undemanding. I was puzzled, but the mother had the answer – 'I couldn't go on doing it. It seemed so unnatural deliberately to upset his contentment by playing with him – and into the bargain rob myself of a peaceful hour.' This mother, who did not hesitate to answer the demands of her baby, could not or would not give him what he did not ask for.

After the fifth month my visits to the home were reduced to once a month, but I also had weekly contact when the mother brought both children to my Mother-Toddler play group. I continued trying to persuade her to play with and stimulate her undemanding baby. Now and again, usually in the days immediately after a visit, she followed the advice and it always resulted in increased liveliness in John. But she did not persevere, and John seemed unable to hold on to his livelier behaviour. Looking at her placid baby she would say despondently but affectionately, 'Well, he may be slow but he is very sweet'.

During the next month his slowness became more and more apparent. At 8 months he was more like a 5-6 month baby. He did not use his shoulders, neck and limbs in an age adequate way. This may sound relatively unimportant, but it threw out of gear his pulling and clutching, held back his sitting and crawling, and thus inhibited the exploration of his surroundings. Furthermore, because he did not try to move, he did not get himself into the awkward positions from which babies often have to be rescued. He thereby missed this contact with his mother.

At 9 months John would not settle to sleep in the evenings and his parents brought him down to join them in the sitting-room. Once downstairs he stopped crying and smiled and babbled to them. They played unreservedly with him, glad that Andrew, safely asleep upstairs, was not there to be made jealous.

These evening playtimes went on for eight weeks. Whereas he had formerly been content to lie quietly alone, his only attainment being to turn on to his tummy, within two weeks of the onset of the sleeping disturbance, and of the heightened attention of his parents, he was much more lively and outgoing. He moved more, held his back and head more firmly, and his muscles generally were less flabby. He complained when left alone. The mother answered to this new level of demand, and John was brought more into the active life of the family. But although this surge forward lessened the gap between him and his peers, his development still fell substantially short of the normal.

At 12 months a normal baby can sit securely at play for long periods, can crawl efficiently and swiftly in pursuit of his interests, and can pull himself up and lower himself at will; he can walk around a room with the aid of furniture, can balance for a few seconds and is almost ready to take his first faltering steps; he will be able to indicate No!, and his resistance will be tinged with aggression; he will show sustained interest in play activities. But when John sat, he slumped forward with a rounded back; he could not crawl, but still moved around the floor like a lumbering sea-lion; he did not try to pull himself up on furniture or the cot bars, and if put into a standing position he was reluctant to take his weight and flopped into a sitting position. He was passive, undemanding and perhaps depressed; he babbled but did not attempt to say syllables.

He was at least two months behind his peers and in some functions still more retarded.[1] It is an open question whether more, or more skilfully applied, stimulation would have narrowed the gap still further.

To the uncritical eye John was a placid, good-natured, compliant and undemanding child. He looked healthy and bonny and responded benignly to attention.

[1] He did not walk until 19 months.

Peter

Mrs O was an intelligent, unemotional young woman; although for much of the time in good contact with her family, she sometimes lapsed into a rather cold efficiency. Betty, the 2-year-old, a serious, depressed little girl, was the apple of her father's eye.

Peter was born normally at home and weighed 6 lb. 6 oz. During the second day he was restless and the doctor ordered three-hourly bottle feeding until the breast milk came in.

Breast feeding was established fairly easily, but supplementary bottle feeding continued as precaution against loss of weight. He sucked well, but was a drowsy baby and fell asleep several times during each feed. By the end of the second week the time between feeds was extended from three hours to four hours.

For a month the breast feeding was satisfactory and Peter gained weight. But the mother was unable to withdraw sufficiently from Betty, the older child, to be fully committed to Peter during feeding times. She contrived to feed him and at the same time to play games with Betty. Though she was skilful in the way she did this, Peter showed by restlessness at the breast that the situation was disturbing for him.

During the third and fourth weeks he was less sleepy and fed better. His movements were strong and his development generally satisfactory. He slept well and was not easily awakened, but during feeding he continued to show sensitivity to noise.

In these weeks the mother did not adequately adjust to her infant's feeding needs; but she was still in the process of adaptation, and there were episodes of gentleness and affection which showed that she could empathize with her infant. However, between the fifth and seventh weeks two events occurred which put further stress on their relationship.

The first was that both the father and Betty caught influenza and were ill for several days. The mother became overburdened by looking after the two patients; her breast milk decreased and the baby became restless. She reacted characteristically to these stresses, managing to keep going but in a dull and affectless way.

A week later, just as the family were recovering from the influenza, the mother's brother became involved in a serious situation which did not begin to resolve itself for more than a week – during which time the mother was in a state of acute anxiety. Again there was a flattening of affect. She became automatic and wooden, and said she could cope only if she 'held tight' to herself.

Whereas John's mother had managed to maintain the physical comforts of her baby despite her anxieties, Peter's mother failed to do so during these two weeks. At 7 weeks I saw them together after a bath and just before a feed. The baby screamed to the point of going blue and losing his breath, but the mother completed his dressing in an automatic and affectless way, down to the last button and ribbon; she stopped only to pinch the baby to make him breathe again, as if quite unaware of his intense distress. His genitals were blistered and raw, but she neglected to apply medication.

Her apathy extended into the feeding situation, which was characterized by the baby's fights and struggles to get food. She went through the motions of breastfeeding, but in a perfunctory and inefficient way which was intensely frustrating to the baby. She held him awkwardly with head too high for the breast, so that her slightest move caused him to lose the nipple. She bent about – attending to Betty, reaching for her coffee, trying awkwardly to light a cigarette – with no concern for the baby who was struggling desperately to get food. Throughout half an hour he wriggled and whimpered, choked and cried. When given a bottle he quietened and sucked peacefully.

The baby was then put on to the floor and the mother, freed from the difficulties of the feeding situation, talked to him and elicited smiles. He was very responsive, gurgling and smiling with much bodily activity and lively facial expression. I was impressed by the extent of the mood variation – from desperate crying to extreme responsiveness.

Earlier there had been nothing to suggest that Peter was a specially active or forward baby. But when at 8 weeks he was put on to his tummy he held his head and looked around; when his eyes caught a bright object about eighteen inches away he babbled and smiled at it. This behaviour was certainly much earlier than usual.

At 9 weeks he reached for his bottle and directed it to his mouth. He was extremely alert to sounds and would turn in the direction of a voice. I recorded the possibility that his unusual awareness of the environment had been accelerated by the struggle for survival that had been forced on him during the difficult feeding situation. This inference is in line with James's theory of precocious ego-development (1960).

At 9 weeks the mother resolved the feeding difficulty by transferring the baby on to the bottle. Her brother was no longer in such acute trouble. Family life became more peaceful except for the minor upsets caused by a series of bronchial infections common to infants in winter time – and from which John, the other infant in this paper, was suffering more or less simultaneously.

Peter's 'forwardness' was welcomed by the family, with its high regard for intelligence and forward development. The parents recalled high intelligence in various relatives, and believed that Peter was showing the benefits of a favourable endowment. His displays of precocity gave further incentive to the mother's trait of courting her children when lively and vivacious, and of withdrawing when they were in trouble. His lively smiling phases were usually rewarded by play and stimulation, and with his strong directed movements he would try to get still more. Often his mother withheld her responses and thus provoked him into still more energetic displays.

Following these two stressful weeks, the extremes of Peter's behaviour were more and more marked – on the one hand his desperation when hungry and unhappy, and on the other his exaggerated responsiveness and gaiety. He was extremely alert in a high-pitched brittle way, and rarely relaxed; a dummy was bought to help bridge the gap between wakefulness and sleep, because for him there was no in-between stage of quietness.

Peter was continually pushed forward in his development. For example, on a visit to the play group when he was 6 months old he was brought in from the garden to lie on the nursery floor. There were three other toddlers in the room, so there was considerable noise; in addition, the room was strange to him. The mother immediately put him on to the floor with toys. He was frightened and cried. Another mother would not in these circumstances have put her infant down, and most mothers would have responded to his crying by picking him up; but Mrs O rattled toys in front of him, gave him a biscuit and talked to him until his crying stopped. He was then left on the floor to play while she sat proudly near by, basking in the comments on his 'forwardness' which came from the other mothers.

The intense interaction between mother and baby continued, in which she stimulated him by a combination of response which pleased him and withholding which drove him to still greater efforts. The more forward Peter became, the greater was her pleasure in him. But in the ensuing months his demands became so insistent that the mother was forced into answering them at his pace in order to get peace.

By 7½ months he was beginning to crawl; by 9½ months he could stand up and walk around his cot; and by 11½ months he walked freely and could say five words appropriately. Before his first birthday he tried to lift the telephone when it rang, and went to the window to look for an aeroplane when the adults in the room had hardly registered the noise.

He was then an attractive, vivacious child, but he could not relax to be cuddled. His alertness had a brittle quality, with an undercurrent of irritation which broke through at the slightest frustration. He was continually trying to do things that were outside his competence.

Conclusion

This presentation is open to the instant criticism that it cannot be known what would have happened

(*a*) had the infants been differently endowed;
(*b*) had the crises not occurred.

I do not know what would have happened had the infants been differently endowed, and I doubt if much is to be gained from speculating about this. These two cases are insufficient to prove anything, but they are consistent with my view that in the early weeks of life innate differences between normal infants are less important than are the similarities of their needs and of their responses when these needs are not met.

I suggest that the disparity between the development of John and Peter at 1 year is to be understood less in terms of inherited constitution than of 'acquired' constitution (James, 1960); that infants as young as were John and Peter when these major upsets occurred are immature organisms, not capable of selective response and able to react only on the basis of primitive adaptation; and that these primitive adaptations become 'acquired' constitution and influence subsequent development.

As to what would have happened had the crises not occurred, this question perhaps implies firstly that the maternal withdrawals may have been of little or no significance; and second, that in so far as environmental influences can affect early development these may in both instances be accounted for by the type of family in which the infant was reared.

It is true that Peter's family had a tendency to hasten the development of their infants, and that he was therefore likely in any case to have been forward. But as early as 9 weeks of age, when most infants do little more than cry when they feel hungry, Peter reached for his bottle. That was ego development disproportionate to the phase. I suggest that inner stimulation, created by the struggle for food, led to precocious development which reinforced his mother's tendency to overstimulate and greatly exacerbated the demands that were made on him for yet more precocious activity.

John, without the early disruption, would have had every chance of a phase-appropriate development. His mother, though neurotic, was warm and intuitive, and adequate in meeting his needs. But just as he was entering upon the phase in which mother and infant stimulate and respond to each other, she suddenly stopped playing her part and his attempts to elicit a response from her were unsuccessful. During his mother's withdrawal he adapted to what was available; and she, consistent with her general tendency to meet demands at the level asked of her, on recovery responded only to the lower demands that he made. As a direct consequence of her temporary withdrawal in the third month, his ability to elicit a response from his mother became inhibited and from that point the interaction between them proceeded at a lower level. This had consequences for his subsequent development.

The ability to interact, to demand or to elicit a response from the environment, is initially experienced in relation to the mother.This capacity, a forerunner of a more general cathexis and mastery of the environment, was inhibited in John. It is probable that had the withdrawal occurred a few months later, in the phase where the ability to make demands is more established, John would have fared better because he would by then have been able to maintain loud and insistent pressure on his mother.

I suggest that the differences in the motor development of these two children can be understood in the same terms. At 12 months Peter was in respect of motor development a 'forward' child; his functions, accelerated by the withdrawal in the second month, had been consistently overstimulated by the mother and by his need to get appreciative response. John, on the other hand, did not exploit functions as they developed; he did not have the incentive to perfect and practise his skills or to explore his surroundings.

I have tried to show that an event which occurred in the second month of life significantly affected the infant and altered the quality of mother-infant interaction, and in consequence affected in a fundamental way development throughout the first year. As this paper is finalized for publication both children are 2 years of age. John is placid and undemanding, with insufficient drive and cathexis of the environment; Peter has low toleration of frustration, a marked inability to relax or regress, and an ego which is perhaps too strong to allow instinctual development fully to emerge. I suggest that this reflects the trends given to their development during the first few months in the ways that I have described, and that these are likely to persist.

Discussion following Mrs Joyce Robertson's Paper

BOWLBY *These two infants developed differently, but I'm not clear whether you see this as being due to the fact that the mothers behaved differently while they were withdrawn or to the different impact that withdrawal had on the babies.*

JOYCE ROBERTSON *Both. They had different experiences partly due to the difference in the mothers' behaviour and partly due to the infants' age and stage of development when the withdrawal took place.*

FREEDMAN *From which you argue that Nicholas's slow development is a direct result of the more complete withdrawal of his mother. But there could be other causes, and my first guess about these two infants is that there are decisive constitutional differences between them. From our study of twins, I can say that if one identical twin is a slow developer the other tends to be slow also and that this is usually not the case in fraternal infants. I don't want to say that learning and experience do not matter, but that you are on shaky ground if you throw out constitutional factors.*

JOYCE ROBERTSON *I certainly don't want to throw out constitutional factors. In this kind of clinical study, I've just got no way of measuring them.*

THOMAS *In taking an analytic approach to the two infants one would say that they used different defence mechanisms, and that implies different constitutions in some measure.*

FREEDMAN *Can I give you an example of what I have in mind? It illustrates the intimate connection between constitutional and environmental factors. It is a case of fraternal twins who were the fifth and sixth children in an unplanned pregnancy, and the mother developed a policy of leaving them alone as long as they didn't cry. Over the first six months they were very 'good' babies in that they rarely cried, and she simply left them in a room by themselves. Their scores were neck and neck on the Bayley Development Scales and both were very depressed developmentally over the first six months. In the seventh month one of them began to crawl, whereas the other was just turning over. The one that could crawl was allowed to get out of the bedroom and mingle with the other children; his developmental quotient shot up well above average, while his brother's D.Q. fell even further. He was the slowest baby of our sample of forty and we were quite worried about him. Well, what is the lesson here? We have two children of different constitutions, both of whom had been deprived at the same time, and both reacted quite differently to the same deprivation. Clearly, one cannot maintain that subsequent characteristics of infants are due exclusively to differences in maternal behaviour, for there are a great number of possible consequences to essentially the same environmental situation.*

GEWIRTZ *This is the sort of frustration one always has with case histories, even when they are as elegant as the ones presented here.*

AINSWORTH *Of course, and that's why one wants to supplement clinical studies with surveys and with experiments. Although Joyce Robertson's observations don't* prove *anything, they do draw attention to all kinds of things – for instance, the importance of the particular phase of development of the infant during which some outside influence comes in, such as the mother's withdrawal.*

OPPÉ *I think it's crucial for Joyce Robertson's hypothesis that she should be able to predict, on the basis of the child's state of development when the crisis occurred, what will happen to the child in the next few months. It's not the sort of prediction I'd be happy to make.*

JOYCE ROBERTSON *I would say such predictions are possible within limits, given adequate knowledge of the history of interaction with the mother; and, of course, provided there are no untoward events, such as prolonged illnesses.*

GEWIRTZ *I imagine your success would be a function of how precise you are prepared to make your predictions. The nature of clinical prediction in single cases, or in a very few assorted cases, I think precludes successful prediction, excepting on rather broad matters.*

ROSENBLATT *In clinical studies like this, there are some controls that can be introduced. For instance, you could look for cases where there have been family crises and no apparent change in the infant; or the opposite – dramatic changes with no crisis.*

JOYCE ROBERTSON *This would mean studying many mother-infant couples from birth, before, during and after any crisis. Mothers and infants coming through a Baby Clinic have given me an impression of what happens but not sufficient detail to support much more than hunches. The main point I'm trying to make is that what happens in the first three months can so affect the baby* and *his interaction with his mother that his future development is affected.*

MICHELL *What was John's speech like?*

JOYCE ROBERTSON *Quite normal, and very much in advance of the rest of his development.*

MICHELL *Which makes him* not *like a typical case of maternal deprivation, where one would expect speech retardation – as in the case Sally Provence reported and which is very much like John in other ways.*

AINSWORTH *I would agree with Gordon Jensen that the emphasis should be on the interaction. For instance, one way of analysing the situation is to say that John's activity got him nowhere. He was fed or not fed regardless of what he did – what the mother did was not dependent on what* he *did. But in Peter's case, he may have had to fight for what he wanted, but what his mother did* was *dependent on his activity.*

JOYCE ROBERTSON *Yes. And this happened to John just when he would normally have been initiating a lot of the interaction and expecting a familiar response.*

APPELL *But it works the other way round too. The child just was not stimulating the mother enough to help her to get back to her previous level of responding.*

AMBROSE *Certainly the two babies turned out to be very different. I would be interested to know what you think of this way of looking at it. In the one case, John, you have a good example of the baby not being responded to as he usually is. He wants the mother to respond, whether by feeding, giving her attention, smiling back and so on. He gives signs that are not answered. As a result of what you might call non-reinforcement, some sort of extinction takes place, and the response strength of the baby's sign behaviour gradually declines. But later on when there was more responsiveness on the part of the mother, more reinforcement, this didn't seem to change the response strength of the baby's sign behaviour; it remained at the low level. A question here is, why didn't it? If the empirical change in response-strength resulted from non-reinforcement, why did this response not increase again when there was reinforcement subsequently? In the other baby, I get the impression that in addition to the non-reinforcement there was elicited a great deal of anxiety, much more than in John; therefore there may be an additional factor here – interference by anxiety in addition to the extinction effect. Again the question arises as to why subsequently this interfering anxiety remained as strong and wasn't reduced when the mother's behaviour changed afterwards.*

JOYCE ROBERTSON *Yes. I agree with your formulation and I have asked myself the same questions. I can't answer them. In John's case I do wonder whether this may point to a sensitive period somewhere in these early weeks. With Peter the hunger served as a stimulation.*

AMBROSE *It tended to provoke anxiety.*

JOYCE ROBERTSON *Yes, that also.*

ROWELL *Don't you get the impression that had Peter got into John's situation Peter would have screamed until something happened?*

JOYCE ROBERTSON *If he had already been roused by the stimulation of the hunger – yes. But not if he had been fed adequately as John was.*

ROWELL *John was odd in that he gave up so extraordinarily quickly.*

JOYCE ROBERTSON *He gave up for the reasons that Tony Ambrose gave a few minutes ago. A new feature of development needing reinforcement failed to get it and extinction took place. Peter's experience was of another order – the hunger acted as a stimulation and premature development followed.*

A Study of Mother-Child Interaction at Thirteen Months[1]

GENEVIÈVE APPELL and MYRIAM DAVID

Research on the effects of separation of mother and child during the three first months of life,[2] has led to a follow-up study of the children in their homes after reunion. The aim of the follow-up was to see whether, after reunion, the child showed signs of suffering, how the mother-child relationship was re-established, and whether or not it was impaired in development. In this study it was necessary to clarify what is meant by the mother-child relationship, how it can be described and assessed in its quality, in its impact and effects. In order to do this we decided to analyse the follow-up material in terms of mother-child interaction.

The following paper concerns a comparative study of interaction between two mother-child pairs, the children being 1 year old. It is meant to be a contribution to a better understanding of the widely used concept of mother-child relationship. The aim is to clarify how the relationship is expressed in mutual behaviour, and to see whether one can formulate hypotheses regarding the effects of different types of interaction on the development of the child.

The follow-up study was organized so that the observers became familiar with the total natural environment of the mother and child, and were able to see how the mother organized it, how the child used it, and how they both related to it and to each other. For this purpose, the raw data were collected by naturalistic observations and recorded in the form of a detailed descriptive, chronological account of whatever happened during the observer's visits – the child's

[1] We wish to acknowledge that this investigation is part of a research programme sponsored by a grant from the Foundations' Fund for Research in Psychiatry from 1955 to 1960.

[2] A Study of Nursing Care and Nurse-Infant Interaction undergone by the same lot of children has been reported on in the 1959 Ciba Study Group (David & Appell, 1961). It has also been published in French in *Psychiatrie de l'Enfant* (vol. 4, fasc. 2).

behaviour, the behaviour of all those around towards him, the most important, of course, being the mother.

Visits were made as follows: every day for the first three days after reunion; once a week during the three first months; once every other week until the age of 15 to 18 months. Visits were made alternately, in the morning and in the afternoon; they lasted an average of two and a half to three hours, which allowed the observer to watch all those recurring events which make up the everyday life of a child: bathing, toileting, feeding, play, etc.

Direct observation was supplemented by talks with the mother. They took the form of spontaneous conversation rather than formal interviewing, and occurred while observation was going on, leaving the mother free to speak whenever she felt like doing so, and about anything she liked. While the mother talked, the observer listened, showing interest, and willingly answered questions, sometimes intervening to get more information and to explore areas left out by the mother.

Besides direct observation in the natural environment, and interviewing, the children were observed in a structured situation during testing. Moreover, at ages 1, 2½ and 4 a visit was organized at our office. Under these circumstances both the setting and the presence of a second observer were new to the child and unfamiliar to the mother. During these visits, the child was allowed to play freely, and given a task. When the child seemed adjusted and at ease, the mother was asked to leave the room for a short while, the child remaining with the unknown observer. By these means, among others, we tested the child's attitudes towards strangers and towards separation.

Though all this material was not collected specifically for studying interaction, it soon appeared that it would be most fruitful to analyse it in such a way, both for longitudinal studies of interaction in each case; and for comparative studies of different cases at a given age. For the present comparative study around age 1, the material used was three home visits and one visit at the office, the children being between 11 months and 13 months old.

To keep an overall picture of the interaction and yet be able to compare different couples, we found it fruitful to analyse it according to:

1. *Quantity of interaction*: its duration and frequency, and the proportion of time it occupies during the total period of observation of mother and child.

2. *Its form*: Interaction can be:

(*a*) A direct and simple interaction when A does to B something to which B reacts.

(*b*) A chain of interaction, when B's response to A causes A to respond so that both partners are caught up in a series of responses to one another.

(*c*) Interdependency without direct interchange as seen for instance during diapering, when mother and child are in touch with each other, but involved in different interests, for example the child with a toy, the mother with the diaper, and with no direct communication.

(*d*) Indirect interaction, when one partner acts upon an environment common to both, the other one reacting in turn to the environmental change, the environment thus serving to mediate between them.

3. *Initiation* of interaction: who starts it and what is the releasing factor.

4. *Termination of interaction*: which partner ends it, how, and what are the responses of the other partner to the termination.

5. *Modes* through which interaction is expressed: looking, touching, holding, etc.

6. *Immediate purpose* of interaction: physical care, relief from pain or fear, stimulating or stopping activity of partner, etc.

7. *Underlying feelings* and ways they are expressed.

The analysis of interaction under these seven headings is carried out systematically in all the different circumstances under which interaction happens, as for instance sleeping, feeding, toilet training, play, etc. It shows that each mother-infant pair has a definite pattern of interaction which is quite specific to them. Their pattern of interaction remains consistent and characteristic throughout, and differs in many ways from the patterns of other pairs. The analysis allows one to get at the interplay of attitudes which both mother and child display in their interaction. Attitudes shown in closeness versus distance, reactions to separation, responses to strangers and relatives, attitudes towards food and cleanliness, attitudes towards activity, objects and environment, mutual attitudes towards protection and daring, zones of mutual satisfaction and frustration, attitudes towards dependency versus autonomy, etc.

Two cases involving the children Molly and Bob will illustrate these points. (Ultimately seven cases will be analysed in the same way.)

Interaction in Molly's Case

Molly is the second daughter of a working-class couple. Her sister, aged 5, has recently started school. The family lives very much on its own, Molly does not go out very often and plays in a somewhat crowded two-room flat. Direct interaction between mother and child is extremely frequent, even apart from physical care, and consists of long and complex chains. Both mother and child do the initiating, and if one stops the other takes the lead.

With regard to the immediate reasons for interaction, almost anything serves. There are, however, three significantly predominant, though non-exclusive, purposes on the mother's part: in response to Molly's direct or indirect request to be picked up or to walk around; each time Molly gets out of sight; preventing Molly from touching or doing this or that.

Interaction is boisterous and noisy on the part of both. All modes of interacting are intensively used, while feelings of cheerfulness, eagerness, contentment, discontentment and irritation alternate with one another at a quick tempo. Enjoyment of interaction is the predominant mood.

Progressive and mutual termination is usual, but pseudo-endings are quite frequent, the mother often being responsible for this. She immediately reinstates the interaction, even if she had been the one to end it. She is the only mother in our sample who does not accept interaction being terminated by the child.

The following excerpt from our records is a good example of what happens:

'Molly, under a table, is playing a peek-a-boo game with observer, and smiles at her. Mother says to the observer: "You see she copies Susan", and addressing Molly "Come, let's go and fetch Susan." Molly, forgetting her play with the observer, comes out of rhe hiding-place immediately, responds to mother with happy sounds, takes mother's hand and they both go towards the door. The mother asks Molly to say "bye-bye" to observer. Molly ignores this but tries to open the door. The mother, wanting to stop her from doing so, picks her up. Molly protests strongly. Mother says "Come along, it is not time yet", and to distract her, gives her Susan's doll. Molly takes hold of the doll and speaks to it. Mother puts Molly down, but Molly goes back to mother and wants to be picked up. Mother says cheerfully "always Mummy" and gives her another doll. Molly smiles broadly at mother and mother announces reluctantly "I won't look at you any more". Molly seems content and retires to play under the table, but mother looks down at her and says "What are you doing there?" Molly comes out and stands up, helping herself by holding mother's legs; she takes hold of mother's hand and pulls at it. Mother says "What do you want?" Molly pulls her towards Susan's doll (though the doll was at hand) and mother seems happy to be pulled by Molly and to comply. She gives her the doll, and Molly takes hold of it and cuddles it, saying "Te-te-te", so mother leaves her and goes to stir the fire in the kitchen next door. Molly, however, follows mother towards the kitchen and sits in the doorway. Mother says "I don't like you to be there" and comes back. Molly rises to her feet and calls "Mum, Mum, Mum"; she holds doll against her heart, then holds it out to mother, going towards her making imitative noises; while doing this she falls, mother says "Boum", Molly gets up and wants to be picked up. Mother does not respond, and Molly proceeds to play with the closet door. Mother rushes to stop her and says "At her age Susan was less demanding", while Molly says "pa, papa", to which mother answers "Papa will come, so take care of your bottom" and mother remarks joyfully that she is scared of Daddy. Molly goes back to fiddle with the closet door, this time mother pays no attention and there the interaction stops for a moment. Molly leaves the closet and quietly goes into the parents' bedroom, while mother speaks of Sue; however, a few instants later, Molly being out of sight, mother goes to see what Molly is doing in other room and a new chain of interaction is set off.'

Analysing now the attitudes which mother and child display in their interaction, we find:

1. *Physical closeness* between Molly and mother is a predominant feature. Mother always manages to have Molly around. She never lets her out of sight; she constantly keeps contact with her by speaking to her, by using any of the child's interests to bring her back to her, and answering all Molly's demands and cries. She seems unable to resist interacting with Molly, takes tremendous pleasure in cuddling, kissing, keeping the child on her lap, and takes advantage of all opportunities which occur.

Molly turns no less frequently towards her mother, calling her to look at things, asking to be picked up, bringing a toy, pulling her hand to take her somewhere, and having cute and inviting ways to obtain what she wants.

The behaviours of the two fit each other and create those long chains of close and warm interchange in which Molly and her mother seem to find endless pleasure.

2. *Avoidance of separation.* This eagerness for 'togetherness' leads mother and child to avoid separation or to keep it at a minimum. Thus, in everyday life, separation is no source of frustration. The threshold of tolerance for separation is low, however, and when at the office a separation was attempted it left Molly the most helpless of all the children in our sample.

3. *Mother's interference with child's autonomous activity.* Her need for closeness leads the mother to interfere quite often in what Molly is enjoying on her own, such as toys, objects or motor activity; and people as well, as will be seen later. She uses such interference, usually if not always, as an occasion to bring back Molly's attention to her.

(*a*) In locomotor activities, the mother interferes to share Molly's interest, to admire and stimulate, by verbal comments, Molly's achievements as she strives on her own; while Molly enjoys moving about and indulging in daring acrobatics, she is rather a show-off in her ways.

(*b*) With toys, mother is often found teasing Molly by withholding, while Molly struggles to hold on. The mother is not seen encouraging or promoting the constructive or symbolical use of toys, and Molly's interest remains at the level of manipulation and possessiveness. This is confirmed during testing, when Molly struggles to obtain objects from the tester, and to keep them, but makes no use of them nor shows great curiosity.

(*c*) Molly is more interested in adult possessions than in toys, and is found struggling hard to reach for them against the mother's will. This is one of the rare areas of conflict between them.

4. *Mother's interference with child's relations with others.* With people, interference takes a different quality, whether it concerns strangers who create acute anxiety in Molly, or a better-known person with whom she is enjoying herself. When Molly faces a stranger, she is the most panicky child of the sample, and rushes helpless to her mother, crying and clinging to her for a long while. The mother responds quietly and warmly, neither pushing nor keeping back, but rather encouraging. It takes a long time for Molly to overcome her anxiety and let interest and curiosity in the stranger take the lead. Even with the observer whom she sees often, she is

fearful at first, moving back and forth between the observer and her mother. After a while, however, she becomes friendly and even quite provocative, and forgets about her mother, and this is when the mother interferes in subtle ways, as in the chain we have just described, diverting Molly's attention from the observer to herself. Usually Molly does not mind, since mother offers her something even more attractive.

Data show that it is a consistent characteristic of the mother to maintain distance between Molly and other people in such a way. The father is always presented as a threat and she rather enjoys Molly's fear of him. An aunt living one floor up is permitted no right to share in Molly's care.

5. *Mutual satisfaction and frustration.* Extreme closeness, though a great joy to both Molly and her mother is also a source of mutual frustration in interaction, the child's demands on the mother being endless and the mother's interference not always being appreciated by the child. Episodes of mutual frustration are quite short but intense. Notes of Molly's whining, grunting, and crying are scattered through the record in the midst of these long happy chains of interaction. To frustration, Molly reacts with a stubborn fight to get what she wants, and, if she has to give in, she screams and turns helplessly towards her mother, who comforts her, bringing a prompt ending to Molly's misery. When the mother is frustrated by Molly's behaviour she responds by inconsistent attitudes, half giving in for a while, then impatient, then putting the child down abruptly, but giving in the next moment.

This angry putting down of the child is the only sudden termination of interaction by the mother to which Molly sometimes reacts by yelling. More often she accepts it and starts playing. The mother then calls Molly back and starts a new chain of interaction.

The same contradictory attitude is seen in toilet training and feeding. On the one hand the mother allows Molly complete freedom to be messy, even laughing about it and not helping her in any ways to become clean, while on the other hand she is happy to comment on how naughty this is, and how Father disapproves of it and punishes Molly for it.

Closer analysis shows also that the mother at times provokes frustration, through teasing or otherwise, as a means of maintaining interaction and of obtaining gratification through the child's happiness when she later removes the source of frustration. This is seen well in frequent instances of inconsistently forbidding the child to do things.

6. *Mutual dependency.* This analysis of the interaction shows Molly and mother to be in a relationship of total dependency. Though the mother recalls how much attached she was to her own mother and declares that she restrains herself so that she will not make her daughters too attached to her, she is seen to use every means to keep Molly dependent upon her. Even when she stimulates locomotor activities, she maintains high emotional dependency. She loves it and on each visit she looks tenderly at the little girl, and comments on how sweet she is and on how much one would like to keep them small. While Molly relies on the mother, both for enjoying herself and, even more, for relief from pain, frustration and anxiety.

Molly shows ability to enjoy a certain autonomy in her whereabouts and dealings with others, but her mother does not give her credit for this and has subtle ways of preventing Molly's normal trends towards autonomy while responding warmly to all Molly's spontaneous movements of dependency.

At age 1 Molly is a happy early walker, quite enterprising learning about her surroundings. She is active. Her level of activity remains at the stage of manipulation and possessiveness with no constructive, nor symbolical use of objects. She is also an early talker and interested in social games. She has great ability in making her wants and desires understood. She is always ready to turn to the mother to share interest, rather demanding, easily frustrated, and then helpless, but easily conforted also.

Interaction in Bob's Case

Now let us turn briefly to Bob, first child of a middle-class couple, living also in a two-room flat. Mother, though not working, has been trained as a kindergarten teacher; Father is an engineer and both are actively interested in community and social life. They remain in close relationship with relatives and friends, the children being often kept in common by each mother in turn while the other mothers are busy elsewhere.

Interaction between Bob and his mother is in sharp contrast with what was observed for Molly. Indeed, outside physical care, direct interaction seldom happens. Chains of interaction are short with long interludes in between; physical care is of brief duration and goes on without interchange, but with a quality of mutual tolerance, and empathy in ways of behaving towards food, cleanliness and handling of the situation.

The factors which release direct interaction are few: on Bob's part, reaction to separation, and reaction to hurt or fear; on mother's part to prevent him from touching or doing something dangerous and to comfort him when hurt. But even then interaction is short, and sober in modes and content. For instance: 'Bob hurts himself and starts crying: mother, who was sewing, watches without a word, Bob comes up to her on all fours, whining; he leans on her lap, mother gently and silently puts her hand on his head for less than a minute, Bob is contented and starts off. . . .' It is striking to see that, during three visits, only one longer and richer chain of interaction is to be observed.

Between Bob and his mother interaction is mostly indirect and carried on almost exclusively through the mode of watching. This watching is very gratifying for the mother and provides her with a fine knowledge of Bob's abilities, likes and dislikes and allows her to arrange an environment rich in thrilling interests in which he gets deeply involved, leaving mother pleased to see him busy and clever, while she is able at the same time to carry on her work.

Bob himself watches his mother a lot and in this way shares her activities. He needs to be looked at and cannot bear it when mother gets too absorbed in her work and becomes remote. He then becomes whiny and frustrated, very much as he does when his mother goes away, as will be seen later.

Mutual watching appears to be a silent agreement, 'We enjoy being here together, but we don't interfere in each other's business'. And indeed, in Bob's case physical distance and non-interfering are as striking as closeness and interfering was in Molly's case.

1. *Physical distance*. Physical contact is reduced to a minimum with no unnecessary picking up, no long stays on the lap, no mutual games of contact, no direct stimulations, little cuddling, and little if any verbal interchange. However, when contact is asked for by Bob it is willingly given to him. But Bob rarely asks for physical contact or attention. He does not seek for mother's approval nor participation in his play. There is indeed mutual agreement between Bob and his mother in remaining distant. However, though physically distant, Bob and his mother are far from being remote towards one another, as is shown by the mother's sensitive and warm comments about

Bob's progress and achievements, and by Bob's acute interest in his mother's activities, his warm greeting when she comes in, and his despair when she leaves.

It was while wondering about this that we found that *constant mutual watching* was a subtle but very active way of interacting.

2. *Mutual non-interference in social relations.* The mother likes Bob to have friends of his age and offers him many opportunities. She enjoys watching the children play, rarely interferes in their games. She also enjoys interchanges between Bob and the observer, and often leaves him alone with her.

Bob is delighted to have people around. Play with children is a source of activity and excitement. He both takes the initiative and follows; he defends himself, hardly ever crying. He is quick and clever at keeping or obtaining the toys he wants, but also quite tolerant when he fails. During the visit to the office he was a little afraid but also fascinated by the unknown observer. He did not turn to his mother for protection, but made cautious and progressive moves towards the stranger, until he was able to enjoy her company. Mother made no comments, let Bob go at his own pace and in his own way but enjoyed his being friendly at the end.

3. *Mother's lack of interference in child's activity.* Bob is seen playing for long periods with a variety of toys and objects which mother generously provides. The room is organized so that Bob may enjoy a lot of freedom. And Bob enjoys himself on his own, looking, listening, exploring and making endless experiments with objects. He is very involved with toys, especially in a Teddy bear, with which he plays out his emotional life in the most cunning and imaginative way.

4. *Mother's lack of interference in child's emotional displays.* Mother comments very little on Bob's emotional displays, although she takes them into account. She lets her son deal with them as well as he can, and comes in only when help is needed. She then tends to make changes in environmental conditions, and, only when Bob clearly asks for it, offers direct support with very few words. As to Bob, he has his own personal means of dealing with anxiety and frustration. and does not rest much on his mother for help.

For instance, when faced with anxiety caused by a stranger at the office, he did not turn once towards mother but watched the observer, not losing sight of her, and stopping what he was doing when he caught her eyes. He slowly came nearer and nearer, but as though ignoring her. He did not take the pencil she was holding and which he wanted. He touched it when it was put on the table but quickly withdrew his hands; finally he took it. He pushed his toys in the direction of the new observer and then dared to play directly with her. Later on one saw him able to fight with her vigorously when she teasingly tickled his neck, not fearful, nor crying. He was not even resentful for he included her in his games a few minutes later.

5. *Attitude towards autonomy.* Here again mutual adjustment seems very good, the mother being favourable in all possible ways to Bob's trends towards autonomy, while Bob shows great capacity in this respect, and mother often comments joyfully: 'He is not a baby any more. He looks like a little schoolboy, doesn't he?'

It is worth noticing that in one area Bob remains totally dependent and passive while mother is definitely imposing herself in a completely domineering way, thoroughly accepted by Bob: this is in physical care either feeding or cleaning. Bob is pleased with the mother's manipulations. He accepts the food that she spoons into him at a quick tempo without making any attempt either to interfere in what she does to him, or to do it on his own. He complies to her demands about toilet training, about which she herself is very matter of fact and not much emotionally involved.

6. *Mutual pleasure and frustration.* Pleasure in one another and happiness strike one as dominant all through interaction, while very few frustrating instances are observed. No whining and seldom crying on Bob's part, and no irritation on mother's part. This is partly due to the reduced number of prohibitions, which are clearly stated and consistent. So much so that at one year old Bob has registered them and prohibitions remain active even in mother's absence.

7. *Attitude towards separation.* Bob's separation anxiety, though within the average range for his age, is quite marked. His mother's comings and goings are a source of concern, and he has long been able to differentiate when she goes out of the room from when she goes out of the flat. He then cries bitterly. The mother is greatly annoyed by Bob's demands on her presence. She feels them as cumbersome and does not permit Bob to intrude in her work and in her social and cultural activities. Though she does not scold nor show overtly her annoyance to Bob, she does not give in and does not spare him.

It is interesting to notice that Bob is the only child of the sample who plays hide and seek with his Teddy bear and a few other objects.

He is also the only one to present some difficulties going to sleep, crying and rocking himself on all fours when put to bed.

At 1 year old, Bob is a happy, contented bright little boy, engaged in many constructive and exploratory activities, already making symbolical use of toys. He is able to develop good social relationships, is independent in many ways and has an advanced ego-development, as is shown by the complex means which he invents in order to master his fears and anxieties, and to master the outside world.

The two patterns of interaction, Molly with her mother, and Bob with his, are both rich and enjoyable for both partners, yet they are contrasted sharply in many respects. At 1 year of age, there is dependency for Molly, and autonomy and early ego-development for Bob. What this will end in during the following years is an open question.

Summary and Discussion

1. Starting from naturalistic observations in an everyday setting we have tried to define a methodology for the analysis of mother-infant interaction which would be valid in every case. Such methodology has led us to a description of interaction in terms of seven main characteristics which define the specific and complex pattern under which both partners are interconnected. From such a description emerged each partner's own emotional attitudes towards the other, and these have also been analysed and classified as a methodological tool. It is likely that other classifications might have to be used in other cases. Since other mother-child pairs might involve new variables, our choice was guided here by those which were outstanding.

This type of study does not answer the question as to what the forces are which lead each partner to have this rather than that mode of interaction. Possibly psychoanalytic investigations of a mother's motivations, studies of individual differences in infants, and socio-cultural and anthropological investigations will one day answer those challenging questions. However, direct observation of interaction between mother and child seems to us to enlighten some points concerning mother-child relationship and its impact on a child's behaviour and development.

2. The two cases we have presented today illustrate a fact which is true of all other cases observed: reciprocal attitudes of partners

towards one another and towards the environment are consistently acted out in interaction and give it its specific pattern. Thus one sees that interaction is the result, and also a complex mode of expression, of these mutual attitudes. Interaction reveals and gives them shape and consistency.

3. These two cases show that the emotional attitude of one partner in regard to one variable affects attitudes to other variables. There is a close interdependency between attitudes. This interdependency between variables results in an attitudinal gestalt which has an invariance throughout the interaction at a given age.

4. In interaction there is a constant adaptation which has three possible outcomes:

(*a*) mutual pleasure in each other's spontaneous attitude;

(*b*) acceptation and easy compliance of one partner towards the other, the latter being a leader readily followed by the former;

(*c*) open conflict.

In both cases presented here, mutual pleasure in interaction is predominant, with obvious reinforcement of mutual attitudes. There are many instances of easy compliance and giving in, and it seems that, in such instances the mother is more often the leader than is the child, for both pairs.

In Bob's case, separation is an area of open conflict and causes frustration and anxiety in both partners. In Molly's case there is not as yet such open conflict though one would be inclined to predict that the frequent occurrences of mutual frustration due to extreme closeness should lead sooner or later to open conflict.

In some other pairs we have studied, compliance is predominant, with low mutual pleasure but with no area of open conflict. Whereas in other cases, conflicting attitudes are predominant, conflicts being both intense and widespread, mutual pleasure is scant, and compliance is attempted but fails.

We believe that such attempt to define modes of adaptation to one another should throw some light on the concept of the mother-child relationship, which is often characterized simply as good or bad.

5. This closely knit mother-child interaction obviously has a strong impact on the orientation and development of maternal attitudes, as well as on the orientation of the child's development and the shaping of his personality, through the reinforcement of some behaviours, while others are completely ignored or punished. We will be inter-

ested, as a next step, to examine zones of correspondences between patterns of interaction, maternal attitudes, and personality features of the child at one year old. Longitudinal studies will be used to follow the evolution of interacting attitudes, and the changes brought about by conflict-solving processes whenever open conflict occurs.

Discussion following Dr David and Mlle Appell's Paper

AMBROSE *One would expect that a child's attitude to strangers would depend very much on his attitude to his mother, especially if the mother is there along with the stranger.*

ROSENBLATT *I think we should make a distinction between anxiety and fear. Fear arises from the actual novelty of the stranger, while the anxiety comes from the child's relation to his mother, and his somehow knowing that the mother objects to having the stranger there. Anxiety in this instance arises from fear of disapproval by mother.*

OPPÉ *The anxiety might arise from imitation. A child will often react to a stranger as the mother does. You see this clearly in a clinical situation, if you get a smile from the mother you will almost certainly get a response from the child.*

BOWLBY *The children were both facing a conflict between curiosity or exploration and fear. Bob seems to resolve the conflict by tending to explore, and Molly comes down on the fear side, and retreats to her mother. And presumably quite a lot of this difference arises from the mother-plus-child's previous history with strangers – very much in the way that Robert Hinde's monkeys showed big differences.*

THOMAS *I think we should note that there's another factor there in Molly's case. Because she was beckoned back by her mother when she approached strangers, she wasn't just exploring, she was also breaking a prohibition.*

ROSENBLATT *Do you think it would be valid to make a value judgment about these children's behaviour, and to consider that Bob is more mature in the way he deals with his anxiety?*

BOWLBY *I personally would be very hesitant in making predictions about their future development. One could argue that, in the case of Bob, his mother is training him to behave too independently with strangers, so that subsequently he will be unable to use any one figure as a haven of safety. This sort of thing can depend on a very fine balance.*

THOMAS *On the positive side, he is encouraged to go out.*

DAVID *But his approach to strangers was a very little bit like what you see in some autistic children – almost pretending that nothing is going on.*

ROWELL *You also see this in perfectly normal animals – going towards something, slightly shying off it, and apparently becoming occupied with something else and pretending the thing isn't there.*

BOWLBY *To what extent did Bob's behaviour depend on his mother being in the room and acting as a haven of safety?*

DAVID *When she left the room, he had already become accustomed to the stranger, but he started crying, went to the door which was closed, then finally went to his teddy bear, which was a very important toy to him.*

APPELL *And when the mother was there, he wouldn't necessarily look at her, but he seemed to use her as a base for his exploring, very much as Harlow's monkeys did with the cloth-covered surrogates* (1961).

JENSEN *Could you tell us more about these children's reactions to toys, especially strange toys.*

DAVID *Well, in the office there were plenty of strange objects, including a box of toys, but the children certainly didn't react to them as they did to strangers.*

JENSEN *I was thinking of a case that Dr Katharine Wolf* (1953) *reported, of a child who developed a definite fear of toys. The evidence was that you were more likely to get such behaviour from toy deprived children.*

MICHELL *On the other hand I would think that there was a definite period when fear of toys occurs, in the way that fear of strangers does.*

RHEINGOLD *Of course, in the case of Harry Harlow's monkeys, the toys were supernormal and moved and made noises, and the monkeys were more or less pathological. We have no parallel case for children.*

FOSS *Is there any reason why one should not submit children to the 'open field test' which Harlow used with the monkeys* (1961)*?*

BOWLBY *That is more or less what Arsenian did more than twenty years ago* (1943). *She looked at the behaviour of young children in a strange room with toys in it, and noted the very different ways they reacted when a mother-figure was with them or not with them. It's a very interesting little experiment, and deserves following up.*

AMBROSE *It's really a very simple set up, and could be used for a number of interesting purposes. One could get evidence, for example, on individual differences in responsiveness to strangers by just having a bare room, with a stranger in one corner, with or without the mother in another corner, sitting the infant in the centre and recording what happens in say fifteen minutes.*

FOSS *I think operant techniques could also be adapted for babies rather in the way Harriet Rheingold has already done* (1963), *or using a modification of the Butler Box* (*R. A. Butler*, 1953). *For instance, one could count how often an infant would press a bar to see or hear his mother when he is in an environment with unfamiliar objects.*

AMBROSE *It might be particularly useful to compare infants' reactions to strangers, to toys, and to their mothers. I suspect we don't pay nearly enough attention to toys.*

ROSENBLATT *It seems to me slightly obtuse to try to infer the mother-infant relationship from the way the infant reacts to toys. Wouldn't it be more straightforward to characterize the mother-infant relationship, and then make testable predictions about the behaviour with the toys?*

AMBROSE *One can do it both ways. I'm interested to know if the attitude to the mother generalizes to other people, and to toys – this is sometimes assumed to be the case in diagnosis through play, and in play therapy.*

DAVID *In Molly's case, toys had another function, which may be quite common. When the mother wanted to interfere with the child, to get her to do something or to attract her attention, she very often used a toy as a means to her end. And she often used toys to tease Molly, a 'who is going to have it?' kind of game. I think this may be connected with the way Molly is very bound up with her toys, hugging them and carrying them around.*

MICHELL *Studies of teasing might be a useful way of getting at maternal attitudes. With Molly, toys were used for teasing, but in some families there is teasing over the bottle, or over toilet training.*

GUNTHER *In the Newsons' study at Nottingham* (1963) *it was found that teasing correlated with class, in that unskilled workers did it a lot with their* 1-*year-olds, but others did it hardly at all.*

PRECHTL *Which makes me want to ask why you haven't looked for the effects of variables like social class in your experiment. Wouldn't it have been wise to keep socio-economic status constant in your sample?*

DAVID *It would be difficult, and I'm not sure that it's important; according to our aim which was to describe and analyse mother-infant interactions.*

KAUFMAN *On the other hand there are many studies which show the importance of sociological factors in child-rearing, attitudes towards children, and so on.*

ROWELL *But you end up just tracing causes backwards. How the infant behaves depends on the mother, and that depends on how she was brought up, and that depends on the socio-cultural background. Where do you stop?*

HINDE *Also it might be disadvantageous to hold class constant, because that might restrict the varieties of rearing. What you need is great variety, so that you can compare the effects of extreme methods.*

GEWIRTZ *It's all a question of where one would wish to focus in a particular investigation. Myriam David and Geneviève Appell are studying sequences of mother-infant interaction. It would seem perfectly proper for them to look at interaction systems isolated from demographic and social status factors. To study the effects of such factors on interaction would represent another investigation entirely. As Robert Hinde has just indicated, it could be useful to sample systematically, or in some way to control, levels of, say, a social status variable, or systematically to confound such a variable in a design. This might be done, for instance, if a given type of rearing condition which effected the quality of interaction were found only in certain class levels.*

FOSS *But even if you don't want to take all your sample from the same class, for the reasons people have given, it is still worth looking for relationships between the mother-infant interaction and the family background, because you might get clues regarding factors which you haven't thought of looking at. For instance, you haven't had much opportunity for observing the role played by the father. It would depend on how much leisure he has, and what his leisure pursuits are, and these certainly depend on the kind of job he has.*

APPELL *But as Thelma says, it's a question of knowing where to stop. I'm sure what we should go on to do is a study of father-infant interaction, mother-father-infant interaction, and then bring the siblings in too.*

KAUFMAN *This is not as far-fetched as it sounds. There are several studies going on in which the father as well as the mother agree to be interviewed, usually several times.*

ROSENBLATT *But the study we have just heard reported is not the result of interviews. Most of these mothers could not provide the information which is needed regarding their relations with their children. We have been hearing very sophisticated reports of the interaction, which can only come from observation.*

KAUFMAN *As a psychoanalyst, I must say that I don't believe a useful picture of the interaction can be given without more information on the mother and father, and some knowledge of their motivation.*

ROWELL *But how much do you know of the background and history of the relations between your monkeys?*

KAUFMAN *Let me illustrate the point. Joyce Robertson described Nicholas who had a mother who thought the father was critically ill. Now suppose she had got it into her head that the father was ill because of excessive activity, that would almost certainly result in her inhibiting Nicholas in his own activity. So that to get insight into this interaction, it would be important to know her ideas about the father's illness.*

BOWLBY *Perhaps this is a matter of faith. I happen to believe that the more experienced we become in making observations the more adequate they will be in their own right. I don't think observations of maternal behaviour need be dependent on our knowing the origins of the behaviour we see,*

KAUFMAN *All I'm saying is that, when designing a study, if it isn't all that difficult (and I don't think it is), one can get the kinds of information about the family structure and about the mother which will enable you to get other clues as to what to look for in her behaviour.*

APPELL *I think we are more concerned with that than we seem to have shown: we certainly pay attention to family relationships, and collect rich material from spontaneous conversation. In this presentation we have attempted to show all that can be given by strict direct observations. I would like to stress our concern not to introduce bias in one's description of mother's behaviour and to maintain an objective and almost photographic, description of what is going on.*

DAVID *When you are thinking of interaction, you can describe it at different levels – the mother does something, the child does something; or one can talk of mutual attitudes; or one can go further and talk of unconscious motivation. Of course they are all interconnected, but for the purposes of this experiment we are confining ourselves to the first two kinds of interaction. For instance, at the attitude level, we got the impression that both Molly and her mother enjoyed their closeness, and found it reinforcing, whereas Bob and his mother seemed to find their independence reinforcing. Perhaps these were two different ways of reducing anxiety.*

Hereditary Control of Early Social Behavior

D. FREEDMAN

We have made a film illustrating selected findings from a month-by-month study of infant identical and fraternal twins over the first year of life (Freedman, 1963). Before presenting the study on which the film is based, it will be worth while to briefly summarize the first report of this research (Freedman & Keller, 1963):

Mrs Keller and I studied mental and motor abilities and personality development in twenty pairs of same-sexed infant twins. We worked independently, each seeing approximately half the twin pairs. We spent at least one morning or afternoon in the homes each month, testing, interviewing mother and photographing; occasionally we paid an evening visit to show the accumulated films to the family. It is pertinent to say that we both became good friends of our respective families over the course of our visits and that with good rapport came a fairly accurate level of observation.

Why did we choose to study *infant* twins? Since imitation which is independent of immediate perception starts after the first year, we could rule out such mutual contagion as a factor in the results. We were also able to postpone zygosity determinations (thirteen blood-group factors) until after the study and thereby avoid contamination from that end. Finally, we wanted to avoid the problems of retrospective histories, a major reason for most longitudinal research.

At the end of the study we found we had an n_1 of eleven fraternal pairs and an n_2 of nine identical pairs. The results from both Mrs Keller's group and my own formed similar distributions on all tests and rating scales suggesting that they are readily duplicable. Within-pair differences were consistently greater among the fraternal pairs on both of our major measures, the Nancy Bayley Mental and Motor Scales ($P < \cdot 01$), and the Bayley Infant Behavior Profile ($P < \cdot 001$). (P values are all based on one-tailed tables of the Mann-Whitney non-parametric test, Auble, 1953.)

We managed to eliminate possible 'halo' effects by a procedure in which our films formed the basis of judgment. We had taken monthly motion-pictures in which each twin of a pair was filmed separately in the same situations, and the film of each was accumulated on separate reels. At the end of the study, the filmed behavior of half of each pair was rated by a group of judges using the Bayley Infant Behavior Profile. Another group of judges rated the films of the remaining twins. Again within-pair differences among fraternal twins were significantly larger ($P < \cdot 005$).

The appendix presents data on the Infant Behavior Profile not yet reported elsewhere. It can be seen that a variety of traits appear to be under genetic control, i.e. they are consistently more concordant within identical pairs than within fraternal pairs over the first year. Two of these items, *Social Orientation* ($P < \cdot 005$) and *Fearfulness* ($P < \cdot 05$) were of particular interest because only in these items was social interaction central. The filmed observations made around these two findings subsequently formed the basis for the present film:

In the first five months *Social Orientation* was scored on the basis of visual fixation of a face and social smiling, and the first part of the film traces the differential development of these behaviors within identical and within fraternal pairs ($P < \cdot 05$ for months 1-5, identicals more concordant). After 5 months of age, *Fearfulness* was primarily scored on the basis of fear of the investigator ($P < \cdot 02$ for months 5-12, identicals more concordant), and the second half of the film deals with this most interesting phenomenon. The film itself is entitled 'Development of Smiling and Fear of Strangers; with an inquiry into inheritance of behavior'.

The following sections on smiling and fear of strangers are intended to illustrate major points of the film. In order to clarify certain developmental issues, data from a non-twin and blind infants are included.

Smiling

In the first month it was common to see smiling for which no specific external stimulation was required, and it occurred most often when the baby was sated, had it's eyes closed and was falling off to sleep (see Plate 21). These were, therefore, not social smiles. This type of smiling dropped out in most infants after the first month.

In the second month it usually took some external stimulation to elicit smiling. This might still occur with the eyes closed but in response to touching the mouth, a voice, the tinkle of a bell, etc. This was the case with Arturo, a fraternal twin, who was a sleepyhead and rarely wide awake (Plate 22*a*). His fraternal brother, Felix, was a remarkable contrast (Plate 22*b*). He was wide eyed and very watchful – but he was unremittingly sober and rarely smiled. This difference in amount of smiling persisted throughout the first year.

Felix not only illustrates contrasting development, so typical in our fraternal pairs, but also his visual fixation of mother's face illustrates behavior that normally preceded *social smiling*. This fixation on the face is further illustrated by Marty and Chucky (Plates 23, *a*, *b*), an identical pair who showed complete concordance for this behavior. Usually, about ten days after such intense visual fixation of the adult's face began, the first social smile occurred.

It is of interest that in identical pairs the age at onset and the intensity of visual fixation of the adult's face was generally the same on both twins even when there were substantial differences in birth-weight. (See Price, 1950, for an explanation of such differences in weight.)

While genetic factors are important we should make it clear that the timing of these events are dependent on environmental factors also. For example, Wolff (1963) has found that, within a small sample from the Boston Irish population, social smiling generally appeared before the end of the first month rather than late in the second month, when it is more commonly seen. He attributes this speedy development to the high amount of stimulation given infants in this sub-population.

As for the cause of smiling in infants, many of the major studies have stressed that visual fixation of a face or some face-like stimulus is a necessary prelude to social smiling (Kaila, 1932; Spitz, 1946; Ahrens, 1954). Consequently the deduction has been commonly made, based on ethological thinking, that a causal connection exists between a moving face-like pattern (social releaser) and smiling. However, it is clear that this conceptualization is far too simple, if only for the fact that blind infants smile. In order to better understand this issue we are currently studying a number of infants who were blind at birth.

In the course of this study, limited because fortunately blinded infants are now rare, we are finding that these infants smile at the usual time, but that their early social smiles are fleeting, much like normal eyes-closed smiling in the first month. Our first example,

Yvonne (Plate 24), could only perceive intense light due to cataracts caused by maternal rubella in fetal life. One interesting observation made was that despite the blindness she nevertheless turned her eyes towards the person holding her, while smiling, as in Plate 24. This occurred with intense petting, cooing, and talking by the adult, and seems to be direct evidence that ocular fixation of the social object is initiated by central rather than peripheral stimulation. Also, although Yvonne's smiling was actually a series of fleeting smiles, the overall impression was that the interaction was as joyous for her as for seeing babies.

The course of early smiling was much the same in David, also a case of blindness due to fetal rubella, and his early smiles were very fleeting. However, by 6 months of age he could engage in normal prolonged social smiling (Plate 25), as was the case with all other blind infants investigated. We also followed the development of several deaf infants and found their smiling to be quite normal.

We have concluded that since seeing infants, blind infants, and deaf infants all smile, sensory channels while important are secondary and that smiling is never a response to just a single sensory stimulus. At present smiling is probably best defined simply as an instinctive response of the infant to 'another'. (See the important paper of Goldstein, 1957, for an elaboration of this definition.)

Fear of Strangers

While infants under 5 months of age will usually smile at any person, after this age they become increasingly discriminating, and smiles are increasingly reserved for familiar persons. Discrimination turns to wariness some time in the third or fourth trimester of the first year, and most infants begin to react with fear when with a stranger. This process is very similar to the development of the flight response in lower mammals and birds. There, too, fear of strangers often follows a period in which indiscriminate attachments are possible. (See Freedman, 1961, for a discussion of this point.)

Lori and Lisa, an identical pair, were both wary of strangers from 5 months of age through 8 months, when fear gave way to rather easy acceptance (Plates 26, *a*, *b*, *c*, *d*). As in the majority of identical pairs, the timing and intensity of their reactions were very similar over this entire period.

On the other hand, Richard and Robert, fraternal twins (Plates

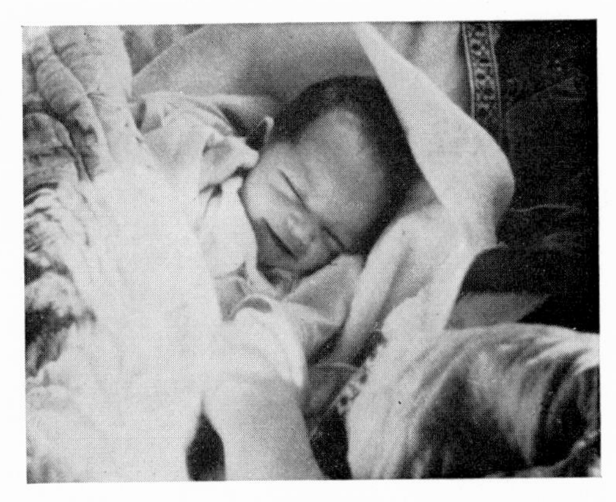

21. Tony, singleton, eleven days of age, example of pre-social smiling.

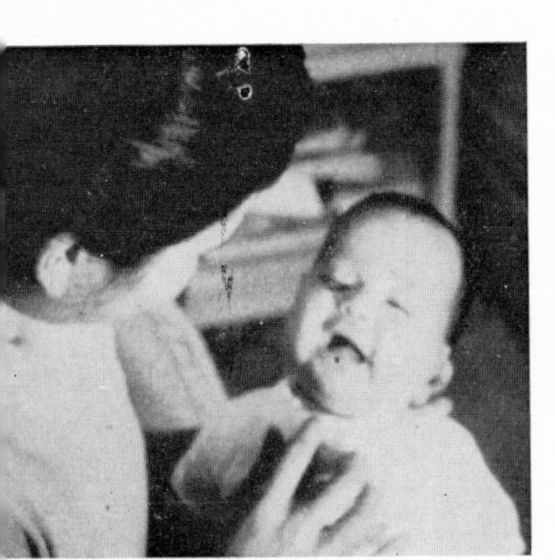

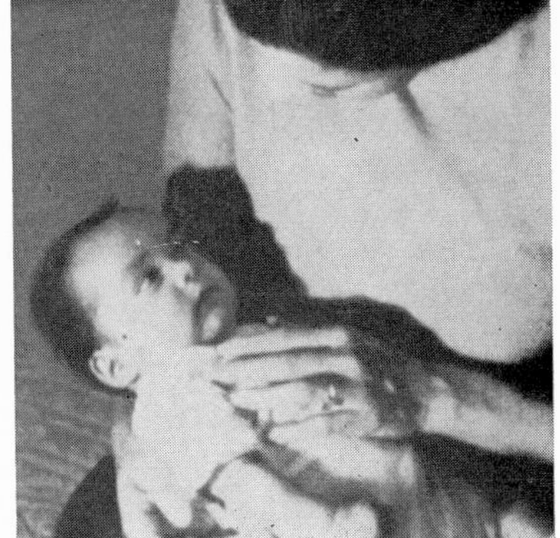

22*a*. Arturo F., two months 4 days, smiling to touch with eyes closed. He was usually drowsy at this age.

22*b*. Fraternal brother Felix F., two months four days, was alert but unremittingly sober.

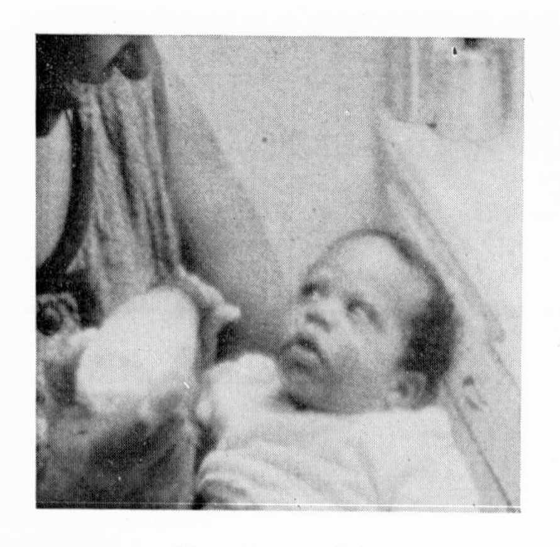
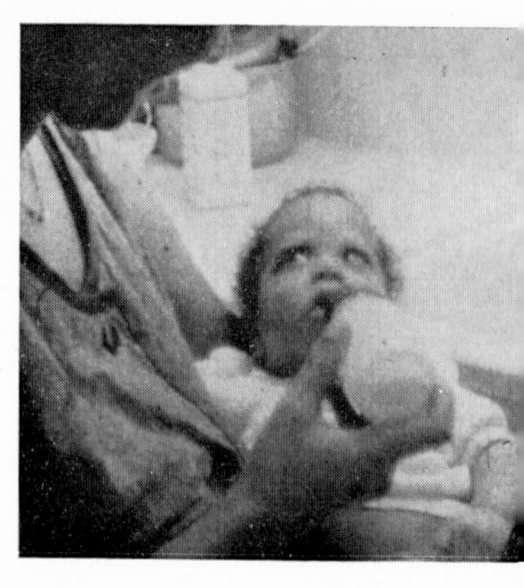

23*a*. Marty S., two months 0 days, staring into mother's face during feeding.

23*b*. Identical brother, Chucky S., two months 0 days, was completely concordant for this behaviour.

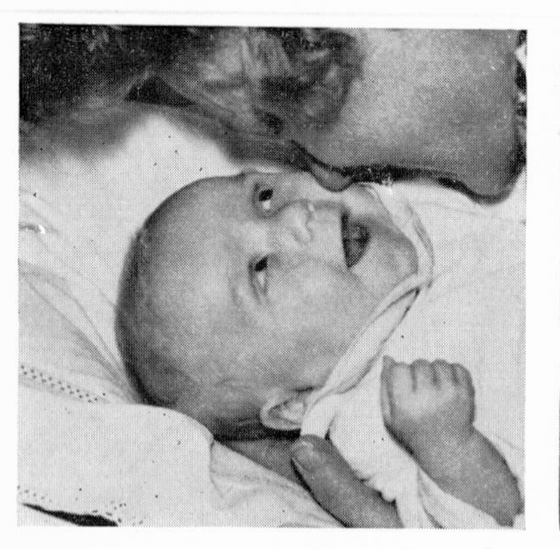
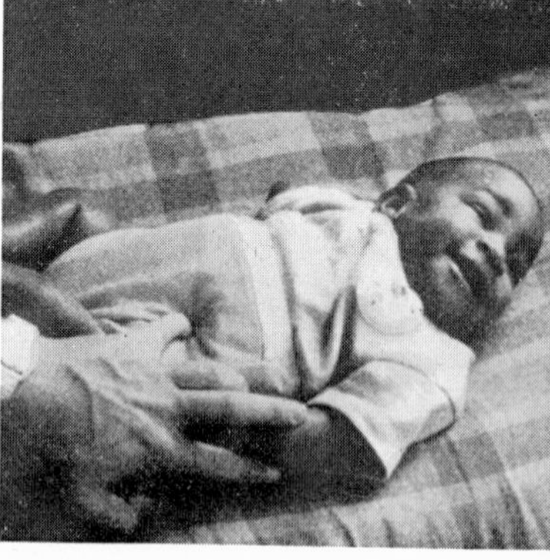

24. Yvonne, two months 20 days, congenitally blind, smiling with "eyes on" mother. Smiles were fleeting at this age.

25. David, six months 10 days, congenitally blind, engaged in prolonged social smiling.

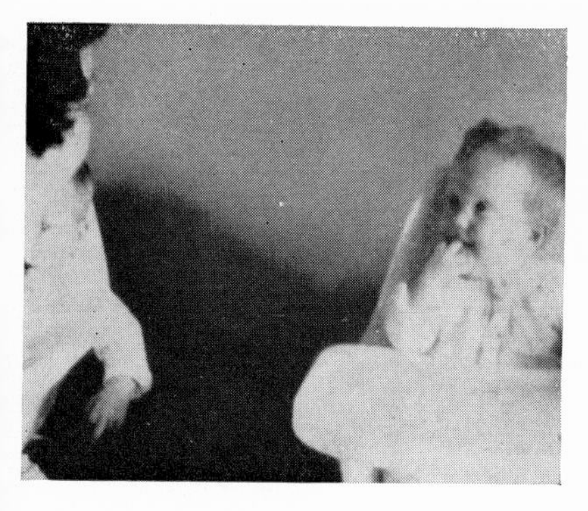
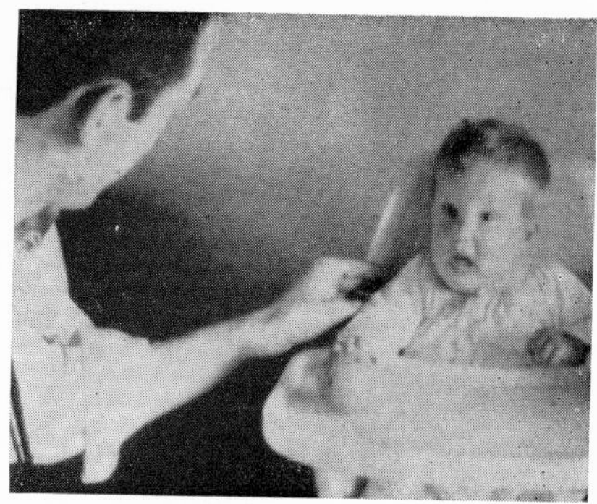

26*a* and *b*. Lisa B., seven months 0 days, with mother and with a male stranger.

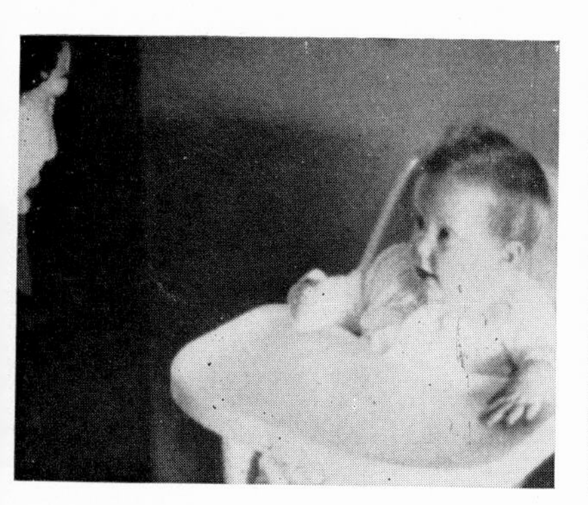
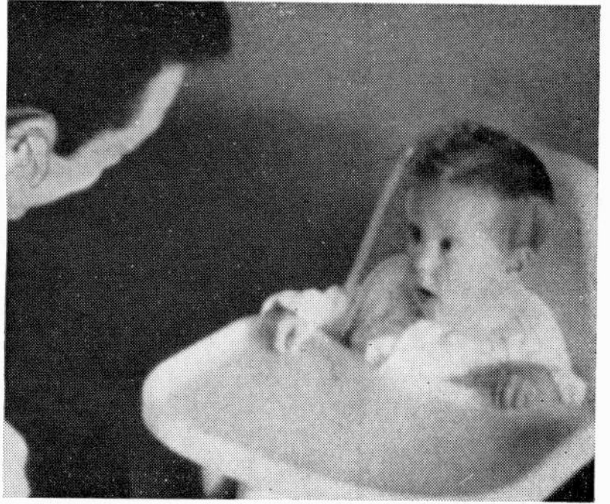

26*c* and *d*. Identical twin, Lori B., seven months 0 days, with mother and with same stranger.

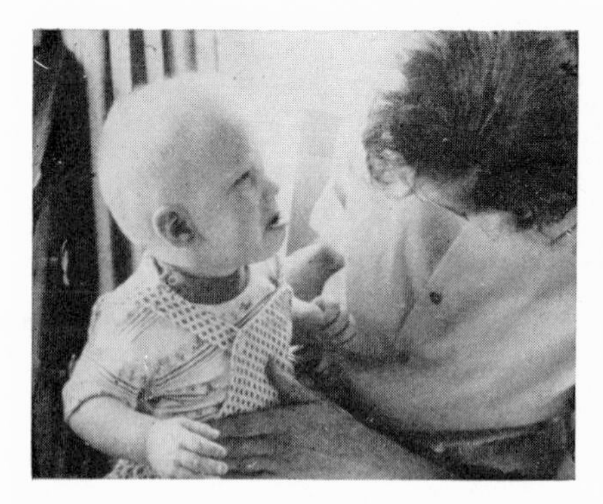

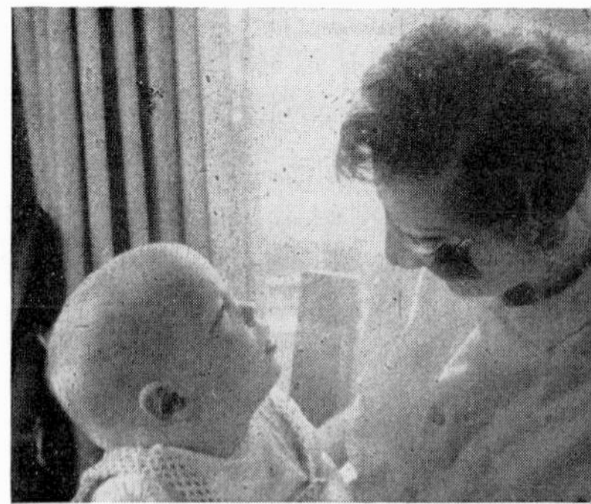

27*a*. Richard C., ten months 3 days, cries when investigator dons Halloween mask.

27*b*. Fraternal twin, Robert C., ten months 3 days, inspects investigator with Halloween mask. His only reaction was 'interest'.

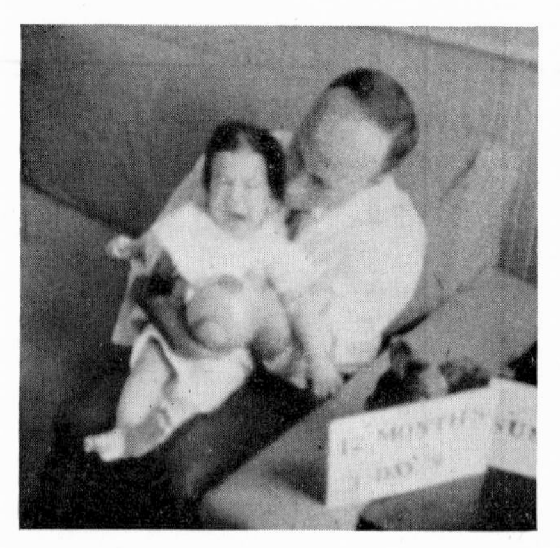

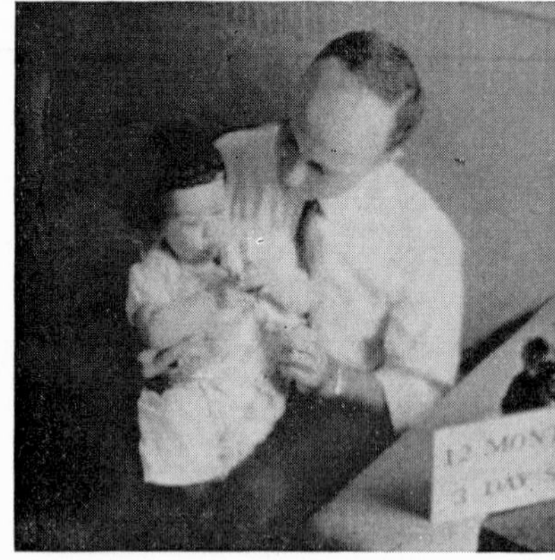

28*a*. Susie W., twelve months 3 days, with investigator, rejecting both him and offered toy.

28*b*. Identical twin, Annie W., twelve months 3 days, sitting comfortably on investigator's lap.

27, *a*, *b*), were highly dissimilar in their reactions. Richard was the more fearful from 5 months and on. For example, he cried when Mrs Keller arrived for the tenth month visit despite the fact that she had made a visit each month of his life. After a while he relaxed, but he cried again when the investigator donned a Halloween mask (Plate 27*a*). Fraternal brother Robert (Plate 27*b*), who had passed through a brief, mild period of fear of strangers at 8 months, provided a clear contrast in that he gave no indication of fright during the entire visit.

While these illustrations are typical examples, the distribution of within-pair differences in ratings of *Fearfulness* formed distinct but *overlapping* populations of identicals and fraternals. Our last example is from the overlapping population, a pair of identical twins who were decidedly unalike in their reactions to fear-inducing situations. Susie (Plate 28*a*), who was easily frightened by noises and the Jack-in-the-Box in the first three months of life, became exceedingly frightened of strangers towards the end of the first year, and remained that way through a follow-up period of two years. Annie (Plate 28*b*), while similar to Susie in a great many aspects of behavior, was only mildly disturbed by fear-inducing situations. There is no unequivocal explanation for such non-concordance: Careful investigation led us to rule out as sole cause either differential treatment by parents, birth order, traumatic delivery, viability at birth, and monochorionic versus dichorionic embryogenesis. The work of Prechtl (1963) does suggest minimal brain damage as a possible factor in Susie's hyperreactivity.

Concluding Remarks

Heredity plays a role in the development of positive social orientation (including smiling) and in the fear of strangers. Our evidence for this is that identical twins show greater concordance than fraternal twins in these two areas of behavior over the first year of life. There seems to be no reasonable alternate explanation of these results.

The phenomena of smiling and fear of strangers are of great importance for they are prototypes for much of later behavior. The smile is the first expression in human life of pleasure with another, whereas fear of strangers is normally the first expression of fear of another. As far as we know, these two phenomena are universal in mankind, and they have doubtless been important in human adaptation and evolution.

Appendix

Nancy Bayley Infant Behavior Profile, survey of individual items. Probabilities are from Mann-Whitney one-tailed tables and refer to items in which identical twin pairs exhibit significantly greater concordance than fraternal twin pairs over the first year. In no case was the opposite true.

Each item was rated along a scale from 'deficient' to 'overendowed', with five steps usually spelled out; a nine-point scale was obtained by adding half-steps. The first and last steps are supplied to clarify the items.

P

1. *Social orientation*: responsiveness to persons. ·005
   (1) Does not modify behavior to persons as different from objects.
   (9) Behavior seems to be continuously affected by awareness of persons present.

2. *Object orientation*: responsiveness to toys and other objects. ·02
   (1) Does not look at or in any way indicate interest in objects.
   (9) Reluctantly relinquishes test materials.

3. *Goal directedness*: ·02
   (1) No evidence of directed effort.
   (9) Compulsive absorption with task until it is solved.

4. *Attention span*: tendency to persist in attending to any one object, person or activity, aside from attaining a goal. ·02
   (1) Fleeting attention span.
   (9) Long-continued absorption with task until it is solved.

5. *Cooperativeness* (not relevant most of first year).

6. *Activity*: inactive-vigorous. Not significant
   (1) Stays quietly in one place, with practically no self-initiated movement.
   (9) Hyperactive: can't be quieted for sedentary tests.

6. 1. *Activity*: level of energy (low to high). N.S.

6. 2. *Activity*: coordination of gross muscle movements for age (smooth functioning to poor coordination). N.S.

6. 3. *Activity*: coordination of fine muscles (hands) for age (smooth functioning to poor coordination). ·04

7. *Reactivity*: the ease with which a child is stimulated to response, his sensitivity or excitability. (May be positive or negative in tone.) ·04

- (1) Unreactive; seems to pay little heed to what goes on around him. Responds only to strong or repeated stimulation.
- (9) Very reactive; every little thing seems to stir him up; startles, reacts quickly, seems keenly sensitive to things going on around him.

8. *Tension*: N.S.

- (1) Inert, may be flaccid most of the time.
- (9) Body is predominantly taut or tense.

9. *Fearfulness* (e.g. reaction to the new or strange: strange people, test materials, strange surroundings). ·05

- (1) Accepts the entire situation with no evidence of fear, caution, or inhibition of actions.
- (9) Strong indications of fear of the strange, to the extent he cannot be brought to play or respond to the tests.

10. *General emotional tone*: unhappy-happy. N.S.

- (1) Child seems unhappy throughout the period.
- (9) Radiantly happy; nothing is upsetting; animated.

11. Endurance or behavior constancy in adequacy of response to demands of tests. N.S.

- (1) Tires easily, quickly regresses to lower levels of functioning.
- (9) Continues to respond well and with interest, even with prolonged tests at difficult levels.

12. *Sensory areas*: preoccupation or interest displayed (none to excessive).

(*a*) Sights: looking.	·025
(*b*) Sounds: listening.	N.S.
(*c*) Sound producing: vocal.	N.S.
(*d*) Sound producing: banging, or other.	·005
(*e*) Manipulating (exploring with hands).	·02
(*f*) Body motion.	N.S.
(*g*) Mouthing or sucking: thumb or fingers.	N.S.
(*h*) Mouthing or sucking: toys.	N.S.

Discussion following Dr Freedman's Paper

OPPÉ *I don't wish to quarrel with your results, which seem clear-cut from the film, and even more so from the study as a whole; but you did give the impression that the mother and the investigators didn't know whether the twins were identical or fraternal until you finished the study, and I find it difficult to believe that you couldn't tell before then.*

FREEDMAN *We guessed correctly by 8 months in all but two pairs. One case was a fraternal pair which looked very much alike, and the other was an identical pair which started off looking very different. The latter were monochorionic, and it's usual to find large differences in birth weight between monochorionic twins because of competition for the mother's blood supply. Usually by 8 months such identicals have come to look alike and similar looking fraternals will have started diverging. However, the fact was that the parents, who hadn't the entire group for comparison as we had, insisted they had fraternal twins in all but three instances. More importantly, the judges who rated the behaviour from films did so of only one twin of each pair, and the judgments could not be influenced by what the other twin was like.*

OPPÉ *I agree that you had an excellent control there. But what I had in mind was that a mother might show greater similarity in her behaviour to each twin if she considered them to be identical. So that the infants' similarity in behaviour would be due to the similarity in maternal treatment as well as genetic make-up.*

BOWLBY *But you did have some cases of identical twins who looked very different at birth, so that presumably the mother would treat them differently. Such a case would be relevant to Tom Oppé's point.*

FREEDMAN *We have several pairs like that. For example, the father of one pair had made a favourite of the smaller and weaker of the two identical babies, but by* 8 *months they were nearly indistinguishable. By* 12 *months the father had to give up his favouritism, for he realized it was a hollow sham.*

ROSENBLATT *I believe that, strictly speaking, you have not carried out a genetic study at all, in that your experiment confounds genetic and environmental factors. It's impossible to tell if the similarities between twins are due to similar environments or similar inheritance.*

FREEDMAN *I agree that it's not a sophisticated genetic study from a geneticist's point of view, but given our controls there seems to be no reasonable alternative to a genetic explanation of the differences between the fraternal group and the identical group.*

GEWIRTZ *One of your more striking results is the close agreement in timing of a fear of strangers in the identical twin pair. I would expect the age of onset of the fear of strangers, in this instance concordant, and any discordant results between members of twin pairs, whether identical or fraternal, both to be very dependent on differences in environment. As has earlier been noted, the maintaining home environment could be dramatically different for the members of twin pairs, which makes it difficult in designs, such as this one of yours, to separate genetic from environmental factors in behaviour. In this context, did you find any relationship between the onset of fear and the conditions of child-rearing?*

FREEDMAN *I can only make a guess about that; it is the rather obvious one that those infants who habitually saw many people showed least fear. This is more likely in a large family, and the one case we had of no fear at all was in such a family. However, his fraternal twin did show a phase of fear.*

AMBROSE *This is consistent with the impression that the institutionalized children show less fear of strangers.*

AINSWORTH *You mentioned one pair who had lost all fear by* 8 *months. That seems remarkably early.*

FREEDMAN *They were precocious in many things and fear of strangers developed early and went early. Their mother was very pushing, always interacting with them and coaxing them along.*

GEWIRTZ *This illustrates once again the point made early by Jay*

Rosenblatt – that it is near impossible in a design such as you used to separate genetic-constitutional factors from environmental factors.

FREEDMAN *Of course they are inseparable, and in this kind of study one attempts to find their rough, relative weightings.*

AMBROSE *With regard to the dropping out of fear of strangers, I would say that there are two main factors – habituation and degree of anxiety. I imagine that individual differences in these might be due to both genetic and environmental factors. The rate at which smiling and approach responses to strangers come in again is a function, I think, of the strength to which they developed before the onset of fear, and I would expect environmental factors to play an important part in this.*

RHEINGOLD *I think it's clear that we need evidence on the time of appearance of smiling, its strength, the time of onset of fear of strangers, and the reappearance of smiling to strangers. And a useful control would be to look at fear responses to strange objects. I believe you suggested a relation between fear of people and of objects.*

FREEDMAN *Sudden noises rather than objects. We have found a significant relationship between the degree of startle to noises in the first three months and later fear of strangers. With regard to perception of the stranger, the sound of the stranger in the house can be sufficient to elicit fear, but on the whole I would say that vision is more important than hearing. We have studied five blind babies, and the fear of strangers appeared to be reduced in all of them. We had one tragic case of fraternal twins of the same sex in which one was blind and the other deaf. This was not a longitudinal study; we found the children when they were 2½. The deaf one had shown a decisive fear of strangers in the first year, but the blind one had not. Had these been identical twins these findings, of course, would be much more meaningful.*

OPPÉ *But it's pretty difficult to find blind children in which the only problem is lack of vision.*

THOMAS *And you have to take into account the fact that the blind twin was probably much more dependent on other people, and had been from very early on.*

FREEDMAN *I agree. But to me, at any rate, an approaching visual stimulus looms in a way an auditory one does not* (*Schiff* et al., 1962).

APPELL *Was crying your main criterion for fear?*

FREEDMAN *The criteria can only be spelled out retrospectively and they varied at different ages. At the fifth month, clenched hands and a drawn-down mouth might be more important.*

APPELL *I was wondering how you would deal with some of the more subtle signs of fear, slight withdrawings for instance.*

THOMAS *And thumb-sucking, which we saw in the film.*

FREEDMAN *Since this study sought to cover general psychological development, we did not elaborate our techniques for assessing fear beyond the pertinent item on the Nancy Bayley Infant Behaviour Profile. Thus the present quantitative data on fear is based completely on a nine-point scale which ranges from 'accepts the entire situation with no evidence of fear, caution or inhibition of actions' to 'strong indications of fear of the strangers to the extent he cannot be brought to play or respond to the tests'. However, we have done extensive filming of reactions to strangers at various ages, and we are in the process of examining this footage and developing specific criteria for various stages of the fear reaction.*

A final remark about the fear of strangers: while the function of smiling seems to be that of a binding force between infant and parent and later between various human diads (Goldstein, 1957), *the evolutional function of fear of strangers is not as apparent. Unlike lower animals, which are highly motile when they develop the flight response to strangers, when a human infant develops its fear of strangers, at about* 6-9 *months, it simply does not have the motor ability to escape a predator. It therefore seems a reasonable hypothesis that in human infants the fear of strangers serves mainly to prevent dilution of primary relationships and to intensify the bonds between the infant and those already close to him.*

Stimulus Conditions, Infant Behaviors, and Social Learning in Four Israeli Child-rearing Environments: a preliminary report illustrating differences in environment and behavior between the 'only' and the 'youngest' child[1]

J. L. GEWIRTZ and HAVA B. GEWIRTZ[2]

Introduction

The data analysis of the study we shall describe is in process. Hence it will here be possible to elaborate primarily on our objectives and method, and to present only illustrative findings. Employing entire-day observations of infants in everyday settings, our study represents an attempt to assess stimulus conditions in the environment of the infant in the first year of life and the impact of these stimuli on his adaptive and social behaviors. The stimuli assessed are provided for the most part in interaction with adults, in and out of caretaking. Infants were observed in four child-rearing environments, namely residential institution, kibbutz, single-child family and multiple-child family. These appeared to represent meaningfully different contexts for early development and learning. The diverse environments could be assumed to provide to children different types, amounts and patterns of stimuli, and therefore differences in opportunity, including that for various learnings to occur. Under our theoretical orientation, these differences, as antecedents, would imply different outcomes, for instance in patterns of social or attachment behaviors. We embarked on this program for reasons which reflect the interaction between our research orientation and the extraordinary opportunity offered for this class of research in Israel.

We have preferred generally an experimental approach to the

[1] This project was supported in part by Extramural Grant No. MH-06779 of the U.S. National Institute of Mental Health to H. B. G.

[2] Of the Institute for Behavioral Research, Silver Spring, Maryland.

study of elementary human behaviors, such as responsiveness to stimuli, smiling, vocalizing and the stimulus conditions that control them, as well as to the more complex integrated systems made up of basic behaviors like these and their relations to or control by stimuli. We might term the latter systems 'information processing', 'adaptive intelligence', 'dependence', 'attachment', and the like. This approach of manipulating systematically stimulus conditions while keeping other conditions constant and of charting effects in selected behaviors (at one or at a sequence of time points) is suited particularly to the isolation of principles governing given stimulus-behavior systems. The necessary step remaining in this case would be to generalize to life settings the relationships found. This could be done by assumption or through a research involving systematic observation carried out in life settings for the purpose. The alternative approach is the one we have found it expedient to follow in the study being reported, given the unique opportunity in which we found ourselves in Israel. It was to observe directly in the life setting the relationships holding between stimuli and behavior. To be complete, this approach would require in addition assumptions about underlying principles that could account for the obtained relationships. Alternatively, it would require a concomitant experimental program in stripped-down contexts to determine definitively the nature of the principles underlying the relationships observed between variables in the life-settings.

It is our conviction that either of the above research approaches is preferable to one in which some gross referent of environmental conditions, operating through long time periods, like that of 'age', 'sex', 'environment' or 'culture' group, 'social class', or 'sibling order' is taken to index aspects of environmental stimulation or experience that are thought to be relevant determinants or antecedents of particular behavioral outcomes, e.g. in smiling, vocal or intelligent behavior. Due to their remoteness from the level of analysis required, there would be no conclusive way of selecting that explanation which best orders a relationship between any such variable and some behavior outcome from among the many psychological explanations possible. (Even so, such gross indices of the independent variables might sometimes be of some use, as in the first stages or as a by-product of an empirical analysis under some reasonably articulate theoretical model.) For a psychological analysis it would be necessary to coordinate the levels of these expedient independent variables with differential patterns of events at the level of stimulus and response. This required analysis would encompass the identities, frequencies, variety and range of stimuli provided, and for an analysis of process, their sequential and timing relationships with such behaviors as smiling which could constitute opportunities for those responses to become conditioned according to the classical or operant paradigms.

We recall that in earlier studies of child-rearing environments the tendency has been to define stimulus and response variables in global terms, and often less at the psychological than at the sociological level of analysis (e.g. in terms of caretaker role descriptions). These definitions have sometimes been in terms of gross abstractions operating through rather long time-spans for the stimuli provided by behaviors of the environment (e.g. 'nurturance', 'acceptance') and for behaviors of the child (e.g. 'dependence'). These gross variables in turn might be inferred from such remote sources as parent interviews, questionnaires or projective tests, some of which might be administered years after the occurrence of the parent-child interchanges being assessed. The long-term aspects of such gross variables necessarily would limit emphasis on the process of interaction between environmental stimuli and child behaviors. At best, there might be implied in such variables details of the interaction process, including the immediate responses of the child to stimuli provided by a behavior of the environment as well as the environment's responses in turn, and so on through entire interaction sequences. This is especially the case when investigators have worked under the aegis of a theory of process, e.g. a learning-behavior theory. In such cases, however, as the process theory implies a use of variables (like those listed in the preceding paragraph) which would permit a direct analysis of process, the gross long-term variables can serve the theory but poorly, and the theory, in turn, can do little more than point, in an indeterminate way, to some possible ways of ordering the relationships found among the gross variables. Hence, the purpose of neither research nor theory is served by this discrepancy between the levels of specificity of research variables and theoretical process conceptions.

In this context we felt a need for the direct observation of functional environmental events which could be described at the 'thing' language level to carry a minimum of surplus meaning. Many of these stimuli would be provided by the behaviors of people, e.g. caretakers. Catching the sequential order of these stimuli and behaviors would permit the analysis of the process of interaction between the infant and his environment, which in turn would permit a functional analysis, in detail, of the stable dependencies between the behaviors of the infant and those of his environment, as well as of the formation of these dependencies. We were fortunate to be residing for a period in Israel, where a range of natural 'laboratory' conditions was available for observation. The variety of Israeli child-rearing conditions included residential institutions of the type which have been disappearing in the United States and the kibbutz in which professional caretakers and parents divide responsibility for rearing the child. Kibbutz child-rearing has been the focus of some research, more speculative than systematic. For these reasons we felt we were in an almost perfect situation to attempt a psychological description of child-rearing conditions, in terms of assumptions of our approach to social learning (see e.g. Gewirtz, 1961). Hence, this study represents a beginning attempt to describe at the required level of analysis the functional environment operating on the developing child in so far as its impact in behavior, both immediate and long-term, is concerned. At the same time, the cataloging of these stimulus conditions would define differences between child-rearing environments in psychologically meaningful terms.

Method

Sample. Our sample was made up of about 110 infant subjects (Ss) distributed among four age-groups (8, 16, 24, and 32 weeks) in the four environments, residential institution, kibbutz, single-child family, and multiple-child family. The 'Only' and 'Youngest' children of the two last-listed environments lived in cities and were, in the Israel context, middle-class. The numbers of Ss in each environment-age group are proportional but not equal, with cell frequencies ranging from 5 to 19 Ss. About twice as many kibbutz Ss as those of any other group were observed (including 8 girls). All other Ss were males.

Each S was observed for a full day, typically divided into two sessions on successive days. After a half-hour habituation period, an afternoon observation was made on the first day. On the average, each S was observed for 12 hours, which ran from morning waking to evening sleep, if possible. S was the focus of the observation throughout the entire period; the woman observer (O) moved with him from room to room, or followed him on his daily outings, as necessary. But at no time did she respond to him or initiate interaction with any other person in his environment. Contact with the family (or institution) was established prior to the actual observation period, and the mother (and/or the caretaker in charge) was generally told only that we were interested in following closely the everyday behavior of a group of healthy infants. No indication was given about our interest in the behavior between adults and the S. Caretakers were asked not to interact with O, and to behave toward S as they would ordinarily, for what they did could not interfere with the observation.

Naturally, we tried to control as many variables as we could in the selection of the sample. Only normal healthy infants were observed, and even those suffering from minor or temporary distresses (e.g. reaction to a vaccine) were excluded. Observations were made only in those town families in which the mother (rather than a regular maid or female relation) was her son's major caretaker and was *not* employed outside the home. Observations were carried out on weekdays only, to avoid confusion of changed routines and work-distributions among parents and caretakers. These selected details should suffice to provide a preliminary picture of our thinking about sampling of Ss and times for observation. There were of course factors which added to the variability among our Ss, over most of which we had little control. For example, when necessary we could begin an observation in an institution or in a kibbutz at 5 a.m., but could not enter a town family's home until 7.30 or 8 a.m. without distorting markedly the normal morning routine of the entire family. Thus, since we adjusted our hours to interfere minimally with the 'natural flow' of the observation, we ended up with differences in the hours of observation among the environments. We are devising weighting procedures to control for some of these differences among groups.

Observation categories and method. Each of our 5 Os was equipped with a spiral booklet, the pages of which were each marked off into five sections corresponding to 30-sec. time blocks, and a portable timer which was set to 'blip' into O's earphone every 30 seconds. O recorded her observations continuously, moving one block down in the booklet each time she heard the signal. The 30-sec. blocks were numbered consecutively from 5 a.m. to 9 p.m. (the earliest and latest observation hours for the total sample). In this way it was possible to keep a complete 'flowing' record of all events (without resorting to time sampling), and at the same time to know the actual time of day for each occurrence.

The observation categories which were recorded can be divided into three major classes, Background, Setting, and Behavior. (*a*) *Background* categories refer to all social and non-social events occurring in S's vicinity which are not immediately oriented towards him and which provide much of the context for S's behaviors; e.g. 'mother enters', 'S's caretaker converses with another caretaker', 'a neighboring infant cries', and 'father leaves room'. (*b*) *Setting* categories characterize general caretaking themes involving S at any time; e.g. 'feeding', 'bathing', 'changing diapers', 'being taken out for a walk', and 'sleeping'. This class included also the designation of S's location, when different from his 'home' room. (*c*) *Behavior* categories represent the central and also the richest class of observation. They contain all discrete acts emitted by the S together with all acts explicitly directed towards him by any person (including children) in his environment, and the interactions between S and other persons. The Behavior categories are comprised of three sub-groups. These include: (1) *S's acts*, e.g. 'S smiles at father', 'S vocalizes a vowel sound', 'S reaches for a toy', 'S looks at O', 'S follows mother with his eyes',' 'S manipulates his fingers', 'S fusses', 'S cries'; (2) *Other persons' acts*, primarily those of caretakers and parents, including, e.g. 'mother touches S', 'mother talks to S', 'mother picks up S, hugs, looks at, smiles to, kisses, or restrains him, or puts a nursing bottle into S's mouth'; (3) *Interaction*, referring to a stimulus-response sequence or interchange between S and another person, in which the time elapsing between the acts of the one and the acts of the other does not exceed two seconds. Any one of the acts of S or other persons might be involved in such a chain. Behaviors in interaction are scored and characterized separately from isolated behaviors. O's training was directed toward catching behaviors in, and the characteristics of, interaction which occupies a central theoretical focus of this study.

Os were trained thoroughly, for several months, in the definitions of the categories as well as in observing in a variety of situations before they were permitted to begin formal observations. The check for observer reliability consisted of having pairs of Os, working independently, watch given Ss during particularly intense periods. They used the same timer signals, and attempted to record the same events. Subsequently, a block-by-block comparison of their records was carried out. Degree of agreement between the observers was calculated by the usual methods, taking into consideration the types of disagreements of omission and comission. The emphasis during the reliability training was on interaction sequences, with particular stress on the correct identification of the order of actors and of responses in the chain, as well as on response content. We have employed several scale-like levels of agreement on interaction, ranging from the most general case of agreement on the identities of the actors initiating and terminating the interaction, to the most specific case of agreement on the precise order and content of the categories. Even though there is no commonly agreed upon criterion of reliability, especially for interaction sequences, and considering the difficult task set for the Os, we have attained what we take to be high levels of agreement among Os about the essential features of the observation. We have calculated in detail the reliabilities, both for isolated categories and for interactions, but shall not present them here.

A final word now about the current status of our method. As must be typical of researches of this type, when we embarked upon this study in Israel in 1961, we did not fully appreciate its scope. It was only after we began to examine the material which had been collected for the purpose of planning the analyses that we came fully to realize the enormous amount of differentiated data we had, as well as the complexity of the variables involved and of the analyses required. It became clear that only a digital computer operating as an enormous sorter would make possible the many and intricate analyses required for us to make maximal use of the data amassed. Hence, since our return we have been concentrating our efforts in that direction. The observation categories have been adapted to a mnemonic alpha-numeric computer code, and the coded records are now being entered on punch cards. At the same time we have been developing computer programs for the desired analyses. Our basic observation unit of the 30-sec. time block is represented by one punch card (and by additional cards in the rare case where the information to be punched would require more than 80 columns). In addition to identification codes for S, time of day and a continuation symbol, each card may contain one or more of the following: 35 codes for designating persons (as actors or objects of acts); 20 setting and location codes; 65 adult act and 45 S act codes; 5 S activity level codes; and 3 unique code classes to characterize interaction sequences. A large number of combinations of these codes may appear on each of about 1100 cards (after eliminating sleep cards) which cover a typical S's day, for about 110 Ss. Aside from programming the required analyses, which is time-consuming and intricate enough (e.g. for interaction sequences), we are told that our analyses might require a great many hours of a large computer's time, and that we could be provided with results sufficient to keep us occupied for years to come. You can see why we are a bit apprehensive at this point.

Some Objectives of the Analyses with Illustrative Data

Now that we have summarized our method, it will be easier to describe our specific objectives in detail, and to give some examples which can illustrate our approach. Our conceptual orientation for possible differences among the environments that might account for differences in infant social behaviors has at least two overlapping trends running through. Each trend is more a different focus for the same phenomena than an independent aspect of them. The first trend is that of environmental richness, in the simple sense of *availability of stimuli.* Relevant here would be such aspects of the stimuli provided as their range, types, variety, frequency, novelty and complexity. Available stimuli could elicit or evoke selected responses, or they could reinforce them. The second trend is that of *types of learnings* that could occur differentially in the child-rearing environments, depending on the sequence and timing relationships occurring between stimuli provided and behaviors.

But even before we deal with the first trend, or focus, it seems useful to establish a *structural* frame for the conditions of the infant's environment (and for the infant's behaviors) which would determine or qualify for S the meaning of the stimuli which impinge on him. The abundance, novelty, or other qualities of the provision of stimuli must be judged relative to an infant's baselevel of experience, which would be a function in great part of caretaking maintenance schedule. For the younger infant, this schedule is the major feature of the structural frame. Thus, our first step is to describe a representative day for apparently typical infants in each environment, emphasizing such structural features as caretaking *schedule* and the availability of persons, i.e. Setting and Background. There would be included, for example: the frequency, duration and time of day of feedings, sleep and play periods with an adult during the day; whether S is diapered or dressed at fixed periods or as frequently and irregularly as S's demands require; and the extent to which S is confined to his room and crib. Of no lesser importance are the features characterizing the *social* environment of typical infants. These would include: the identity and number of different persons who enter his room during the day, the purpose and duration of their visits, the association of particular persons with specific caretaking acts, and so forth. As far as we know, even a simple minute-by-minute log of such elementary ecological themes which constitute the context and limits for the stimulus conditions impinging on the infant has never been carried out effectively. It has not been attempted for the child-rearing conditions of the kibbutz, which have aroused so much curiosity because they seem so different from our conception of stimulus conditions in the modal middle-class nuclear family. Indeed, such a structural analysis has not been attempted even for the middle-class family with which all of us are so familiar.

A pertinent example here is our observation that quite a few 2- and 3-month-old institution infants emptied their milk bottles in two to three minutes, in contrast with the much longer feeding periods among their middle-class family peers. Such elementary structural differences in maintenance conditions can mean much when we consider that the opportunities of institutional infants and of many family infants for contacts with adults are almost completely limited to the periods of instrumental caretaking, as during feeding. Thus, also, an institutional child may actually see and have contact with many more people who come into his vicinity during the day than does the only child of a middle-class family. Our point here is that an ecological description in terms of caretaking structure and schedule is a necessary first step for any evaluation of the effective functioning of environmental stimuli for behavior. Our method of observation should enable us to construct the required contextual picture.

The illustrative data presented in the tables that follow are taken from the records of two middle-class family infants, one an 'only child' the other a 'youngest child' having a 3-year-old sister. Otherwise, these Ss are remarkably similar in demographic characteristics and in the conditions of observation, which were the sole bases for the selection of their records: both were boys, 32 weeks old; their parents were of the same occupational level, and lived in apartments in Jerusalem; both were observed by the same O, and for the same total time, if we exclude sleep time. The summaries presented are based on hand-tally operations. No definitive generalizations about 'Only' and 'Youngest' children should be drawn from the data of such arbitrarily selected cases, for without summarizing the results for all Ss in the relevant environment and age-groups (for which we are not yet quite ready), it is impossible to determine how representative this pair of records actually is. We note only that these two family Ss did not seem to be atypical in any way, and that the differences seen between their structural environments and their behaviors are, in the main, plausible.

In the context of our earlier points about the limitations inherent in employing gross independent variables, a few words are in order on why we selected these two sibling-status groups. First, one of our purposes is to define these gross sibling-status conditions in terms of the environmental conditions we think they index (correlate with) so imprecisely. Our focal interest remains the stimulus conditions themselves. Second, these sibling-status groups can help us to sample what we think are widely spaced points along the postulated dimension of (patterns of) stimulation provided to children. The environmental heterogeneity introduced by this sampling procedure could facilitate our analysis of functional stimuli, and the conditions under which they have differential impact on behaviors. And, third, of our four Israeli environments, these two sibling-status conditions are the only ones which appear also to be represented in a similar form in western countries. Hence, as our listeners would be familiar with such sibling conditions and their implications for the child, they would have a reference basis for evaluating the possibilities of our method and the plausibility of our preliminary findings (by 'triangulation' as it were). Apart from these bases, our tactical reason for comparing the two middle-class town family environments was this: if we would find differences in the direction of our expectations on the variables that should illustrate our assumptions between Ss from two most similar of our four environments, then we could assume plausibly that even greater differences would hold for groups of Ss representing even more diverse environments.

The summaries of Setting and Background information presented in Tables 10 and 11 can begin to illustrate the point we have made about the structural caretaking description as the context for stimulation and behavior. In Table 10 are seen some striking similarities in the schedules of the two Ss: (1) both Ss were awake for an almost

TABLE 10

Daily Schedule: Frequencies and Durations of Mother's Caretaking in Settings

	'Youngest' Child		'Only' Child	
	Number of Periods	Total Time (minutes)	Number of Periods	Total Time (minutes)
Total Time Observed	—	676	—	800
Sleeping	2	166	3	294
Awake	—	510	—	506
Setting				
Feeding	5	53	5	43
Eating (S by himself)	1	5	—	—
Changing diapers	5	13	6	17
Dressing	3	7	2	7
Bathing	—	—	1	4
Outing	2	60	—	—
Playing	—	—	6	7
All Settings	—	140	—	80
Time Awake less Settings	—	370	—	426

identical period; (2) caretaking was provided solely by the Ss' mothers, with no marked difference in the frequency and duration of Feeding, Diapering and Dressing periods; and (3) if the Outing periods of the 'Youngest' S is disregarded, an identical total time period (506 and 510 min.) of being cared for by their mother through the day results for both Ss. The Background similarities shown in Table 11 are: (1) an equivalent period for both Ss (166 and 170 min.) in which they are awake *alone* in the room; and (2) the total amount of time spent by the mother in her son's room is, again, very similar for both Ss.

These similarities serve to put into relief some of the differences between the Ss' environments. Thus, Table 10 shows no play periods between the 'Youngest' S and his mother in contrast to six (brief) play periods between the 'Only' S and his mother. (A single two-minute play period between the 'Youngest' S and his sister is not shown in Table 10, nor is a three-minute play period between the 'Only' S and his father.) Other minor differences in the Settings also 'make sense' in terms of our expectations. For example, the 'Youngest'

TABLE 11

Background Events: Frequencies and Durations of Visits by Persons in Infant's Vicinity

	'Youngest' Child		'Only' Child	
	Number of Visits	Total Time (minutes)	Number of Visits	Total Time (minutes)
S's Time Awake				
S awake	—	510	—	506
S alone	—	166	—	170
Mother alone with S	—	29	—	161
Visitors				
Mother	22	298	41	276
Father	—	—	5	96
Sister	11	153	—	—
Visitor A	—	—	8	49
Visitor B	3	97	3	26
A child	2	90	1	42
An infant	2	105	—	—

S slept half as long as the 'Only' S, possibly due to his sleeping conditions not being as sheltered as those of the 'Only' S. Also, the possibly busier and more experienced mother of the 'Youngest' S might let him handle some food by himself (Eating Setting), or neglect to bathe him for a day.

Further interesting differences emerge in Table 11. Each mother spent a total of between 4½ and 5 hours in her son's presence during the day. Still, the mother of the 'Only' S made twice as many visits, and of these, half were short 'peeks', i.e. of one to two minutes in duration. In addition, the total period she spent alone in the room with her son when he was awake was five times as long as the equivalent period spent by the mother of the 'Youngest' S alone with her son.

Our next objective represents a further step in the direction of a psychological specification of the infant's day. We shall add to the structural aspects previously described the identification of selected behaviors of environment and of child which occur during the 'typical' day. We intend to catalog the types, frequencies and rates of stimuli originating in the acts of persons which are explicitly directed towards S, when different persons do enter S's environment. Thus, under this heading we are interested whether there is a systematic trend in the relative frequency of visual, auditory or tactile stimuli to which infants are exposed, whether fathers talk more while mothers touch more, whether there is more social stimulation during bathing than during feeding, whether there is more physical contact between caretaker and infant in one environment than in another, and whether the adults' response patterns toward the infant are different during a caretaking period from a 'pure play' situation in which an adult's presence is clearly not necessary for the infant's survival. Similar to this catalog of all adult acts, we shall seek in the same way to catalog selected responses emitted by S, especially those directed towards persons in his environment. For example, we would want to establish various rate measures as developmental indices, but also as related to the stimuli provided by the immediate presence of various persons (and their identities), or as related to the duration of absences of persons in the vicinity.

To illustrate this type of analysis, Tables 12 and 13 present summaries of such selected acts. Table 12 presents the incidence of talking and smiling by different adults to S, and Table 13 presents the incidence of vowel vocalizations and smiles by S. A number of trends are seen from the distributions of adult responses in Table 12. Mothers and other persons talk to Ss more often than they smile to them. Further, many more talk and smile responses are directed to the 'Only' child than to the 'Youngest' child, by all persons but especially by their mothers who interacted most frequently of all. In addition, in interaction the 'Only' child's mother may have smiled somewhat more (·37) than the 'Youngest' child's mother (·23), in frequency relative to talking responses. The 'Only' child's mother exhibited more responses, primarily vocal, outside interaction (i.e. that received no reply from S) to her child than did the 'Youngest' child's mother. The implications for differences in interaction sequence patterns will be examined further when we consider Table 14.

We see in Table 13 that both Ss smiled more frequently than they vocalized vowels within interaction, which interestingly is the opposite of the adult pattern, and that both exhibited more vocalizations than smiles when with adults who were not interacting with them, and when they were each alone. This differential pattern may indicate, among other things, that at 8 months the smile is relatively more under social stimulus control than is the vowel vocalization.

TABLE 12

Frequencies of Adult Smile and Talk Responses to S During the Day

	'Youngest' Child						'Only' Child					
	By Mother		By Others		Total		By Mother		By Others		Total	
	Talks	Smiles	Talks	Smiles	Talks	Smiles	Talks	Smiles	Talks	Smiles	Talks	Smiles
In Interaction	75	23	24	11	99	34	218	127	68	35	286	162
Outside Interaction	—	1	—	—	—	1	32	2	5	—	37	5
Total for Day	75	24	24	11	99	35	250	129	73	35	323	167

TABLE 13

Frequences of Ss' Vowel Vocalizations and Smile Responses During the Day

	'Youngest' Child			'Only' Child		
	Single Vowel Vocalization	Repeated Vowel Vocalization	Smiles	Single Vowel Vocalization	Repeated Vowel Vocalization	Smiles
In Interaction	28	13	47	69	9	134
Outside Interaction						
Adult present	30	97	13	64	81	80
Adult absent	8	10	5	37	51	36
Total for Day	66	120	65	160	141	250

Further, both in and out of interaction the 'Only' child exhibits more numerous smiles and vowel vocalizations than does the 'Youngest' child. It is possible that the former is responding more than is the latter to the social stimuli provided by the presence of the observer. Further, vowel vocalizations, especially those repeated with minimal pause between successive instances, are more frequent outside of interaction than in it, for both Ss, provided an adult is present. When adults are absent, the 'Only' S emits his repeated vowels at a slightly decreased rate, while the 'Youngest' S's rate drops dramatically. Again, the greater incidence of these behaviors of the 'Only' S might be due to his greater sensitivity to O's presence.

We have illustrated two of our objectives, determining the structure or frame of the typical caretaking day and cataloging behaviors of both environment and infant. Similarly, the tables have presented illustrative summaries within categories ('vertically'), and have only implied the complicated interrelationships among events occurring simultaneously in the Background, in the Setting, and in the Behaviors of S and others. Our objectives are being presented separately only so that they might be clear, for in fact there is much overlap and interdependence among them. We are even now working on ways to assess these contingencies as the central focus of our study. Some of our preliminary conceptions are illustrated in the next section.

The third of our objectives involves the analysis of *interaction sequences*. This represents one of the theoretical foci of the whole study, and is also perhaps the one most difficult to master technically in an analysis. We have begun by classifying interaction sequences according to the number of shifts in behavior between actors they contain (which we term the number of 'actor positions'). In this preliminary step, the number and the identities of the concurrent responses of each actor at every time point (position) are ignored. And all persons interacting with the infant (C) are coded as adults (A). Some examples of sequences follow: 'mother approaches – S smiles' would be termed an AC (adult begins – child terminates) 2 position interaction sequence, as would be 'mother approaches and talks – S smiles and vocalizes'. But 'mother approaches – S smiles – mother talks' would be an ACA (3 position) sequence, while 'S fusses – mother picks up – S quiets down – mother hugs' would be a CACA (4 position) sequence. In this classification scheme, the number of positions and the identity of the actors beginning and terminating sequences are independent of each other and of the number and content of individual responses at each actor position. These would constitute criteria for further classification, but we need not go into such detail for our purposes here. However, we anticipate that even while interaction sequences are classified in Table 14 only by the identity of the actors and the length of sequence, for some of our theoretical purposes it would be sufficient to emphasize only the identities of the actors beginning and terminating an interaction sequence. [The four possibilities are: adult begins – adult terminates (A–A); adult begins – child terminates (A–C); child begins – child terminates (C–C); and child begins – adult terminates (C–A).]

Table 14 illustrates the distribution of interaction patterns for the two cases with differences that conform with several of our expectations. While there do not appear to be substantial differences between the Ss in the percentages of occurrence of different interaction patterns, the overall number of interactions differs sharply: The 'Only' boy participated in more than twice as many sequences as did the 'Youngest' boy. The largest proportion of interaction sequences of each was with his mother. (To our regret, the 'Youngest' child's father did not appear during the observation day. We might have expected a similar difference between the incidence of fathers' interactions with their sons.) This trend is even more striking when we recall that there appeared to be no difference between Ss either on the total time during the day each spent with his mother or on the distribution of caretaking settings. Thus we see illustrated a difference between the potential and the actual availability of stimuli, and, by implication, between their structural and their functional meaning. If the interaction patterns would be filled in with responses like those illustrated in Tables 12 and 13, we might conclude that the two mothers have quite different types of 'relationship' with their sons. Further, the learning contingencies inherent in the interaction sequence patterns of Table 14 are the reverse sides of the coin, as it were, of the control over each other's vocal and smile behaviors, of infant and mother (and others), that is reflected in Tables 12 and 13. Those tables indicated that, relative to the 'Youngest' child, the 'Only' child shows a greater incidence of social behaviors, as does his environment to him. At the same time, the 'Only' child may be provided with a relatively greater number of opportunities for social learning.

TABLE 14

Frequency Distribution of Each Interaction Sequence Pattern with Different Persons

Actor (A)	'Youngest' Child (C)							'Only' Child (C)						
	Interaction Pattern							Interaction Pattern						
	AC	ACAC	ACA	CA	CACA	CAC	Total	AC	ACAC	ACA	CA	CACA	CAC	Total
Mother	67	0	10	61	3	23	164	148	6	48	115	3	37.	357
Father	—	—	—	—	—	—	—	47	1	20	31	1	3	103
Sister	27	1	2	12	0	1	43	—	—	—	—	—	—	—
Visitor A	—	—	—	—	—	—	—	15	0	1	3	0	0	19
Visitor B	11	0	2	4	0	3	20	4	0	0	0	0	0	4
A child	0	0	0	0	0	0	0	7	0	0	6	0	0	13
An infant	0	0	0	0	0	0	0	—	—	—	—	—	—	—
Total	105	1	14	77	3	27	227	221	7	69	155	4	40	496

One of our central interests during this phase of analysis will involve the search for systematic relationships between interaction sequence patterns and response rates in non-social contexts. If, for example, the vocal responses of middle-class family infants are much more frequently reinforced, in interactions, than are those of institutional infants, we might expect to find a difference in the rate of vocalizations of both groups, in and out of social and interaction contexts. And this difference could increase with age. Relationships such as this one would be relevant to our basic theoretical assumption (which is but a corollary of the conception of learning) that selected classes of environmental stimuli could have an impact (in behavior) as a function not simply of whether they are available, but also of whether they are provided in effective contingencies with the infant's behavior.

To conclude our comments on the technical aspects of the interaction analysis, we do plan to analyze closely the response content of interaction sequences as well as their form. Thus, we are interested in whether there is a tendency for specific infant or adult response classes to occur together, e.g. whether smiles evoke smiles and what the probability is of adult talk being followed by an infant's vocalization, whether physical-contact stimuli constitute more potent or effective reinforcers than visual events, what are the conditions under which vocal responses accompany smiles, and similar issues. We are involved at the moment in the complicated task of developing a method for response sequence analysis in adult-child interaction.

As you may have guessed by now, one of the underlying emphases in our classification of interactions is our assumption that classical (Pavlovian) and operant conditioning patterns may be differentially implied in the interactions between infants and caretakers in diverse environments or in different settings of the same environment. We would expect that the institutional infant must work harder (i.e. exhibit more frequent and discriminable operant responses) for the attention of the caretaker, competing with other infants as well as with other responsibilities of his busy caretaker. Further, we would expect fewer interactions in the institution than in the other environments, and would imagine that proportionately more interactions in the institution (e.g. in frolic play) involve eliciting stimuli. Hence, the acquisition and performance implied there would be more of the Pavlovian than of the operant type. 'Pavlovian play' might often emerge in situations where a caretaker, however well-intentioned, has limited time available to interact. Her behaviors to the infant would be a function more of this limited time than of what he might be doing at any moment. She might approach the infant during her brief free periods, and flood him with contact and similar proximal stimulation, to which he might respond wildly. (But as she typically must soon leave, the infant would soon be left 'up in the air'.) In both middle-class family and kibbutz there may be relatively more 'operant play'. That is, responses *to* the infant's initiations would comprise interaction chains often terminated by the adults' reinforcing response. Also, there may be more instances where adult initiations are answered or terminated by the infant's response, which could be reinforcing for the adult's behaviors. We might even pick up some of these differences between the two middle-class families. The mother of the 'Only' child, who can hardly wait until her baby wakes to play with him, might show a different quality of interaction with him (e.g. intensity), and might be much more likely to reinforce his initiations, than the busier and perhaps more relaxed 'multiple' mother who might be happy to have her baby sleep as long as possible, and might frequently leave him in a room alone for long periods, unless he would be in distress.

Summary

We have illustrated our purpose in attempting, in four diverse child-rearing environments in Israel, a functional analysis of the conditions of environmental stimulation, and their effects, particularly in the social behavior of developing infants. When our aim would be achieved, we shall have defined functionally differences among these child-rearing environments, not in terms of global, remote or inferred constructs, but in terms only of the different patterns of stimuli they provide in relation to the capacities and the behavior repertory of the developing infant. We expect an analysis like this one would be useful for the understanding of the psychological processes underlying the effects of child-rearing. But we would hope to illustrate the potential fruitfulness of our approach to the complexities of the phenomena of human interaction, even in an observation study carried out in a life-setting as is this one. This study employs elementary stimulus and response units, and the basic conceptions of learning. While we think that the underlying processes thus identified in the main could best be validated under controlled, stripped-down, laboratory conditions, assessments and analyses based on observational studies such as this one have a definite place. Variables which might most fruitfully be experimented upon could be identified in the very 'real life' situations (with all their variability and complexity) to which the laws best isolated in the laboratory would ultimately be generalized. These approaches of laboratory and of systematic naturalistic observation are complementary for an understanding of the processes involved in human social learning.

Discussions following the Drs Gewirtz's Paper

AINSWORTH *As you say, the big problem in this kind of study is knowing what sequences of behaviour to look for. It seems to me that to carry your programme through you will have to ask your computer a great many questions.*

GEWIRTZ *Yes, and I suppose we would have had fewer questions had we used fewer behaviour categories. Our recording task would certainly have been simpler with fewer behaviours to score! We might be able still, on the basis of frequency counts, to combine some observation categories having a low incidence of occurrence with categories defined similarly. To simplify our analysis it would, of course, be possible to look primarily for contingencies between caretaker and child behaviour that we strongly expect, for instance because of gross differences between child-rearing environments. But that approach would be too simple. We must do much more.*

FOSS *With regard to knowing what sequences to look for, I imagine your computer would be programmed to do some of this for you? Supposing behaviour* X *is frequently followed by behaviour* B, *then it would be possible to focus on* XB *and find those behaviours which most frequently precede it, and those which most frequently follow it. In this way you could build up sequences of high probability.*

AINSWORTH *Even then I think you'll either be stuck with your computer for years, or you will have to be selective in what questions you ask of it, and presumably lose some of your data.*

BOWLBY *I think it's very important to lose a lot of the data. It's in the nature of scientific method that selection and abstraction must go on the whole time; and that selection is bound to depend on some kind of hypothesis, even though only implicitly.*

FOSS *I know that traditionally one should do that, but psychology is in an odd position in that if the experimenter has a hypothesis, especially if it's too strong, then the observations he chooses to select, the way he makes measurements and the way he treats the data are all determined by that hypothesis. As a result the psychology journals are littered with experiments supporting the experimenter's point of view. Why not, for once, get a computer to select for you? It might discover some reliable sequences of behaviour which none of your hypotheses would suggest. Your observation would to some extent be theory-free.*

GEWIRTZ *If that were only possible! I can't imagine a situation in which data collected would be 'theory free', where in effect behaviour categories would have evolved independently of some theory of the researcher, however informal or preliminary. We've chosen some categories of behaviour to score, and we ignore others, using an eclectic sort of consensus based on past theorizing and research in the field, of what behaviours might be important. Thus there are different theories, and especially learning assumptions implied in our behaviour categories. There is one way I can think of where the efficiency of a computer would make it possible at low cost to examine relationships among variables that one's theory would not predict specifically. A large number of possible relationships, with low or zero antecedent probabilities, could be examined, and in this way some could be identified which, because they would be unanticipated, would be theory-free, at least until the researcher's theory could be changed to take them into account. But this is a limiting case.*

KAUFMAN *Supposing we did what Brian Foss suggests in analysing the function and causation of the len or jaw thrust in monkeys. The computer could be asked to do a frequency count of what comes before the jaw thrust, and what comes after it, but I suspect that when you looked at the table of results you would still pick out those antecedents and consequences which your theory says are important.*

FREEDMAN *So much of the theoretical bias goes on at the observing stage. When people looked at human chromosomes through microscopes they would always report seeing* 48, *but we know now that in some of the earlier studies they must have been seeing* 46. *They counted* 48 *because they thought there should be* 48.

KAUFMAN *Well, we have the jaw thrust clearly defined, and we have established the reliability of the people observing it.*

FOSS *And that's where filming is so useful. One can subsequently compare the interpretations of people with different viewpoints.*

ROWELL *I still think that you must have a hunch what to look for. Supposing a monkey only made a jaw-thrust when it had its back to another monkey (which I'm sure is not the case), neither your computer nor your notes would tell you that, if you had not had a hunch to make the relevant observations in the first place.*

BOWLBY *I think it's in the nature of science that one should always be thinking up theories – you have them whether you like it or not – and much of science is concerned with collecting data to test theories. I have a great unease about anyone who collects data and then says 'to what theories should we apply these data?' I think that's putting the cart before the horse. I think it's perfectly right and proper to get a computer to analyse data so as to test theories, but it cannot test theories which you arrive at after the collection of the data, because the data will probably not be relevant to them.*

FOSS *I would say that theories, or at least hypotheses, sometimes arise out of observations, or exploratory experiments, and I don't see why one shouldn't use a relatively unbiassed computer to select one's observations for one. It might help to break the impasse of being too theory-bound in one's observations.*

GEWIRTZ *While the need not to have our theories generate our results as artifacts is clear, many of us have been concerned through the years that, in the area of mother-child relations, there have been special problems in relating theory to research. Thus we have had, on the one hand, far too much straight empiricism in which norms were collected or lay theories 'tested'; and, on the other hand, a parallel sterility of apparently articulate theories that were not subjected to the discipline either of conceptual consistency or of rigorous empirical research.*

ROSENBLATT *I would say that rather than being in a position to develop theories we are still working out an approach to the study of mother-young relations. Dr Hinde's work, I would say, is in this stage as well as my own. By an approach I mean that we still have to work out the basic concepts to deal with mother-young interaction and the basic relationships within which specific factors need to be tested, as hypotheses towards the development of a theory. In my own work I feel I am doing this by showing that the maternal behaviour cycle does not arise endogenously but is a product of the mother's relationship with her offspring.*

BOWLBY *But you still have dealt with hypotheses.*

ROSENBLATT *Yes, an approach generates hypotheses which serve as a means of testing this approach as against others. However, an approach is usually broad enough to serve as a basis for several specific theories about a particular phenomenon. For example, there may be a number of theories to explain the way in which the offspring regulate the maternal behaviour cycle of the mother all of which fall within the outlines of the general approach.*

FREEDMAN *My problem with Jack Gewirtz's study is not so much that there is a theory behind it – reinforcement theory – but that the theory is too catholic. Because you are so saturated in this theory, and think of it as covering so many different kinds of behaviour, aren't you likely to end up in a vicious spiral, in which all the evidence fits?*

GEWIRTZ *Let me consider Jay Rosenblatt's and Dan Freedman's comments at the same time. I suppose we do have a basic theoretical approach or orientation which suggests various relationships among variables we might look for, and sometimes also the forms of the relationships. Under our approach, the relationships we find should be reconcilable under a number of theories, at the same or at different levels of conceptual abstraction. There are several reasons for this. First, for the most part we scored stimuli and behaviours that have been identified as important in many writings in the field. Second, our theoretical approach is one in which extant learning and behaviour principles, proven in human and animal research in stripped down experimental settings, function as assumptions that could organize a variety of environmental stimulus and behaviour contents operating with respect to the infants we have observed. Lastly, we scored events at a fairly basic level of analysis (e.g. smiles) which involved minimal interpretation by the observer. Since the learning and performance assumptions we use would be fundamental relative to the more abstract conceptions typically employed in the area of parent-child relationships, we would expect the responses scored and assumptions used to be compatible with those more abstract constructs. Now let me move on to Dan Freedman's point that our theoretical approach is perhaps too general, hence indeterminate, and that any result would fit it. We have found the learning theoretical approach to caretaker-child interaction useful, as others have found before us. While the ultimate test of a theory is its utility in organizing an area, and we must await the completion of our research project for a definitive answer on how well ours has served us, I think the learning-behaviour approach we are following would stand up at least as well as any other theory I know, with strengths and limitations not unlike those involved in generalizing to parent-child interaction settings from the smaller body of basic research in ethology, or in perception. It has the strength that stems from its underpinning in principles derived from basic research phenomena, stemming from a large variety of contexts. Its major weakness (if that is what it is) is that those principles must still be found to operate 'in vivo', in the everyday settings of our study, where they could be qualified in different ways by conditions operating there. While emphasizing the systematic impact of recurring environmental conditions on behaviours of the developing infant, our general approach has been to attempt to take account of the basic behaviour properties of the infant, including non-learned factors. It is thus aimed at identifying behaviour repertoires and their controlling stimuli in early life, and is open with respect to behaviours that appear to be unlearned, species-specific, and those representing developmental stages. In the early stages of research in an area, there is little theoretical or research precedent. Hence, there is not yet an understanding of which of the stimuli and which of the behaviours we score as separate stimuli or responses are equivalents for the infant organism, and of how our learning and performance assumptions would be qualified by such factors as infant's capacities, developmental stages, and the like. There are also vicissitudes of sampling of persons and settings to contend with. In this context, it could be difficult to interpret negative findings, for it would not be a simple matter to tease out their bases – whether for instance a learning or performance assumption of the theory was faulty or some sampling aspect was wanting. On the other hand, positive results could be articulated much more readily and definitively with the theoretical approach.*

Imitation

B. M. FOSS

Although the members of this study group come from several different backgrounds there is often agreement in the interpretation of infant behaviour. Perhaps it occurs because the group spends most of its time discussing the results of observations and experiments rather than theoretical concepts. I have chosen to talk about imitation because I consider it to be a central theme in the development of personality, and because it is approached so differently by psychoanalysts and behaviourists. It could be regarded as a topic with which to test whether or not a rapprochement between psychoanalysis and neo-behaviourism (for want of a better word) is possible.

All the important theories of personality which derive from Freud use the concept of identification, and for all of them it is a central concept. The behavioural evidence that identification has occurred is that the identifier imitates the behaviour of the person he identifies with. Freud himself took this to be the case (e.g. Freud, 1922, p. 222) and many behaviour theorists would agree (e.g. Mowrer, 1950, p. 582f.). So that identification-imitation provides a link between the contrasting theoretical approaches. The importance of the topic is immediately clear to parents and educators who assume that a great deal of a child's behaviour is 'learned by imitation'.

This may sound like an apology for raising the topic, and indeed it is; because until recently imitation has been curiously ignored by psychologists (Bandura & Walters, 1963, is a splendid sign that things are changing). If it is mentioned at all in introductory books, one is likely to find either a picture of a pole-vaulter or high-jumper being watched by spectators who are empathically lifting a foot off the ground; or a description of Miller and Dollard's famous experiment in which rats learned to follow other rats if they were rewarded for doing so. Which of these two examples is given will usually indicate rather clearly the fundamental attitudes of the author. Among psychologists there are those who consider 'imitation' to be an explanation of behaviour; and at the other extreme there are those who regard it as an ill-defined class of events, all requiring further analysis and explanation in terms of more basic behaviour. Now obviously this second kind of psychologist is right in thinking that many different kinds of behaviour get classified as imitation, and, at least for some purposes, they should be defined separately. However, before considering definitions I should like to digress from the main theme to consider the various kinds of explanation used in psychology. This digression is based on the belief that controversies often arise because different people ask different questions, and consequently get different answers.

Explanations

There have been many classifications of different kinds of explanation, but usually not taking into account some of the more peculiar ones used by psychologists. Rather than adopting an existing classification, I am going to propose one based on the kinds of question which children ask, and the answers they get. The questions and answers of psychologists are not very different. It is necessary to use names for these explanations, and the ones chosen are familiar, but in some cases used with a slightly different connotation.

Child's question	*Answer*	*Name of explanation*
1. What's that?	A cow.	Naming, classification.
2. Why do the clouds move?	Because the wind blows them.	Causal.
3. Why are we going to town?	To see grandma.	Teleological/Purposive.
4. Where do babies come from?	A black bag.	Historical.
5. Why must I go to bed?	Because Daddy says so.	Rule-following.
6. Why must I drink my milk?	Because it's good for you.	Functional.
7. How does my engine work?	(The child takes it apart to find out.)	Structural.
8. Why is Daddy late?	He's always late on Saturdays.	Contingency, correlation, necessary and sufficient conditions.

This list is almost certainly not exhaustive, but it will cover most of the explanations used in psychology.

1. Naming is usually thought of as descriptive rather than explanatory, nevertheless it sometimes masquerades as explanation. It is characteristic of the taxonomic stages of a science. In many cases where instincts have been classified, for instance in McDougall's scheme, the psychologist is presenting a taxonomy rather than an explanation. When behaviour is called imitative, this act of naming classifies and describes the behaviour, but does not explain it, unless certain other questions about imitation have already been answered.
2. The example chosen for a causal explanation is a poor one, in that there is an implication of pushing. S – R psychology is heavily committed to causal explanation, so is much of physiological psychology.
3. Teleological explanations need not, of course, be purposive. A useful way of describing the behaviour of a guided missile is in terms of its target, but one would hesitate before calling the behaviour purposive. However, when this kind of explanation is used in psychology, as for instance in McDougall's hormic psychology, it is clearly purposive. When people are asked *why* they are doing whatever they are doing, the most usual answer is purposive. At least part of the explanation offered by concepts like feed-back and the TOTE (G. A. Miller *et al.*, 1960) are teleological, in that end-states are emphasized.
4. Historical explanations are explanations in terms of previous events, but with a time interval, and therefore no implication of direct causality. This class might be profitably divided into subclasses; for instance 'recent historical' to cover explanations in terms of transfer of training, set, practice effects, etc.; and 'historical' to cover explanations of personality in terms of what happened during the first five years of life. Such historical explanations are most frequently used in theorizing about personality, both by 'dynamic' psychologists and behaviour theorists.
5. Rule-following explanations are sometimes used by social psychologists. A tendency to conform is postulated, and from this, behaviour can be predicted to some extent. A clearer example is to be seen in axiom systems, such as Euclidean geometry, where the theorems follow in a law-abiding way from the axioms or postulates. The clearest example of this in psychology is to be found in Hull's 'hypothetico-deductive' system, in which explanations follow from the rules laid down in the postulates.
6. Functional explanations are especially found in the writings of

zoologists, and are most purely seen when behaviour is explained in terms of its biological or survival value. An example of a mixed historical (or pre-historical) and functional explanation is the following: 'Why do I have goose pimples?' 'Goose pimples are a vestigial form of a reaction which originally caused the hair to stand on end when your ape-like ancestors were cold or threatened. In one case it helped them to keep warm, and in the other it made them look bigger and presumably more frightening to their adversaries. Notice that we get the functions mixed when we say "a cold chill ran down my spine".' If functional explanations are tied to evolutionary theory, they should presumably be restricted to behavioural mechanisms which have an innate basis. However, functional explanations are often used for behaviour which is clearly acquired, and here they often shade over into purposive explanations. 'The function of lever-pressing is to obtain reinforcement'; 'The function of smiling is to retain the mother's attention.'

7. Structural explanations, as the term is being used here, are those which refer to the general structure of a system and the inter-relation of the parts. (There is usually reference to the function of the parts, so that functional explanations are also involved.) Several kinds of psychology use structural explanations in this broad sense: information flow diagrams; id, ego, super-ego; the Gestalt analysis of perception and Lewin's field theory; much of physiological psychology; the reflex, the TOTE and the feed-back loop, to the extent that their structures matter; and machine analogies in general.

8. Probably, most psychological experiments are concerned with 'what goes with what?' Under what conditions does the behaviour appear? What is the relation between dependent and independent variable? What is the correlation between A and B? The ideal goal of this kind of explanation is to be able to give the necessary and sufficient conditions for an event or process, but in practice this can be done only in terms of probabilities. (Sometimes the relationships are expressed mathematically, e.g. DL=0·9S, meaning Daddy is late on nine Saturdays out of ten, but the explanation still belongs in this general category.) *Causality is not implied*, nor is any other of the explanations so far mentioned. Of all systematisers, Skinner exemplifies the users of this kind of explanation.

It will be noticed that there is overlap between the various explanations. S – R explanations are causal, structural (in that they imply a reflex arc, or something like it), and correlational (in that they imply a correlation between stimulus and response; or, more often, between independent and dependent variables).

The Compatibility of Explanations

All eight kinds of question-and-answer can be applied to any one event, and there need be no incompatibility. McDougall made fun of the way Watson explained 'instinctive' behaviour in terms of chain reflexes. McDougall thought the behaviour made sense only if you followed the animal and discovered its goal. But there is no incompatibility. Watson was using a causal-structural explanation, McDougall a purposive explanation. Köhler thought that the insightful behaviour of his apes involved a restructuring of their perception. Others (e.g. Birch, 1945) showed that such behaviour depended on appropriate prior experience. Köhler underestimated the importance of transfer of training. Nevertheless, his structural explanation is not incompatible with the behavioural explanation of the learning theorists (who were just not interested in the structuring of perception). Thorpe at one stage was struck by the way some birds mimic sounds very readily, whereas others do not, and concluded (along with many others) that some birds had 'more' of an instinct to imitate. Mowrer (1960, p. 74) objected to this, and suggested that birds differed from each other in that some have the necessary motor equipment, neural and muscular, to mimic. But the presence or absence of such equipment can be regarded as presence or absence of part of the instinctive equipment. Mowrer is giving a structural explanation where Thorpe had simply named or classified.

Which Explanation is Best?

If the purpose of an explanation is to provide predictions, then contingency and correlation explanations are adequate, though often limited in range of predictions (as compared with for instance structural explanation). Knowing that Daddy is always late on Saturdays permits that, given it is Saturday, one can predict he will be late. Knowing that a response is followed by a reinforcer, one can predict that the probability of the response recurring will increase, since this is how the reinforcer was defined. (But one should not argue that, if response probability increases there *must* have been reinforcement – any more than one can argue that, if Daddy is late, it *must* be Saturday.) Contingency explanations are amenable to testing more readily than are other kinds; and since causal explanations imply a contingency of cause and effect, they can be considered as a sub-class, and the above remarks apply. But in general, although contingency explanations are predictive and testable, they leave many questions unanswered. Sooner or later the child is going to want to know *why* Daddy is always late on Saturdays.

If one wants to *understand* why some stimulus events are reinforcing (in Skinner's sense) it is necessary to seek other explanations,[1] usually functional explanations. Food to a hungry animal, the removal of noxious stimuli, the attentions of a mother, warmth, are all reinforcing because they have biological (and psychological) functions of value for survival of the individual. Communication between individuals has survival value for the group, and one would predict that (at least some) acts of communication should be reinforcing. Being forewarned of danger, or of places of safety, has survival value, so one would predict that being able to explore and learn about the environment should be reinforcing. Many people eschew such functional explanations on the grounds that they are in principle untestable. The fact that one can make predictions as to what may be reinforcing shows this to be false; and as John Bowlby has pointed out, it is in principle possible to test functional value directly in some cases. One could, for instance, paint over the red spot on the beak of several generations of herring gulls, and observe the results.

It could be argued that the description of behaviour in terms of instincts has often been a functional explanation as much as a classification. To talk of instincts of self-preservation, of the maternal instinct, even of the sex instinct is frequently to do no more than to highlight the fact that certain behaviours have valuable functions for individual and group survival. The same is true of descriptions of behaviour in terms of goals. Goals stand out not because they terminate a sequence of behaviour. As C. A. Mace once said, a psychologist holding such a belief would have to conclude that the

[1] Alex Comfort (1961, Chap. 1) has discussed two kinds of explanation, 'hard-centred' and 'soft-centred'. He argues most persuasively that a man may stick to one kind of explanation and avoid further analysis, since it might be damaging to his beliefs; so that one's personality is reflected in one's preferred mode of explanation. Certainly individual preferences among psychologists are very striking, and in themselves require an historical explanation.

goal of much human behaviour is washing up. If one looks for the functional reason for goals, one finds that they usually have biological or psychological value of greater importance than the behaviour leading up to them.

Before applying some of these considerations to imitation, there is a point to be made regarding the role of experiment in psychology. The assumption is sometimes made that, if a psychological mechanism can be demonstrated under experimental conditions, then that mechanism plays the same part in behaviour outside the laboratory. For instance, one can show by using inverting spectacles that the visual world can, to some extent, become reoriented. The demonstration shows that visual orientation can be learned, but it does *not* show that a person's up-down orientation *must* have been learned in the first instance. Similarly, it is possible to demonstrate classical conditioning in children under the age of 1 year, but the demonstration shows nothing more than that the nervous system provides such a facility. One cannot logically conclude that any learning in the first year of life is dependent on the mechanisms of classical conditioning. Indeed, such conditioning is sufficiently difficult to demonstrate experimentally – the mechanism is so sensitive to timing – that it seems unlikely that everyday life could provide appropriate contingencies repeatedly.

Explanations of Imitation

Naming, classification. A miscellany of behaviour has been labelled imitative. Other names used are copying, mimicking, modelling and matching. 'Empathy' has been used as an explanation of why imitation may occur (compare 'identification') rather than as a straight description. Certain attributes provide the basis for further classification, without any appeal to theory. For instance, the time interval between the behaviour of the actor (person or animal being imitated) and the behaviour of the observer or imitator may vary greatly. It may be a matter of months, as when birds in their second season reproduce song heard in their first season (Thorpe, 1961, pp. 74-5); sometimes it is a matter of days, as when a child will start playing with bricks when he thinks he is unobserved, and some days after having seen his father play with them, or will reproduce words after a similar time interval; the time interval may be of the order of minutes, as in typical 'observational learning' experiments (Riopelle,

1960, pp. 224-233) or in the experiments of Bandura with children (*op. cit.*); of seconds, as in contagious yawning; and occasionally the matching of behaviour seems to be simultaneous (see p. 198). It is unlikely that the same explanations will fit such a range of time intervals.

Another, and well known, sub-classification arises from the distinction between imitating the goals or end-results as opposed to imitating actions. The chimpanzee Viki (Hayes & Hayes, 1952) was presumably copying her own *actions* when she imitated the facial expression and posture of a photograph of herself, whereas, in observational learning, it is often said (e.g. Crawford & Spence, 1939, pp. 133-4) that the actor or demonstrator 'draws the attention' of the imitator or observer to salient features of the problem being solved. Here the imitation is of goals, or sub-goals, rather than of actions. In practice, the distinction between means and ends may not be clear. The imitator may use the same actions as the actor to achieve the same goal simply because these are the most available in his repertoire; on the other hand, when a baby monkey continually looks in the same direction as his mother (Harlow, 1963, pp. 4-5), he may be merely copying gestures rather than goals.

A regard for antecedent events may show that what appears to be imitation is not so at all. The level of carbon dioxide may rise sufficiently to make several people yawn, even if they cannot see or hear each other. Such a case of common stimulation leading to common response must be distinguished from that which occurs when the yawning is facilitated through people seeing each other. A group of babies in a nursery may all start crying because the temperature has dropped rather than because of any contagion. The behaviour of following gives an impression of imitation. If one animal aims to follow another, either on an instinctive basis as in ethological observations or on a learned basis (Miller & Dollard, 1941, chap. 7), the second animal will appear to be copying the goal of the first, and will also appear to copy the same actions, since the locomotion of both animals will look similar.

Causal and teleological explanations. We have already seen that by focusing on antecedent events it is possible to rule out some behaviour as non-imitative since its immediate cause has not been the behaviour of another animal; and by focusing on the goal, other behaviour can be ruled out on the grounds that the purpose of an animal may be simply to follow.

Historical explanations. Studying the previous history of an animal allows a distinction to be made between imitative learning and imitation of performance. Many writers have suggested that for imitation to be demonstrated, it is necessary to show that the actor or observer produces *novel* behaviour as a result. Only if there is novelty can one be sure that learning has occurred. If the behaviour is already in the animal's repertoire, then learning may not have occurred, and a better description would be imitative performance. It is possible, of course, to think of several sub-classifications in this context. When an animal eats or drinks an unaccustomed food as a result of seeing another animal doing so (Weiskrantz & Cowey, 1963) he is performing an act already in his repertoire. What is new is the appearance and smell of the food. The novelty in imitative learning may lie in many places: the aspects of the environment to which the behaviour is directed, the sequence with which acts are carried out, the way in which the voice is modulated, and so on. In many cases one can expect the distinction between imitative learning and imitative performance to be difficult to make.

Rule following. In all social interaction, but also in ways of dressing, eating, and walking, can be seen the results of pressures to conform to the 'rules' of society. The rules are complicated, in that they vary with the role a person is playing. Whatever the social pressures may be, they all tend to direct behaviour so that, for a given group of people, it is more predictable. It is puzzling that there should be so many pressures to conform. Possibly one biological and psychological function lies in this very predictability, since this in turn will lighten the load of social learning for members of the group. The more predictable the environment, the less learning there is to do. The uniformity (within limits) of behaviour which results does not usually look like imitation; but it might be plausible to regard all kinds of imitation as having the function of increasing conformity, and, therefore, the predictability of behaviour.

Functional explanations. Besides the functions just mentioned, many kinds of imitation may also have the functions of making communication more efficient, and also of expediting the learning of the individual in a general way. Imitation may be a means of furthering the mores of a group, but may also speed up the acquisition of established methods of communication and of coping with and manipulating the environment; so it may be an important mechanism for passing on tradition, in a wide sense. (Klopfer, 1960, has pointed out that imitation should be considered as a third mechanism, after inherited patterns and individually learned patterns.) Arguing from this, in a quite untestable way, one might conclude that imitation of different kinds probably plays a part in the following situations:

1. learning means of communication. These include birdsong (to identify the species); distress, and other calls; gestures communicating the presence of danger, food, etc.; 'emotional' expression; language;
2. learning means of manipulating the environment and solving problems, especially if in doing so there is an outcome of great value for the animal;
3. learning to eat some foods, etc., and avoid others;
4. performing (rather than learning) acts which make for group cohesion and group survival. Various contagious behaviours may function in this way.

Instinct, imitation or individual learning may serve the same end. In general, the required behaviour appears most rapidly (in the life of the individual) if it has an instinctive basis, takes longer if it is learned imitatively, and longer yet if it is learned individually. On the other hand, if the environment is relatively unpredictable, or if new kinds of behaviour are to emerge, individual learning shows the greatest plasticity. This concept illustrates the fine division between the different mechanisms. It is clear that, in behaviour, many different means may achieve the same ends; different mechanisms may have essentially the same function.

This is true for imitation itself. If imitation plays a useful function, then any mechanism which makes it possible is likely to be selected. Perhaps physiologists are more aware of such multiplicity of mechanisms than are psychologists. Communication and control *within* an organism have functional benefits for survival, and many mechanisms exist – neural and chemical, and combinations of these. Similarly there are several defence mechanisms which the body uses when it becomes infected. Perhaps dynamic psychologists are aware of this multiplying of agencies when they talk of several psychological defence mechanisms. Behaviour theorists have tended to go for single mechanisms, to the extent that any one theorist may for instance emphasize a single kind of learning. It is, of course, good scientific strategy to be parsimonious, to postulate one mechanism and then see how much it will explain. Those who postulate several mechanisms can be accused of trying to have the best of all worlds. I believe that here lies a fundamental conflict in psychological methodology: nature welcomes a multiplicity of means serving useful ends; science requires a parsimony of means serving as many ends as possible.

Structural explanations. Here I am referring to structure in the sense 'does imitative behaviour involve the use of feed-back loops, or reflex arcs?'

The imitation of noises is an interesting and special case to consider, in particular the copying of speech sounds. There is some consensus for a model based on the circular reflex first suggested by Humphrey (1921). The point about sounds is that the imitator can match his own utterances against those of the actor – the same sensory organs are involved in perceiving both (though when listening to himself the imitator obtains additional feed-back from bone conduction and from kinaesthesis). When a budgerigar mimics a human, the characteristics of the auditory stimulus must be very different for the human voice and for the bird's own utterances, nevertheless it is assumed that the bird can make the match. If such matching is possible, then various theoretical interpretations of this kind of imitative learning follow. For instance, in Mowrer's system (1960, p. 72f.), if the bird during the course of its babbling produces by accident noises which it hears to be similar to human noises and if those noises have already been associated with reinforcement, then the bird will reinforce itself. Its own noises will generate 'hope'. As a result it will tend to repeat these noises, the more so the more they approximate to the human noises.

For other kinds of imitation, some different structure will be needed, especially in those cases where the feed-back produced by the imitator cannot be matched against the stimulus provided by the demonstrator. There is evidence (anecdotal, as far as I know) that an infant of 5 months will put out his tongue in reply to a similar gesture. Here the feed-back is mainly kinaesthetic and tactile, the original stimulus is visual. How does the infant know which muscles to move so that he produces the same result as the demonstrator? The same sort of thing is said to happen, at a later age, for rapidly blinking the eyes. There would be no explanatory problem if the infant had already practised putting his tongue out or blinking in a mirror. Given that he has not, and given that the evidence is correct, one must conclude that certain physiognomic stimuli tend to elicit responses which look the same as the stimuli. It is difficult to believe that this is the case, although people have believed this state of affairs to be true for smiling – a smile automatically eliciting a smile without the intervention of learning.

Contingency explanations. What conditions favour the occurrence of imitative learning and imitative performance? There are several theories about this, but few experiments and few reliable observations. The infra-human studies are summarized in several places, including Thorpe (1956), in Riopelle (1960), and Bandura & Walters (1963). Until recently there has been a paucity of experiments with human subjects, but the series carried out by Bandura and his colleagues, and reported in the book cited, should provide a useful impetus. Of major interest are the findings on the effects of variables such as the role of the actor or demontsrator; whether or not he is rewarded for his behaviour; and the kind of behaviour being demonstrated (with the finding that aggressive acts are particularly likely to be copied).

Theories of Imitation

Bandura & Walters also give a useful summary of several of the more important theories of imitation. (Klopfer, 1959 and 1960, gives an interesting analysis from the point of view of a zoologist.) Two only will be considered here, on the grounds that they provide links between the approaches of behaviour theory and psychoanalysis, and are also theories which aim at relatively global explanations of behaviour.

Skinner's system (it is really an anti-theory, being interested only in prediction and control) is almost ignored by Bandura and Walters as a description of imitative behaviour. However, Lundin (1961), who has written a Skinnerian account of personality, has given a small amount of space to the question. He says (p. 109): 'Freud recognized a kind of imitative behaviour and called it identification. A child receives his reinforcements by acting like his father or mother.' If a reinforcer is contingent on a response, the probability of the response increases. The argument is that parents and others reinforce children for imitating them, so that imitation is encouraged. No one would doubt that this sequence of events occurs, but the explanations seems incomplete, since the ideas of operant conditioning have been worked out from the effects of reinforcement upon responses. Imitation is not a response. It is a word for a relation (or contingency) between the response of one person and a similar response of another.

Supposing a mother has a repertoire of responses R_1, $R_2 \ldots R_n$ and her infant has a similar repertoire $r_1 \ldots r_n$. If the mother emits R_j and the child by chance emits r_j, and the mother then reinforces the child, R_j will become a discriminative stimulus for r_j so that the sequence is likely to be repeated; but it does not follow that if the mother emits R_k the child will copy that, and produce r_k. This contingency would have to be learned independently. There is no reason for any transfer of learning. One way out is to say that reinforcement of one response spreads to other responses with which it forms a class, so that a sub-repertoire, say r_h to r_n becomes reinforced. It will also be necessary to postulate that there is stimulus generalization, from the infant's point of view, between the mother's responses in this class, so that the appearance of any one of the responses provides a discriminative stimulus. Given these assumptions, if the child is reinforced for emitting r_j when he sees mother emit R_j, this would lead to the child producing any one of r_h to r_n when the mother produces R_h to R_n. But he might produce *any* one. There is no reason why R_k should lead to r_k rather than r_i.

There is in fact one experiment performed with Skinnerian techniques (Baer & Sherman, 1963) which shows that reinforcing some imitative behaviour produces a spread of effect to other behaviour which was not reinforced. It remains to be explained. One is tempted to have recourse to a naming explanation, by saying that the child has a 'concept' of imitating someone else, or perhaps he is 'identifying'.

Mowrer's theory (already mentioned under structural explanations) perhaps provides the closest link with the concept of identification. Imitation occurs because the actions of the imitator provide him with sensory feed-back which is positively affective, since it resembles sensations associated with reinforcement. The child hears himself making noises resembling those made by his mother, and which are therefore associated with reinforcements of all kinds. The greater the attachment of the infant to the mother, the greater the variety and potency of the reinforcers. Being attached, being identified, being in love should be associated with greater amounts of imitation. (We have seen that this should apply particularly to noises.) Mowrer first elaborated this theory by discussing the ways of teaching birds to mimic, since he considered that such training might present a paradigm for other kinds of imitation (Mowrer, 1950, chap. 24). His views disagreed with those of some bird trainers, and a recent experiment was performed to test the theory (Foss, 1964). Two groups of Indian myna birds were played whistles either in association with the presence of the experimenter and primary reinforcement (food) or in their absence. The birds imitated the whistles played under the two conditions equally well. However, it could be argued that both kinds of whistle belonged to a class, one member of which was associated with reinforcement, and a spread of effect might be expected. However, if this were the case, it would follow that *any* kind of whistle falling into this class, and which the bird produced by accident, would come to be learned. One would also expect (given the usual reinforcement gradient) that the whistle *primarily* associated with reinforcement would be produced more often, which it was not.

The birds did tend to produce the whistles while they were alone, and this would favour Mowrer's argument that by doing this, they recapitulated the presence of reinforcement. It would argue against the presence of the experimenter being a discriminative stimulus for whistling. Bearing in mind previous cautions (p. 191) on extrapolating from experimental situations to real life, I would prefer not to make any generalizations from the experiment, except to say that if mimicry in mynas is a paradigm for anything, it is probably not the best paradigm for the kind of imitation learning Mowrer had in mind.

An incidental finding from the experiment may show a new category of imitative performance. Once the birds had learned the whistles, if they were then played the stimulus whistles they would occasionally join in, in syncrony, and often exactly in pitch. The behaviour was striking, and I would hesitate to speculate on its causality, purpose, function or underlying structure.

Conclusions

My conclusions are on the whole negative. I do not believe that any behaviour theory has yet accounted for the phenomena associated with the Freudian concept of identification. This may be because the theories have attempted to be too global. By arguing from the functions of imitative learning and performance, I am led to conclude that there are many mechanisms involved, and possibly explanations should be more restricted in their scope. Some kinds of contagious behaviour (yawning) might be explained in terms of simple conditioning; others (food preferences) are more complicated. And I would be very surprised if the explanations of Mowrer and Skinner did not have some validity for some aspects of human imitation.

Discussion following Professor Foss's Paper

BOWLBY *Imitation is a new theme for us, and clearly it's of special importance in primates. Am I right in thinking that you doubt if your own experiments with birds can help us much in understanding human behaviour?*

FOSS *Well, birds and babies are rather far removed from each other. It seems to me that, for many animals, imitation, and also various kinds of contagion, for instance of vocal and other expression, may be biologically useful. So that one might expect that any mechanism serving imitation would become selected. Which leads me to think that there may be many mechanisms serving imitation, but there is no reason why they should be the same in birds and babies.*

ROWELL *If you watch somebody who is good at getting birds to talk, the situation is very different from the one in your experiments, where you try to use control conditions, and where the noises to be learned are produced regularly and monotonously, and where birds just don't seem to get interested. The successful bird teachers spend a great deal of time with their animals, and are continuously interacting with them, so that the birds attend and seem to be involved. I don't think it's right to work on the assumption that, if you want to test the effects of reinforcement, food will do.*

FOSS *I'm sure it's the case that many kinds of imitation occur more readily when there is some kind of attachment to the person or animal being imitated. For Mowrer, if I understand him rightly, the attachment is built up through the person being associated with primary reinforcement, like food, and he considers that this should apply to talking birds. What you are saying is that this is not enough, that the attachment must arise from an interaction.*

ROWELL *That's right. Myna birds love food, and perhaps for them it's an important reinforcer; but I doubt if it would make much sense to think of a budgerigar's affection depending on food. The millet is always there, and not specially associated with people.*

FOSS *So that what one should do is to use something visually exciting – especially since birds are such visual animals – as a reinforcer instead of food.*

BOWLBY *No, I don't think so. In your bird experiments you seem to have tapped one kind of imitation in which attachment is of minimal importance. But I am quite sure that for some kinds of imitation, especially with humans, some kind of personal attachment is very important. Even with monkeys, the infant tends to imitate its mother rather than any other monkey; and this is true of humans too. Particularly in the second year, infants have a tremendous urge to copy their mothers, in a way which can be quite embarrassing. And this can happen both with monkeys and humans even when the mother is inclined to reject the child. What seems to matter is not so much primary reinforcement like food, or something visually exciting, as someone who has been constantly responsive, with whom the infant is continually having interaction.*

FOSS *To an analyst, presumably some kind of identification comes first, and copying comes second.*

BOWLBY *I think that's an open question. My own feeling is that this compulsion to copy is the core of what we mean by identification.*

ROSENBLATT *By selecting imitation in the mother-child relationship you are missing an important way of looking at what the child does. Perhaps one ought to say that the child fits his behaviour to the mother's, so that they integrate with each other. Sometimes this will result in imitation, but in some kinds of relationship the infant's behaviour may be complementary rather than similar. That sometimes the child appears to be imitating may result by accident, so to speak.*

FOSS *But there are some instances which look clearly like imitation. For instance, an infant of 5 months putting out his tongue when you do.*

ROBERTSON *I very much doubt this. What happens is that the mother selects random movements which the child makes, and* she *copies them. If this is done repeatedly, then you get the impression that the baby is imitating.*

FREEDMAN *I have been in correspondence with a number of child psychologists about imitation. One can assume that they are reasonably accurate observers, and they do report what looks like imitation even at 5 months. In my film you will see a kind of imitation at 7 months. The mother plays pat-a-cake, and the baby bangs the palms of his hands rhythmically, but not against each other.*

AINSWORTH *Very much as in language learning, where the first copying is only an approximation. But in the case you are mentioning now, it's difficult to see how an approximation to the mother's action can be reinforcing.*

JOYCE ROBERTSON *I find it easier to understand imitation of hand clapping, but I can't see how imitation of facial expression can happen in the very young.*

OPPÉ *Of course, after some facial expressions there may appear to be copying for fortuitous reasons. For instance, blind babies smile quite early, but obviously they are not doing so because their mothers are smiling. And, incidentally, blind mothers smile at their babies.*

FOSS *Which suggests that smiling in response to a smile looks like copying but is not. It's simply that certain situations tend to elicit smiles, and there is probably an innate element. A blind man once told me that congenitally blind people do not smile. He seemed not to know that he himself smiled a great deal – which brings home this point: how do you know which muscles to move when copying someone else's gesture, or better still, facial expression?*

KAUFMAN *Even monkeys seem able to match their gestures and postures with those of other monkeys. In Mirsky's experiment* (1958), *a monkey was conditioned so that when it was severely shocked it switched off a light, and this also switched off the current. This habit was then extinguished, and the monkey was put to watch another monkey being submitted to the same routine. When the second monkey was shocked, the observing monkey ran to switch off the light. It seemed to have matched the behaviour of the other monkey with its own behaviour.*

ROWELL *On two occasions I have seen female monkeys watching another giving birth, and they have fingered their vulvas and arched their backs as though in empathy.*

BOWLBY *Were they primiparas?*

ROWELL *I believe one was and the other not.*

AMBROSE *I think we should keep in mind the distinction between imitating a movement, which I think is more difficult to explain, and imitating so as to produce the same end-result. With the mynas, the movements made in vocalization are quite different from those a human would use, but the end-product, the noises, are matched. With the baby attempting to play pat-a-cake, what he's probably doing is trying to produce the same noise as the mother. Now in the cases you've just mentioned, and in the case of smiling, it's the movements which match. The results could only be matched by using a mirror.*

FOSS *There is another matching of movements which is said to occur at about 7 months which is more difficult to explain than smiling – that is the copying of rapid blinking. But as with so many of these things, the evidence borders on the anecdotal.*

HALL *Apart from the two kinds of imitation Tony Ambrose has mentioned, there is also the sort shown in observational learning – in which an animal observes another solving a problem, and as a result learns it more rapidly when his turn comes. The usual interpretation is that the demonstrating animal draws the attention of the observer to salient features of the task.*

ROWELL *And the interesting thing about such a situation is that imitation can lead to a worse performance. Peter Klopfer* (1959) *showed with finches that if the demonstrating bird, which already knows the trick, is allowed to watch the other bird learning, then its own performance deteriorates, as though it were copying the learner's mistakes.*

GEWIRTZ *I'd like to consider for a moment John Bowlby's earlier point that a strong attachment is a pre-condition for much imitation in humans, and that the direct association of the behaviour-to-be-copied of the model with primary reinforcers, like food, may be relatively insignificant. I think it is important not to underrate the possible role in early human childhood of direct reinforcement for imitative-modelling responses and the shaping of infant response repertoires to be like the repertoires of models. The distinction I am here making may be simply one between imitating learning in the phase* before *and in the phase* after *encompassing attachments are fully formed, on the basis, I would assume, of the parent mediating so many reinforcers for the infant. For our purpose here, the term 'attachment' would imply primarily that the infant will do different things (including imitate) to bring on the variety of stimuli from the model that would maintain or permit to occur key behaviour chains. Before the conditions that we index by the term 'attachment' are operating, i.e. before or during the formation of an attachment, various of the infant's behaviours will be shaped and reinforced articulately by their mother's, into a repertoire which would not be unlike the mother's or that of some other model valued by the mother. In this context, also, much behaviour would be shaped that would be appropriate to socialization values, and which in that sense would constitute copies of adult patterns. And in this process, also, there could be specific learning to copy, that is, learning sets for one's behaviours to be shaped, employing cues from the adult's behaviours. This learning might be more extensive, to be sure, the better the interaction generally and the relationship between child and caretaker-mother.*

The Course of Infant Smiling in Four Child-rearing Environments in Israel

J. L. GEWIRTZ

Introduction

Smiling may be assumed to be a key human response system, since it mediates, and thus could index efficiently, much of initial social development and learning. A preliminary report is herein presented of an attempt to chart the course of the smile response, in the first eighteen months of life, in groups of infants reared in diverse child-rearing environments in Israel. These environments appear to offer different contexts for early development and learning.

The course of social development in the first months may be a key for understanding much of subsequent human behavior, in social and non-social contexts. The theories of human behavior which have set the tone in this area have placed emphasis on the earliest phases of development in which the child's first 'ties' are formed, and some have dealt, if grossly, with the limitations and disorganizations effected by various disruptions of early social development. Even so, there is a dearth of detailed knowledge concerning the origins, nature and course of early human social development. And while smiling has long held a central place in theories of early infant development, the information available on the smile response is also limited.

It is to fill this gap in the literature of early human development that the research program, from which this is an early report, was undertaken in Israel. Israel provides a unique variety of child-rearing environments which constitute differential behavior contexts. These could facilitate an understanding of the bases of early human smiling. It is thought that many of the peculiarly human qualities of the adaptive infant are acquired through the opportunities, particularly for learning, provided in interaction with his caretaking environment. Hence, apparent differences among these Israeli child-rearing contexts are most interesting theoretically, for they can be taken to represent various levels of availability of selected classes of stimulus conditions, which would index differences of opportunity, including those for a variety of learnings. As antecedents, these differences would imply dissimilar consequences in the social behavior patterns, including smiling, exhibited by the children reared in those settings. Infants from hospital-like residential institutions and day nurseries, who could provide a developmental picture of the early course of smiling under relatively limited conditions of environmental stimulation, are compared under standard conditions of observation to those from kibbutzim (collective settlements) and middle-class town families. Thus, the age course of smiling is contrasted in infants coming from widely differing child-rearing settings, having, it is assumed, different backgrounds of experience.

On Smiling

There exist a variety of conceptions of the role of the smile. As with other key human behavior systems, there are a number of aspects of smiling that have been emphasized differentially in various contexts. These include: the stimuli which at first, and subsequently, evoke smiles; smile response qualities; the stimulus qualities of smiles for the behavior of others; how the smile is shaped through experience and learning; and combinations of these. It is sufficient for our purposes here to note that the conceptual approach underlying this study (detailed in Gewirtz, 1961), emphasizes both the stimulus and the response qualities of smiling in a social learning analysis. We have assumed that the behavior repertoires of the highly adaptive developing infant are mostly acquired through learning opportunities provided by recurring conditions in his interaction with the caretaking environment. We have been actively interested in identifying, in the initial phases of life, behavior repertoires and the stimuli which control them. Our approach is entirely open with respect to responses to stimuli which appear to be unlearned ('released'), 'species-specific', or which represent 'stages' in developmental sequences. In this frame, two assumptions about human social learning are stressed. Detailed here for the case of smiling, these are: first, that the infant's smile is a key response in that it occurs frequently in social contexts early in life, and could be reinforced heavily by conditions typically present in social environments, e.g. provided through caretaker behaviors; and, second, that the infant's smile in itself could provide a most effective reinforcing stimulus for, and hence could exercise considerable control over, the behavior and learning of caretakers. Both bases would foster the 'ties' between infant and caretakers.

The course of the smile response in the first year

Observations of the course of the human smile response in the first year are dependent on many factors, including the stimuli employed, the response measures taken, and the samples used. A brief summary of findings follows:

'Spontaneous' or 'reflex' smiling: the first phase. This earliest phase of human smiling is thought to be relatively brief; smiles occur in the absence of readily identifiable stimuli (e.g. 'gastric smiles') as well as to a variety of kinesthetic, tactual or contact stimuli (e.g. stroking lips or cheeks). The early developmental form of the smile elicited in the first days of life may not involve the entire configurational pattern of the face which is taken to define the smile response at later months, when it usually occurs to identifiable social stimuli. Koehler (1954) and Wolff (1959) have reported such 'reflex' smiles in the first twenty-four hours.

'Social' smiling: the second phase. The second smiling phase begins somewhere between 2 and 8 weeks (Jones, 1926; Bühler, 1933; Shirley, 1933; Gesell & Thompson, 1934; Söderling, 1959; Bayley, 1961). Here it appears that the smile is evoked by a variety of stimuli, many apparently visual in character and social in origin, in addition to some of those operating in the first phase. In typical infant environments, the most prominent stimuli for smiling seem provided by the human face (sometimes paired with a voiced sound); hence, the term 'social' smiling (Watson, 1925). As the infant's capacities develop, the critical properties of the human face which evoke smiling may change (Ahrens, 1954). At least two theories have been advanced for infant social responsiveness and smiling to social stimuli in earliest life: the first has assumed they are already conditioned, emphasizing the concepts of classical conditioning and its variants (Darwin, 1872; Watson, 1925; Dennis, 1935; Gesell & Thompson, 1934; Spitz & Wolf, 1946); the second has proposed they are initially unlearned (Bühler, 1933; Piaget, 1952; Bowlby, 1958; Rheingold, 1961).

'Selective' social smiling: the third phase. The beginning of the third phase of smiling is placed before 20 weeks, when it is assumed to be

at peak level to familiar and stranger adult faces (Washburn, 1929; Dennis, 1935; Spitz & Wolf, 1946; Ahrens, 1954; Ambrose, 1961). Whereas in the second phase the infant's smile appears to occur indiscriminately to social stimuli, in this phase only selected social stimuli are thought to continue to bring out the smile. In so far as infant smiles continue to be evoked by human faces, the rate is thought to remain unchanged or to rise to 'familiar' adult faces, but to decline, even disappear, to 'unfamiliar' (stranger) faces. It has been noted also that concomitant with this decline in smiling, the infant might sober, even withdraw or cry, at the sight of a stranger's face, however responsive it might be.

Rationale of the Present Study

Even while some studies have been qualitative, and on institution Ss, several represent steps in the direction of providing a basis for understanding the developmental age course of the smile in the first year. Kaila (1932), Spitz & Wolf (1946) and Ahrens (1954) have concentrated on identifying dimensions of stimuli evoking smiles at different age points. Spitz and Wolf also have attempted a preliminary charting of smiling through the first year under more or less constant stimulus conditions. And Ambrose (1961) has used a standard condition of minimal social stimulation and quantitative response indices to chart the course of smiling during the first half-year. Still, the stimuli which control the response, both initially and subsequently through learning, remain obscure. In part, this may be because the tendency has been to attribute apparent declines in smile rates around 6 months not simply to a change in the discriminative stimuli for smiling and the correlated decline in smile response strength to the earlier controlling stimuli, but to the sudden onset of a 'fear of strangers' process conceived to be incompatible with smiling.

This study was mounted to chart the course of the smile response through the first eighteen months. It was thought the learning-experience basis of smile response strength could be clarified by examining differences in its age course in what appear to be heterogeneous child-rearing environments. Quantitative response indices were devised, as was a standard stimulus setting selected to focus attention on the shifts in smiling from apparently unconditioned to conditioned stimulus control, and from gross social to selective social stimulus control, under conditions in which the smile response would be relatively unconfounded by incompatible responses or processes (e.g. 'fear', 'curiosity' and 'exploration', and those generated by internal or external discomfort as might be brought on by fatigue, hunger, illness, or soiled diapers). Observers were to follow a brief standard procedure for approaching infants when they appeared to be at their peak of comfort and alertness, for presenting themselves to these infants, and occasionally for responding briefly and making initiations to a small portion of them, prior to but not immediately preceding the observation proper. In this way, the likelihood that a zero smile score would index the operation of a process incompatible with smiling was lowered; and the study became oriented towards getting from every infant a score for a single measure, smile frequency, which would reflect mainly smile response strength. Even so, other measures of overall responsiveness of the infants to the observer and to the experimental setting were obtained, at the same time as was the measure for the frequency of smiling, to provide a broader context for understanding the implications of the use of this relatively unencumbered smile measure. The light shed on the smile scores by these ancillary measures will be considered in a subsequent report.

Method

Sample

Institution. Subjects (Ss) received complete care in one of six residential institutions for infants in Israel. Many Ss were from lower socio-economic backgrounds, but few were orphaned. Most never received visits from parents. In general, caretaking routines in institutions at the time of observation followed this pattern: five or six infants of the same age in a living-room might be in the care of a female caretaker, usually professionally trained. In institutions which had training programs for children's nurses, a trainee might be in charge of a group for several months, until rotated. If the group contained more than six infants, the major caretaker might have help. During days off, holidays and illnesses of caretakers, substitutes would serve. Caretakers and/or their assistants might rotate in and out of groups. Relief caretakers might come into a group during the day, to diaper, to give medications, sometimes to feed.

Day nursery. Infants would spend some eight or nine hours per day, six days per week, in the custody of caretakers, some of whom might be professionally trained. Most Ss would receive all meals in the day nursery. Mothers of day-nursery infants generally represent lower socio-economic strata, have lived in Israel for only a few years, have several other children at home, and are day workers. Some day-nursery infants are from 'broken' homes. The ratio of caretakers to children in the day nurseries sampled is low, there being typically more infants per caretaker than in the residential institutions. The care given is for the most part routine, and the environment seems less differentiated than that of the residential institution.

Family. Ss were from families dwelling in Jerusalem apartments. Their values and style of life would be termed 'middle class' in Israel. Infants were sometimes housed in their parents' bedrooms, but often their cribs were situated in separate rooms which they sometimes shared with older siblings. Typically the mother was at home during the day. Apart from the hot period around noon, these Ss would spend much of the day during warm seasons out-of-doors on terraces. They were typically taken on walks at least once daily, by their mother or substitute caretaker, and sometimes by their father late in the afternoon and on Sabbaths. Usually free at those times, fathers might spend much time then with their infants.

Kibbutz. The kibbutz or collective settlement in Israel is a small, typically rural for the most part agricultural, self-contained social and economic unit. Educationally above average, Kibbutz memberships represent voluntary highly select groups made up of persons ideologically committed to living out their lives on collective settlements, to owning little personal property, and to having their children raised collectively. Members of a kibbutz would devote much thought and effort to the care, socialization and education of the children of their collective. Children's needs would be paramount for them, transcending many economic and practical considerations. Usually from birth onward, a kibbutz infant is reared in a separate children's house, in the continuing care of a particular female kibbutz member, trained as a caretaker ('metapelet') and herself usually a parent. The interweaving of all spheres of kibbutz life makes of the children's house not only a place of 'work' for the caretaker, but also a 'home' in which her own children might be reared. A kibbutz caretaker is therefore highly committed to her four or five children. Caretaking would be supervised by an active kibbutz education committee.

Typically nursed and fed in the children's house for much of the first year by their mothers, young infants receive frequent visits from their parents, about whose room they would spend several hours during the latter part of each day, in addition to much time Sabbaths and holidays. A portion of each visit is spent in the parents' room (apartment), in which the ambulatory child has a 'corner' which is his alone, and which becomes one of the two foci of his life. The children's house provides the other focus. Each focal place will involve different patterns of duties and privileges, with different sets of stimuli provided and different classes of responses that are appropriate. Yet in the first year of life there is considerable overlap between the two focal environments, for the parents also attend to the infant during the day in the children's house. Further, infants would often interact with adults who visit neighboring infants, and who would have become familiar. The kibbutz provides infants with a differentiated environment, in terms of the frequency, variety and complexity of available stimuli. This environment is quite different from those of even the better Institution, the nuclear Family, and the Day Nursery.

Number of Ss from each environment. These numbers of normal infants were observed in the various settings: in Institutions, in the 1- through 18-month range, 228 Ss were approached at least once and 226 of those not eliminated for crying, fussing, or sleeping were observed for two full minutes; in Day Nurseries, where only Ss between 8 and 18 months were observed, 107 were approached and 105 were observed for two full minutes; in Families, where only infants between 2 and 18 months were observed, 91 were approached and 91 were observed for two full minutes; and in Kibbutzim, 236 infants were approached and 235 were observed for two full minutes. The two-minute score was generally gotten on the first approach to each S. In keeping with the custom set in the smiling literature (e.g. Spitz & Wolf, Ahrens, Ambrose), in the preliminary analysis being reported here the simplifying assumption is made that there are no sex differences.

Observation context

A Manual described the standard conditions under which observers (Os) were to approach S and respond to him in a brief habituation phase, as well as those under which the observation was to be con-

TABLE 15

Numbers of Infants Observed for Two Minutes in the Four Environments (Sexes Combined)

Age in Months	Child-rearing Environment			
	Residential Institution	Day Nursery	Town Family	Kibbutz
1	11	—	—	6
2	35	—	10	8
3	18	—	12	16
4	17	—	8	23
5	16	—	12	17
6	18	—	7	18
7	17	—	6	11
8	16	11	—	24
10	31	20	11	24
12 & 14	25	39	8	51
16 & 18	22	35	17	38
Total	226	105	91	236

Note. In the Institution group, six 9-month Ss, twenty-one 10-month Ss, and four 11-month Ss are pooled at the 10-month point. Four Family Ss at 7 months and two at 8 months are pooled at the 7-month point. All Family Ss at the 12–14-months point, are 12 months old; at the 16–18-months point, one Family S is 16 months old, and sixteen are 18 months old.

ducted. Ss were observed within the range from five days before to five days after the relevant monthly anniversary. O selected Ss who were normal, and not ill, sleepy, hungry, or thirsty at the beginning of an observation, nor any who evidenced soiled diapers. O neither fed nor diapered Ss. Infants who had been crying in the preceding five minutes, or who resided in a room in which another child was fussing or crying, were not observed until a later time.

Pre-observation experience of Ss with O. A brief standard procedure was followed for approaching and interacting with infants who qualified as Ss, in a period which did not immediately precede the observation proper. Its purpose was to make of O a not completely unfamiliar figure for Ss so that responses incompatible with smiling (e.g. avoidance, crying) would be less likely to occur in the test setting, permitting implications of the social stimuli to be reflected completely in the incidence of smiling. In group settings, the pre-observation experience of Ss with the O was limited, in about 75 per cent of the cases, to their witnessing O's movements in the room (*a*) in the twenty- to thirty-minute period during which O spoke with the caretaker(s) to become familiar with the routine and to gather information about potential Ss, and (*b*) while O was observing other Ss in the room, not necessarily on the same day. Older Ss were likely to have more of this experience with O than were those below 5-6 months of age. In family home settings Ss generally could observe O while she conversed with the mother before the observation proper. Otherwise, O behaved in the individual home setting as in group settings. For over three-quarters of Ss observed this procedure constituted all the preliminary familiarization contact that O judged was required. If O caught the eye of a potential S, she might smile or talk to him at a distance, and even approach particular Ss or groups of children, concentrating on potential Ss. Then, after a ten-minute waiting period during which O absented herself from S's room, she would approach in turn each apparently receptive S for the formal observation.

To our regret, it proved impractical for Os to keep a systematic record of pre-observation interaction. However, from Os' detailed reports, it could be determined that they may have employed forms of preliminary interaction more intense than those outlined in the preceding paragraph with approximately 18 per cent of Institution Ss, 17 per cent of Day Nursery Ss, 21 per cent of Kibbutz Ss and 35 per cent of Family Ss. These Ss were for the most part older, except that in the Family environment some younger Ss also were included. A preliminary examination of group age curves excluding Ss who received more intense forms of interaction does not change the over-all curve patterns from those in which all Ss are represented, as qualified in the next section; hence, only the latter curves are presented in this report.

Environmental settings for observation. With the exception of some instances in kibbutzim (considered in a later section), in every environment S was observed in his own bed in the room where he resided. Toys regularly present in S's crib were allowed to remain. With rare exceptions, no adults or ambulatory children were permitted in a room during an observation. O was to approach S when all pre-conditions for observation listed earlier were fulfilled. (She was to wait at least ten minutes before beginning a formal observation after any interaction with S, or after effecting a change in his position.) O would align her face approximately two feet above S's (when he lay supine), in his line of vision, with S in what appeared to be his regular or preferred position. O sat or stood depending on whether S lay on his back or stomach, sat or stood. With certain standard exceptions for O's changing position, O attempted to keep her initial position during the entire observation period, moving head or eyes minimally. O's mode of dress conformed to the standard dress of caretakers in the setting; she would wear a white coat where caretakers and visitors wore uniforms (in institutions and some day nurseries), and street clothes where caretakers wore street dress.

Stimulus conditions established by O during observation

Upon approaching S, and for two minutes thereafter (constituting the initial portion of a twelve-minute observation), O exhibited to S an unresponding 'blank-face', aligned with S's face at a distance of two feet. O remained motionless, except for periodic glances at the sweep-second hand of the timer she held in her field of vision and at her notebook while recording, neither responding to S's smiles nor to any other of S's behaviors. While they should be random in relation to S's behaviors in the two-minute period, under this procedure O's head and eye movements would depend to an extent on the rate of a S's scored behaviors. Hence, it is conceivable that the discontinuities in eye contact between O and S for Ss exhibiting high rates of scorable behaviors might have inhibited smiling, at least in younger Ss, by bringing on responses in S (e.g. turning away from O) incompatible with smiling. Alternatively, the increase in O's head movements might have constituted evoking or reinforcing stimuli further to increase smile rate in Ss already smiling at a high rate. Our assumption is that this factor could play but a small role in the indices used.

Smile behavior categories

The topography of the smile response is known to vary with developmental level during the first year. In the early months, the smile complex would seem to be composed of several discrete response elements in sequential and concurrent pattern relationships with an early developmental form of the facial smile, and with each other. Thus, near the peak period of 'social' smiling, while S fixates an expressionless face, very quickly his smile appears, involving perhaps a movement of the chin and mouth. As his smile continues, S's overall motility level may rise, with arms and/or legs shooting out or kicking, sometimes repeatedly. At the same time, S may emit a vocal response. This pattern may recur relatively often in a short time span, even while the unresponsive stimulus face appears constant; and S continues to fixate the stimulus, even between discrete smiles. However, when S is several months older, as in the second half-year, the facial smile alone would be involved (perhaps with a vowel sound as in laughter), almost completely restricted to a sequence of behaviors involving the face. Since our aim was to investigate smiling through the first eighteen months, during which there are these and other possible developmental changes in the character of the smile, the smile definition employed emphasized those essentials of the smile pattern which appear to be present throughout this age range. For the most part, facial behaviors are emphasized in the definition, and vocal and gross motor behaviors are not. The definition then does not cover all elements of the smile complex in infants below 6 months. Therefore, developmental differences in the quality of smiling are deliberately obscured in order to establish a behavior variable which could be employed in the entire age range. Smiles to O's face were categorized into three classes: the '*Quarter-smile*' includes any change toward elongation of mouth, outward and upward, traces of the naso-labial folds may appear, cheeks may bulge, mouth may open; the '*Half-smile*' includes the 'Quarter-smile' pattern, in addition to which there is a deepening of naso-labial folds (lines) from corners of mouth to wings of nose, mouth is open; and the '*Full-smile*' includes the 'Half-smile' pattern, in addition to which wrinkles form at outer corners (canthi) of eyes which narrow (squint) with upper and lower eyelids moving together, cheeks bulge and raise under eyes. (In rare cases when wrinkles form at outer corners of eyes but mouth remains closed though elongated, the response is scored a 'Quarter-smile'.)

Method of recording smiles. Her face aligned with S's, O stood or sat with a note-pad in the palm of one hand and a pencil in the other. She kept a small time-piece with a sweep-second hand in her line of vision and ticked off a ruled record sheet line every thirty seconds. Behavior symbols were employed to record S's smiles and behaviors which fell under related categories (e.g. vocal behaviors, mouthing objects, turning away, turning to another person, crying, fussing). The symbols referred to the onset of behaviors, so that sequences and combinations of behaviors were recorded but durations were not. If a smile dissipated and then rose again to its original level (e.g. 'Full' declined to 'Half' and rose again to 'Full'), two responses were scored.

Behavior criteria required of S during observation. An observation was discontinued as soon as any *one* of the following conditions obtained: (1) S cried or fussed continuously for thirty seconds *or* in at least three consecutive thirty-second periods *or* five different times; *or* (2) S fell asleep. If S did not fulfill these behavior criteria, he was left for at least ten minutes before O might approach him again. If S did not meet the criteria after three attempts on each of three different days, he was not approached again that month.

Dependent variable for smiles. The three smile categories were pooled for the dependent variables 'frequency of (all) smiles' and 'proportion of an age group that smiled at all'. 'Full' smiles comprised about two-thirds of all smiles. The indices are based on smiles to O's unresponsive face in the initial two minutes of the first successful approach (when S was not eliminated for crying, fussing, or sleeping).

Determination of observer reliability. Six women Os were successfully trained to serve. [The data of this report stem from five of these, as the sixth O observed relatively few cases, neither sufficiently frequent nor well distributed in the cells of the design, and hence have been discarded from this report and from a preliminary report (Gewirtz, in press).] During training, Os were paired to make independent observations of infants through the 18-month age range, when these were alert and responsive, in institutions and family homes. Independent paired observations were lined up to determine percentage O agreement. The six Os served in twelve different pairs to observe 110 infants for a total of 854 minutes. Twenty-five sessions provided 1966 instances of smiles. The percentage agreement index for smile categories takes account of errors of disagreement and of omission. Its formula was: % agreement = # agreements/(# agreements + # disagreements + # omissions). This index was thought conservative since it is sensitive to *un*-reliability due to confusions among categories, inadequacies of the method in coping with high rates of behavior, and inefficiencies in recording. The pooled mean percentage agreement over twenty-five sessions for all smiles was 95.

Methodological Qualifications

Our goal is to examine and evaluate in a preliminary way the relationships between the pattern of age curves of smiling, our dependent

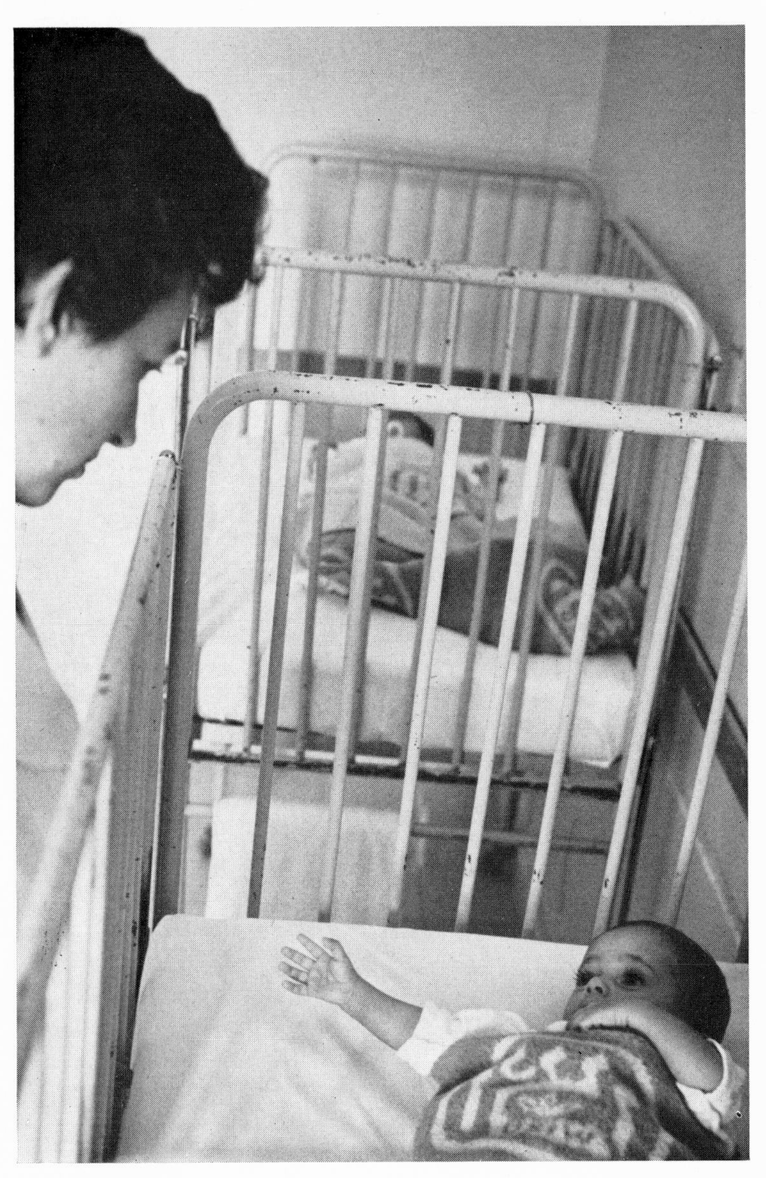

29*a*. Observer presenting unresponsive face 3 feet from face of supine Institution infant to evoke smiling. (Distance was 2 feet in formal observations).

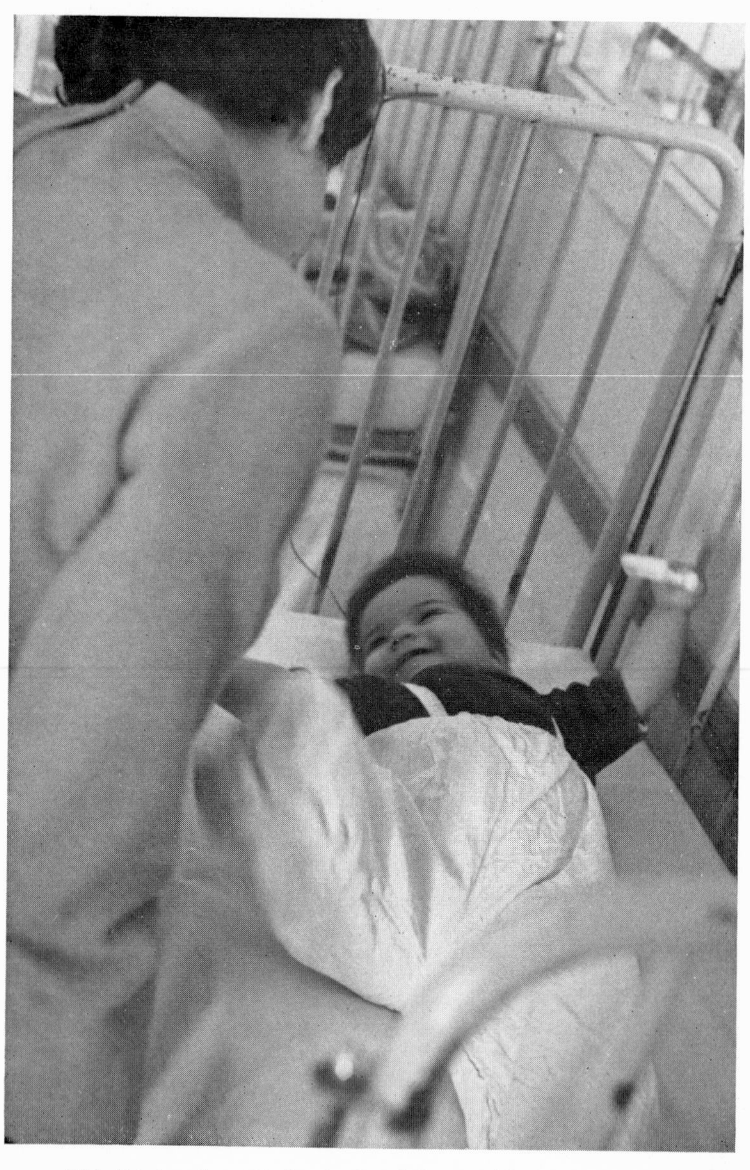

29*b*. Supine 6-month Institution infant smiling to observer's unresponsive face. (Bed-side would remain up during formal observations).

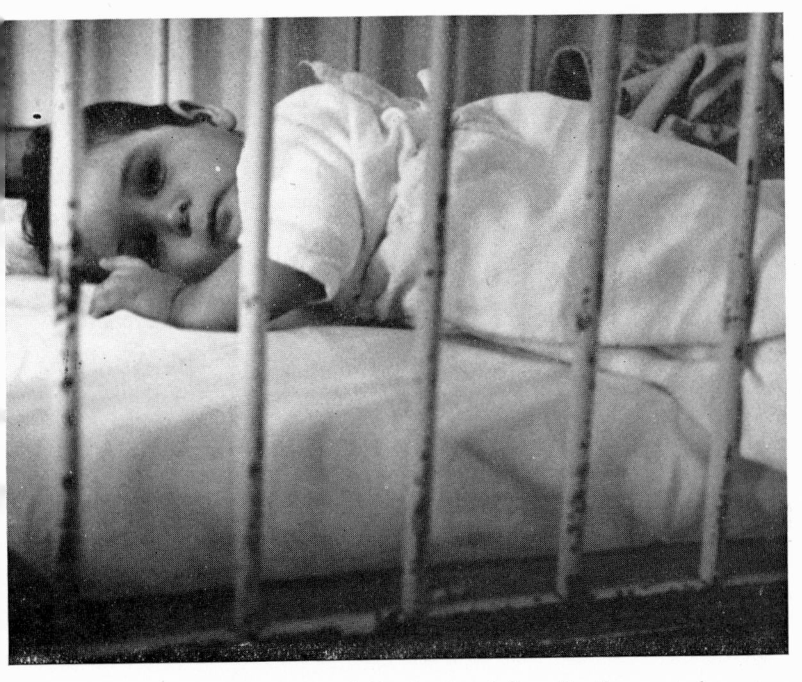

29*c*. Non-smiling 7-month Institution infant fixating seated observer's unresponsive face (out of picture).

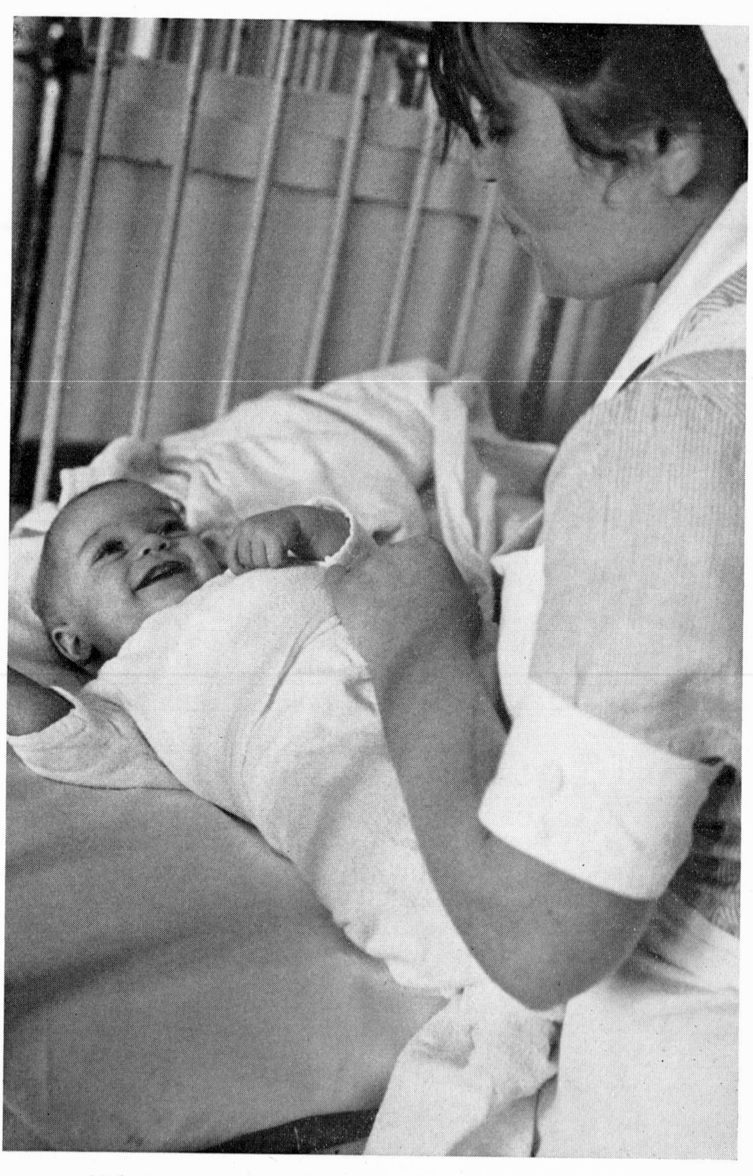

29*d*. Four-month Institution infant smiling to caretaker while being dressed.

variable class, and antecedent conditions derived from assumptions about differences in stimulus patterns characteristic of the several child-rearing environments. The antecedent differences to which we will attend are those considered relevant in extant theoretical approaches in which the dimensions of experience and learning are related to particular behavior outcomes. An adequate test of whether the age course of smiling differs as would be expected among the environments in the first eighteen months requires that the assessment of smile rate in all environments and age-groups be made under comparable conditions. Therefore, before attending to this our main question, we must consider the possibility that the gross fundamental differences among the four child-rearing environments might have led to differential changes in the observational procedure, and that these procedural changes themselves might account for the different outcomes in the age curves of smiling associated with each of the environments. Further, we must attempt to take such factors into account when evaluating our results. From interviews with Os about their procedures in each setting, and from an analysis of the characteristics of each environment studied, some possible procedural differences were identified. These include procedural differences of which the Os were aware at the time of observation, and more subtle ones which might have operated outside their awareness. Both types of procedural difference might have operated in part or completely to determine the different smile result patterns obtained.

In this section there are identified three possible types of deviation from standard conditions of observation, which might have differed among the environments due to differences inherent in their fundamental natures, and which in themselves might plausibly determine individual smiling rate scores and the resulting age curves for smiles of the environmental group to which these scores contribute. These determinants are not directly relevant to the conditions of differential early experience and learning in the several environments, in which our theoretical interest lies and which our focal hypotheses involve; thus, if any of them were operating in this study, it would be as an artifact. Possible effects in this study of such incidental conditions as these must be taken into account and weighed carefully before we might, with some confidence, refer environmental differences in the age curves of smiling residually to differences in the early experience and learning patterns of infants reared in these environments.

Saliency of stimulus setting. The first possible artifactual determinant of the form of the age curve for smiling considered would be due to differences among the several environments in the saliency of the stimulus setting in which the smile response is evoked during the observation, in particular the saliency of the standard stimulus provided by the unresponsive face of the woman O. These differences would be due to the presence in the environments differentially of distracting stimuli, of competing stimuli for smiling (e.g. distant faces), or of competing stimuli for responses incompatible with the smile response (those evoking, e.g. curiosity, fear or frustration). Due directly to a fundamental ecological difference between conditions prevailing in the Kibbutz environment and conditions in the other three child-rearing environments, a deviation from standard observation procedure was occasionally necessary if some Kibbutz Ss were to be observed at all. This deviation may have determined differences in group smile scores as artifacts. In mild weather these infants typically spent much of their time awake out-of-doors in playpens or on lawns, and at other times indoors in playpens or on floors. If moved from outdoor or indoor playpen to crib for formal observation according to our standard procedure, Kibbutz infants would sometimes cry or fuss, which might have resulted from the custom of their being placed in bed mainly to rest or sleep, e.g. after baths. In this context, the procedure of observing Kibbutz Ss in their beds was sometimes impractical, and a small number of these Ss was observed in playpens. This procedure modification was required on occasion in kibbutzim for Ss below 6 months of age (a few of whom were observed in outdoor playpens) and relatively more often, though still not very frequently, for Ss above 1 year of age (a few of whom were observed in indoor playpens). One artifactual outcome of these deviations from standard procedure, particularly in the portion of the age range below 6 months and in that above 12 months, could have been to depress and cause to be understated the group smile rate of Kibbutz Ss to O's unresponsive face, relative to the smile rates of groups from the other environments, and in particular to Family rate. In these other settings, there could be followed more closely the standard procedure of observing Ss lying alert in cribs in the absence of competing stimuli.

Stimuli provided in the environments preceding the observation. A second artifactual determinant of differences in the form of the age curve for smiling among the several child-rearing environments might be due to differences among environments in stimuli provided in the period immediately preceding the observation. A function of the fundamental characteristics of each environment, differential pre-observation stimulation might also affect the strength of the smile response during the observation. Thus, as was indicated in the description of the procedure, O employed relatively more intense forms of pre-observation interaction with Family Ss, possibly because they appeared less immediately responsive than did Ss in other environments. On this basis, the age curves for Family Ss could be overstated relative to those of the other groups. Apart from O's familiarization behaviors toward S, there is also the possibility that regular conditions in the setting would evoke smiles repeatedly in the period preceding observation, and hence, that the occurrence of smiling during the observation would be understated, due to its having become habituated. A second possibility in this class is that the smile might be reinforced frequently in association with an adult's smiling face, on either a Pavlovian or operant basis, in the period directly preceding the observation, and hence that its rate of occurrence during the observation would be overstated. These two last points would seem to be most pertinent in the case of Kibbutz Ss, who would often have in their vicinity many responsive adults, though the points could apply to a lesser degree to Institution Ss as well. Kibbutz infants are breast-fed through most of the first year and hence would have much contact with their mothers and those of other nurslings during that period. Further, there are frequently caretakers in the vicinity caring for neighbor infants, and there are frequent visits made to S by relatives and similar persons, who also would be acquainted with, and responsive to, other infants in that group. Thus, at any particular time Kibbutz infants might be relatively more habituated for smiles to social stimuli, leading to fewer such responses during the test; or, as seems *less* plausible to this writer, the receipt of reinforcement for smiling in the preceding period could cause its strength to be relatively high during the test, as a result of which their group results might be overstated relative to those of other groups.

In this context, it is noted also that it was occasionally necessary for caretakers in Kibbutz, Institution and Day Nursery environments to transfer Ss from outdoor settings to their cots indoors. Such transfers occurred more seldom in Family settings. Caretakers were asked to interact minimally with their charges while transferring them; still, it is possible that some habituation of smiling might have occurred in the process of transfer. On this basis, the age curves for smiling of those three groups could be understated relative to that for Family Ss. In this context also, the possibility comes to mind that because given Os returned repeatedly to the same few institutions, less often to the day nurseries, and rarely to the numerous kibbutzim and families, they might have become more familiar to institution (and perhaps nursery) infants and, hence, provide more effective stimuli for their smiling. It is difficult to judge the extent to which this condition might have operated; however to the degree it did operate, Institution (and possibly Nursery) smile age curves would be overstated relative to the other group curves. (While the procedure did not permit a formal assessment of Ss' *initial* reactions to totally unfamiliar Os, it is the impression of Os who observed in every environment that, relative to Institution Ss, older Family and Kibbutz Ss, and perhaps even Day Nursery Ss, responded to them more as they might to strangers. This interesting impression might reflect only the relative frequency of return visits to installations of each type, as noted earlier.)

State of Ss during the observations. The third class of artifactual determinants which might have operated to determine differentially the group outcomes in smiling could be due to differences in state of Ss at the time of observation, which differences would stem directly from the need for the O to conform to fundamental dissimilarities in the opportunities and constraints for observation which characterize each environment. These S state differences might be subtle, e.g. due to different sleeping times or to different reasons for Ss lying in their cots, and Os might not readily be aware of them. We have in mind here the possibility that in some environments more than in others Ss might have been observed when more alert. Thus, Kibbutz Ss found in their cots might have been put there to rest or sleep, and hence might be relatively less alert and responsive, while Family Ss found in cots might just have awakened from sleep, since Os would attempt to time their home visits to catch infants after a nap, when they were likely to be both alert and available. This factor might have played a similar, though lesser, role in the other two settings, and at the very least would tend to understate Kibbutz smile scores and to overstate Family scores. Thus, we see that due to basic dissimilarities among environments, differences in Ss' state could operate as artifacts to determine differences in group smiling rates, similarly as might the two classes of possible artifacts already considered. Our observation procedure was devised to preclude the possibility that Os might observe Ss under diverse states either in the same or in different environments. While Os following the observation rules should have made it unlikely that such S state differences would be operating, it seems important to remind ourselves at this point that it is likely we were not entirely successful in this purpose, and that group smile rates might have been qualified differentially in spite of our precautions.

Other examples of artifacts are possible in theory. Our purpose here is to alert ourselves to the possibility that the standard observation conditions might not have been engineered with complete success so as to insure a pre-observational context across the environments that was sufficiently homogeneous to preclude the operation of factors like those listed as artifactual determinants of the smile results. Hence we must attempt as best we could to weigh the possible effects of the operation of such variables before we relate the smiling age curves to postulated antecedents which are theoretically relevant.

In the preceding sections, there was attempted a preliminary evaluation of three classes of artifacts that could possibly be operating in the procedure of this study, and of how these might qualify differentially the smiling results for the several environmental groups. Thus it seemed possible that the age curve for smiling of Kibbutz Ss might be understated, in the lower as well as in the upper portion of the age range, relative to the age curves of all other environmental groups, and that this factor would qualify especially its contrast to that of the Family curve to which it was closest in form. Moreover, it was thought the smiling age curves for Institution Ss and Nursery Ss might have been qualified relatively little by gross or subtle changes in the procedure of observation.

The qualifications mentioned in the sections preceding remain to be evaluated more fully at a later time. Even so, considering that this paper constitutes an early report of results intended to provide but a foretaste of subsequent analyses of a larger body of data, it would be unwarranted in the discussion that follows to attempt closely reasoned theoretical distinctions among our four environmental groups. The preliminary distinction it seems reasonable to maintain is one between the results for Family and Kibbutz Ss on the one hand and those for Institution and Nursery Ss on the other. This is because our reservations thus far have been primarily about the levels of the Family and Kibbutz curves relative to one another, and rather less about their levels relative to those of the Institution and Nursery curves. Hence, it seems parsimonious in the preliminary discussion of the results that is to follow, wherever it is reasonable to do so, to treat the Family and Kibbutz age curves of smiling as representing one basic pattern, relatively higher at initial and final ages, and to treat the Institution and Day Nursery age curves of smiling as representing a second basic pattern, relatively lower at initial and final ages.

Results

The age course of smiling in the four environments in the first 18 *months*

Mean frequency of smiles. The basic group index of smile response strength is the *mean frequency* of all smiles emitted by Ss in given age-groups to O's unresponsive face. These cross-sectional data are available for comparison of Ss in the Institution and Kibbutz environments from 1 through 18 months, in the Family from 2 through 18 months, and in the Day Nursery from 8 through 18 months. Mean frequency age curves are shown in Figure 24. It is seen there that the stimulus of the 'unresponsive' face of a relatively unfamiliar woman O has evoked some smiling in the two groups represented at the first month, Institution and Kibbutz. From initially lower levels, it appears that the age curves for the three environments represented in the early months all display rapid increases in mean smile rate, after the second month in the Kibbutz and Family curves to peaks at 4 months, and after three months in the Institution curve to a peak at 5 months. Thereafter, no decline from its peak is seen in the Family curve, and a moderate decline is seen in the Kibbutz curve. (This decline relative to the Family curve is discounted for the reasons detailed in the preceding section.) The Institution curve declines from its peak (and the Nursery curve parallels it after 8 months) in a gradual and most orderly manner, to the terminal point at 18 months. At no age point after its peak month does any environmental mean curve decline to a zero level; and where a decline in smiling is seen after 16 or 20 weeks, it is nowhere abrupt.

Reliability of mean age curve patterns in the first 4 *months.* To de-

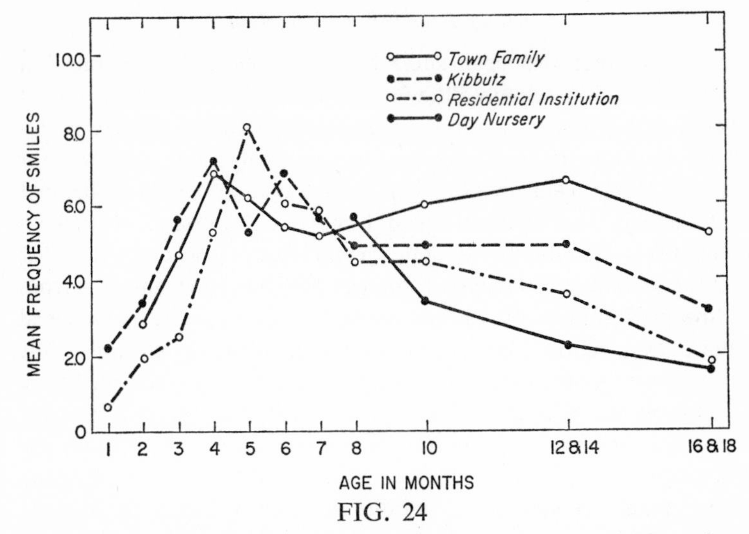

FIG. 24

Age curves for Mean frequency of smiles *in 2 minutes for infants from four Israeli child-rearing environments, in the* 1- *through* 18-*lunar-month range. Indices in all figures are based on smiles to a woman's unresponsive face in the first approuch of* 2 *minutes during which the infant exhibited less than a defined minimum of crying or fussing, and during which he did not appear sleepy. Note that in Figures* 24 *and* 25 *Day Nursery and Family Ss are not represented at every monthly point.*

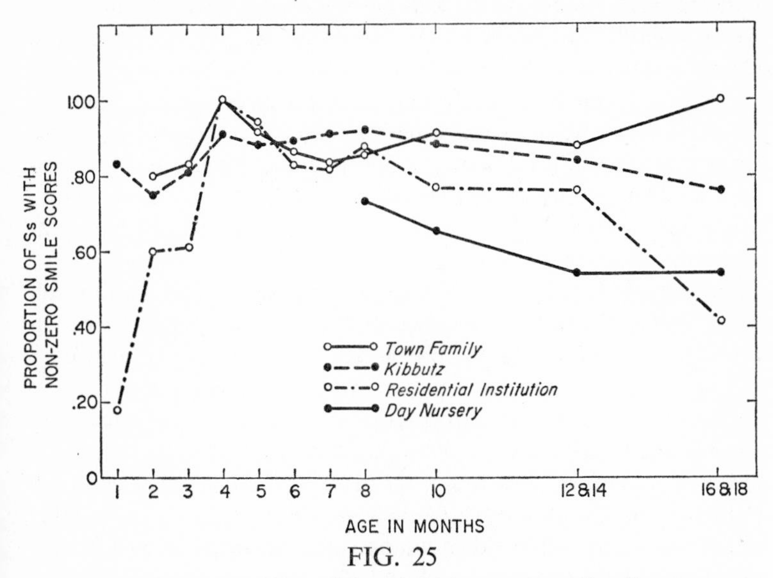

FIG. 25

Age curves for Proportion of Ss exhibiting some smiles (*i.e. non-zero frequencies*) *in* 2 *minutes, in lunar-month groups, for four Israeli child-rearing environments, in the* 1- *through* 18-*month range.*

termine whether the mean smile frequency age curves in the first 4 months exhibit reliably different patterns of rise (i.e. slopes) and overall levels, the data for the three environmental groups represented in that range are subjected to two analyses of variance (for disproportionate subclass numbers) which take into account the fact that there is no Family mean at 1 month: the first 2×4 analysis compares Institution and Kibbutz groups from 1 through 4 months; and the second 3×3 analysis compares the three environments from 2 through 4 months. Performed both on frequency and transformed square root scores, the analyses yield identical conclusions. The relevant raw scores frequency means are found in Figure 24. In the Institution vs. Kibbutz 2×4 analysis, both the Main effects for Environment and Age are found reliable at $P < \cdot 001$, while the Interaction effect is not reliable. Hence, the Institution and Kibbutz mean curves are seen to be parallel in slope in the 1- to 4-month range, with the overall mean smile rate reliably higher for Kibbutz than for Institution Ss. Given that the mean curves are parallel, the Age effect reflects the fact that in both environmental groups the smile mean at every monthly point is higher than the mean of the preceding month (i.e. $4 > 3 > 2 > 1$). The companion 3×3 analysis also shows no Interaction between Environment and Age, indicating that the three environment mean age curves are parallel; further, it yields reliable Environment ($P < \cdot 05$) and Age ($P < \cdot 001$) effects. Overall comparisons between 2 and 4 months via *t*-tests indicate that the Kibbutz and the Family mean smile curves are each reliably greater (at $P < \cdot 02$) in average height than is the Institution curve, while the average heights of the Kibbutz and Family mean curves do not differ reliably from each other. Again, the Age effect shows across environments that there is more mean smiling at 4 than at 3 months, and more at 3 than at 2 months.

No attempt is made here to interpret the fact that the peak mean smile level of the Institution curve, at 5 months, appears higher than the other environmental curve peak levels, for the peak mean does not fit into an interpretable pattern with the means at nearby age points in the Institution curve. Simple analyses of variance were carried out to compare all three environment means at 5 months, and to compare the Institution mean at its 5-month peak with the Kibbutz and Family means at their 4-month peak. As no reliable difference was found in either comparison, the means of each set are taken to be homogeneous.

Reliability of age curve patterns from 8 *through* 18 *months.* For the formal examination of the mean smile age curves in the upper portion of the range, the 7- and 8-month Family groups were combined into an 8-month group. Also combined in every environment were the separate 12- and 14-month groups and the separate 16- and 18-month groups. With the means at 10 months, the frequency and square root data were each subjected to a 4×4 Environments *by* Ages analysis of variance. By inspection, the environment mean curves show a distinct tendency progressively to diverge between 8 and 18 months, after appearing relatively homogeneous around 8 months. Nevertheless, the analysis performed indicates that the Interaction effect which would reflect this pattern is not reliable; hence, in terms of this particular test, the age curves must be considered parallel within the 8- to 18-month range. At the same time, the Main effects for Age and for Environment are each reliable at $P < \cdot 01$. Appropriate *t*-test comparisons indicate that the reliable Environment effect (across ages) was due to the fact that the over-all Family mean was reliably higher than the means for Kibbutz ($P < \cdot 05$), Institution ($P < \cdot 01$) and Nursery ($P < \cdot 01$), while the second ranking Kibbutz mean was reliably higher than the Nursery mean ($P < \cdot 01$) and, at a borderline level, higher than the Institution mean ($P < \cdot 10$). The basis of the Main effect for Age (across environments) is that mean smiling seems to be decreasing in the 8- through 18-month range. A preliminary 5×3 analysis of variance was also carried out from 5 through 18 months for the three environments represented throughout that range, Kibbutz, Family and Institution. Scores at ages 5 and 6 months were combined, as were scores at 7 and 8 months for the three environments. As in the earlier 4×4 analysis, the Age×Environment Interaction effect again was found not reliable, while the Main effects for Age and Environment were each reliable at $P < \cdot 01$. As it was possible that an Interaction effect was being obscured in the two preceding analyses due to the way the ages were grouped, a more precise parametric test was performed (on square root scores) for whether the group mean curves diverge across uncombined age points from 5 through 18 months, in the post-smile-peak age range. Given the observed pattern of age curves, a test of differences among the linear regression b coefficients of each of the four mean curves, if significant, would suffice to indicate the presence of an Environment *by* Age Interaction. The larger negative b coefficients reflect steeper linear declines of the age curves in the

5- to 18-month range. The *b*s rank-ordered: Family (·02), Kibbutz (−·06), Nursery (−·10) and Institution (−·13). An overall analysis of variance indicated at $P < \cdot 001$ that the *b*s were heterogeneous. Exploring further by means of *t*-tests of differences between pairs of *b* coefficients, it was found at $P < \cdot 05$ that the Family curve showed reliably less linear decline than did every other environmental curve. And while the Kibbutz curve declined reliably less than did the Institution curve, it did not decline reliably less than did the Nursery curve; the latter in turn was not reliably less steep than the Institution curve.

Proportion of age-groups smiling. Four environmental age curves are presented in Figure 25 for the index 'proportion of a monthly group which smiled at least once' (in two minutes of the first successful approach). While this dichotomous proportion index is not entirely independent of the smile frequency from which it derives, its all-or-none aspect may make it more sensitive than the mean frequency for comparing the relative potency of different stimuli in evoking smiles at different age points. Relative to the mean frequency age curves, the orderly proportion age curves rise more rapidly to, and decline more slowly from, a peak at 4 months. While overall the pattern is quite similar to that of the age curves for mean smile frequency, there are interesting divergences. In particular, the difference between the homogeneous Kibbutz and Family proportion smiling curves and the Institution curve is greatest in the first months, and the curves draw together as they approach their 4-month peak. It is recalled that while the mean smile frequency age curves were found to be parallel, the peaks were also at 4 months for Kibbutz and Family groups, but the peak was found at 5 months for the Institution group. The differences between Kibbutz and Institution proportions of those smiling is greatest in the first month. While 5/6 of Kibbutz Ss smile then, only 2/11 of Institution Ss do. Fisher's exact test for fourfold tables shows this difference is reliable at $P < \cdot 05$ (2 tails).

Discussion

Age curve differences among environments in level of smiling

In this section there will be attempted heuristic analyses of the possible bases of the differences between the Family-Kibbutz and the Institution-Nursery age curve patterns of smiling to the standard stimulus of the woman's unresponsive face. This speculative analysis has two independent foci: the first involves the possible bases for different rates of smiling in the early months, where the Family and Kibbutz curves were higher and rose to an earlier peak than did the Institution curve; and the second involves the possible bases for the difference in level in the mean smile age curves in the post-peak portion of the age range, where the Kibbutz and Family curves were higher generally than were the Institution and Nursery curves, and where they declined less.

Possible bases for environmental curve differences in rise to peak smile rate

There have been identified what seem to be differences in the age course of smiling among groups from diverse environments, which could provide differential opportunities for the occurrence of smiling and for its conditioning. Hence, it seems appropriate to attempt to identify those differences among the environments which might be bases of the pattern of results. Even for this heuristic purpose, it will here be possible only to list in a loose, schematic way, but not to identify definitively, how the child-rearing environments studied potentially could differ, according to some of our current conceptions of processes through which stimulus conditions could have systematic, long-term, impacts on behavior, to account for the pattern of obtained results. Several theoretical cases for learning processes are outlined in the following sections. However, due to the gross nature of our two independent variables, 'age' and 'environmental group', there would be no conclusive way of selecting from among the possibilities listed there the cases which best order the results we are here attempting to explain. For the psychological analysis required, it would be necessary to coordinate these independent variables with events at the level of stimuli and responses. This analysis would consider the identities and frequencies of stimuli provided, their pairing and timing relations with smiles, whether preceding or following, and the opportunities for the classical and operant conditioning of smiles which the patterns of these variables differentially could constitute. A companion study (J. L. & H. B. Gewirtz, this volume) is in progress in three of the same environments. Its formal observations should ultimately provide information at the required level of analysis on antecedent and contemporaneous determinants of the smile response, and of other key behaviors, as well as on the learning processes which, to different degrees and at different times, may be involved to determine the results we are here attempting to order.

With these cautions in mind, we may now turn to an heuristic analysis of the possible bases for the apparent differences in the age curves for smiling to the standard stimulus of the woman's unresponsive face in the *early* months between Kibbutz-Family and Institution groups. This analysis will take into account some conceptions found in the literature of the bases of human smiling as well as the data from which these conceptions have evolved. The heuristic attempt is made to consider which of the available conceptions most plausibly could represent the relationships evident in the literature between smiling and its determinants, environmental and organismic, as well as the relationships presented in this paper. The present section will concentrate on conceptions which, while they stress the importance of different kinds of learning in the developmental course of the smile response, are entirely open to the operation of 'innate' processes. This conceptual analysis of possible differences among the environments that might account for differences in early smiling will have two complementary themes throughout. The first theme is the relative 'richness' of the environment, in the sense of the simple *availability of stimuli* for smiling (and other behaviors). The second theme is the differential *opportunities for learning* of various types involving smiles (and other interaction behaviors) in the environments, which would depend on the sequential and temporal relationships holding between available stimuli and smiles. Both themes overlap, and are involved in every one of the conceptions that follow.

Differential availability of stimuli (for smiles). Pertinent to the dimension of the relative availability of stimuli would be such attributes of the stimuli provided as their type, frequency, range, variety, novelty, and complexity. Such stimuli could elicit or evoke smiles and/or could reinforce them. In the context of the availability or provision of particular relevant stimuli, the infant's smiles (like many of his earliest behaviors) may be viewed initially as unconditioned responses (URs), either (*a*) *elicited* by (e.g. 'releasing', 'sign') stimuli which could increase the rate of a specific reflex, or (*b*) *evoked* by stimulus events which could increase non-specifically the likelihood of occurrence of various occurring behaviors, including smiling among others. On the *elicitation* point, *a*, we have noted that early smiling to stimulation has been conceived by some as being essentially *unlearned* (e.g. Bühler, Piaget, Bowlby, Rheingold); and it is possible, to the extent that eliciting or evoking unconditioned stimuli continue to control occurrences of smiles, that these stimuli might change in strength with developmental level. On the *evocation* point, *b*, we note that recent studies (e.g. Berlyne, 1958) have shown that infants tend to respond by attending, approaching, exploring, and/or smiling to complex or novel stimuli presented in their environments. The critical feature of this first conceptual focus then is, if a variety of stimuli were simply available, that Ss might: *first*, habituate disagreeable stimuli and hence become less encumbered in approaching and smiling to these and to stimuli generally; *second*, respond to instances of effective positive stimuli within classes and ranges, and, hence, as one consequence, acquire the *capacity to discriminate* along diverse dimensions of stimulus difference; and *third*, employ responses which could be *conditioned* (on a classical or operant basis) in circumstances conducive to learning (the second theme which follows). These circumstances would depend on the sequential and temporal relationships between stimuli and responses. On this last point also, in addition to evoking such responses as smiles, complex or novel stimuli and those permitted to recover from satiation might also operate more effectively (relative to simple or familiar stimuli) to *reinforce* such behaviors if made contingent upon them, as under the operant conditioning case detailed below.

On this basis, then, the apparent difference between child-rearing environments in the first 4 months might be due primarily to the fact that Institutions provided fewer stimulus possibilities for smiling to occur than did Kibbutz and Family environments, perhaps at an early point when the organism had the capacities required and was relatively unencumbered by the results of past learnings. (Some might term this a 'critical' age range.) Further, the environments may differ on the complexity and novelty of stimuli they provide, and hence in the potency of potential evoking stimuli for smiling (as well as for attending, approaching and exploring). Environments might differ also in the reinforcing potency that stimuli with these attributes (relative to simple or familiar stimuli) might have differentially for such behaviors if made contingent on them, as under the operant conditioning case detailed below.

Lastly, the differential effect of environment could be based on the conception that the smile response might acquire strength in the early months as a function simply of the opportunities to emit smiles, i.e.

of *practice*. In an analysis of gross independent variables such as ours here it would be difficult to separate a practice from a learning basis of smiles, for learning as conventionally conceived also involves the passage of time and practice. Moreover, even if a valid residual concept of practice could plausibly be defined, it would be most difficult to rule out the role of learned components of smile response strength. Even so, it seems worth while maintaining this distinction for our heuristic purpose here.

Differential opportunities for smile learning. Several conceptions of the smile as a learned response may be advanced also. Not incompatible in principle, smile learning may be taking place concurrently under several of these cases. One basis for smiling may be *classical* (Pavlovian) conditioning (Darwin, 1872; Watson, 1925). There are some difficulties in applying this basic paradigm to the early acquisition of smile response strength. First, the term 'reflex' typically has been reserved for cases in which a *specific* unconditioned stimulus (US) or those within a quite narrow stimulus range, upon *discrete* presentation, exhibits the capacity repeatedly to elicit a *specific* narrowly defined unconditioned response (UR), which UR usually involves directly elements of the autonomic nervous system (e.g. pupil constriction brought on by an intense light US). The conditions under which smiling is typically evoked in the early months seem to differ considerably from these: *First*, it appears that USs in a wide range, rather than in an exceedingly narrow one, may be capable of eliciting smiling. These USs would include visual, auditory, kinesthetic, and tactual stimuli (provided, e.g. through jogging, lifting, tickling, caressing, throwing or dropping the infant through space, or by distant or disjunctive sights and sounds). *Second*, rather gross stimuli, in particular the human face, when presented not discretely but continuously and which are apparently unchanging, seem capable for periods of evoking smiles repeatedly. *Third*, the to-be-conditioned stimulus (CS) complex, the most likely one for infant social smiling being some discriminable aspect of the caretaker's appearance or face, must (*a*) have no initial US value for smiling, and (*b*) permit discrete presentation for effective pairing, on both of which counts the caretaker's appearance-face may not qualify. For these reasons, it would be difficult to specify with confidence whether and exactly how the smile would be conditioned classically.

Even while it is difficult easily to assume that these three requirements hold for the case of infant smiling, it would be instructive to follow through how the classical conditioning model might apply. It would emphasize that the smile could come rapidly under the control of CSs through their regular association with the US. For this case, a variety of USs might operate, like those earlier listed. Assuming that it is not a continuous and unchanging event, that it could be presented on discrete occasions (trials), and that it has no US value for smiling, the caretaker's appearance-face could function as the to-be-CS complex. On the assumption, then, that it would systematically precede USs on a sufficient number of occasions with proper timing relationships, the caretaker's appearance-face would soon come to function as the CS class for the infant's smiles. Thereafter, the caretaker's appearance-face would elicit smiles from the infant, assuming the continuation of maintenance pairings between CS and US. Thus, from the viewpoint of learning opportunity, one way in which environments could differ in the early months is in the pattern of stimuli they provide, specifically in the sequence and timing relationships between those stimuli and smiling which would constitute opportunities for the Pavlovian conditioning of smiling. To explain our findings, relative to the Institution, Kibbutz and Family environments might earlier provide more instances of readily discriminable to-be-CSs, which precede uniformly, in effective timing relationships, the occurrence of USs for smiling.

Dennis (1935) has suggested that smiling could become a classical CR to any stimulus which brings about a cessation of fretting, unrest and crying, and that it is *not* elicited by an US. Gesell & Thompson (1934) and Spitz & Wolf (1946) in a not too dissimilar vein have assumed that the smile as CR somehow comes to be produced by the 'satisfaction' inherent in 'need-gratification', and that somehow it then could become an *anticipatory* response to that 'satisfaction', for which the caretaker's face becomes the CS. In so far as classical conditioning is the actual or implied model, the implicit assumptions of these conceptions would be even more tenuous than those required for the straightforward application to smiling of the Pavlovian conditioning paradigm. In this section, we have noted the difficulties involved in a straightforward application of the classical paradigm to smile learning. As will be detailed in the following section, many of the phenomena these theorists have attempted to explain may be ordered readily with the conception of the S-R chain, i.e. operant conditioning and the conditioned discriminative stimulus (cue). The stimulus of the appearance-face would signal, as it were, that a smile response could lead to a reinforcing consequence (e.g. food, water, being held). Hence, appearance would come to control (evoke) smiling.

The second potential learning basis for smiling is that of *instrumental* or *operant* conditioning. This conception may be applied to the case of smile learning with far fewer reservations than that of Pavlovian conditioning just considered. For this paradigm, aspects of freely occurring responses of the infant are differentiated out ('shaped') and conditioned by those immediate environmental consequences which function as 'reinforcing' stimuli (cf. Gewirtz, 1959). Any stimulus event which follows a free response (e.g. smile) of the infant and which systematically increases some index of that response, would be termed a (positive) reinforcing stimulus. Accordingly, smiling as an operant response could become conditioned to occur more frequently in the context in which it has been followed by reinforcing stimuli, of which a great variety is provided in most caretaking environments. Reinforcing stimuli might be provided through the potential USs listed for the classical conditioning case, through the provision of relatively more complex and novel stimuli, and through such responses as talking to the infant and picking him up as was demonstrated by Brackbill (1958) with 3-4 month Ss. [For other examples, see Gewirtz (1961).] Indeed, due to the great value placed on infant smiles by most caretaking communities, it would be most unusual for smiles to remain long unanswered (unreinforced) by the responses of witnessing caretakers who are not encumbered or occupied. As was indicated in the preceding paragraph, a minor extension of this operant paradigm would be one in which a discriminative (cue) stimulus occurred to signal that a response, if emitted, could be followed by a reinforcing stimulus. For example, the caretaker's appearance or face could provide the cue to the infant that he might be reinforced (e.g. by his being picked up) if he would smile; hence, he might smile to the appearance of the face.

Therefore, another possible way in which environments might differ is in the opportunities they provide for the operant conditioning of smiling. As in the Pavlovian case above, it is axiomatic for this case also that stimuli be available to the child, particularly those which could function to reinforce behaviors if made immediately contingent on them. Specifically, if occurrences of smiles would be followed as consequences closely and frequently by any of a variety of stimulus events which function as reinforcers, the incidence of smiling in that setting would increase; i.e. the smile would become conditioned. To explain the differences in results among environments, it would be assumed that caretakers in Institutions might have relatively less time for each infant in their care. Further, even when in the infant's vicinity, they would often be busy with neighboring infants. Hence, it is thought that relative to Kibbutz and Family caretakers, Institution caretakers might respond to the infant's smiles (and other behaviors) relatively less often and less quickly (it is recalled that the most effective reinforcement follows immediately the response), perhaps also providing potential reinforcing stimuli in a narrower range and of less complexity or novelty, and in fewer settings.

Lastly, we emphasize two additional ways in which environments may differ, deriving from or extensions of the two preceding conditioning paradigms. We have seen that the operant paradigm may be extended to where an environment would provide stimuli so that the smile as operant is reinforced only on occasions when it is emitted in the presence of (or when it is preceded by) a particular stimulus (e.g. a woman's face), which then would become a *discriminative* (or cue) stimulus for smiling. This paradigm may be relevant to the test procedure of this study. In the Institution environment this learning might occur rather later than it might in the other environments, either because the stimuli are not presented as often or because effective contingencies between stimuli and the smile response do not occur until much later there. Finally, the environments may differ in that they provide stimuli in contingencies with the smile to make it possible for elements of the Pavlovian and operant paradigms to occur in sequence. In essence, once elicited by an US or CS, or evoked, some elements of the smile functioning not unlike a free operant might be in a position to be reinforced by stimulus consequences. The same environment patterns would hold as were earlier detailed separately under the classical and operant cases.

It is perhaps important to point out once again that the preceding analysis of possible differences in smiling between the Institution and the Family-Kibbutz environments was an heuristic one. Several theoretical ways in which stimuli might have been provided differentially by those environments in connection with smiling were detailed. The observation study surveying stimulus conditions and their relations to behaviors (including smiles) in the early months in the same three environments, just concluded by Dr Hava Gewirtz and the writer, should provide pertinent information for evaluating the role of each of the possible bases outlined for the pattern of differences in smile curves found in the earliest months between the Institution and the Kibbutz and Family environments.

Possible bases for environmental curve differences in post-peak smile rate

Our method deviated from the modal procedure found in the smile literature, which has involved the approach to Ss of a complete stranger. Instead, our O employed a brief preliminary habituation-familiarization phase on first approaching S, before the formal observation but not immediately preceding it. This habituation phase was established to limit responses incompatible with smiling, for the purpose of making it possible to study that response system when relatively unencumbered. Hence, the smile curve patterns found and the difference in level between the two curve patterns (neither of which reflect a sudden onset and continuing state of a hypothesized 'fear of strangers' response pattern) do not bear directly on the issue of whether there is a decline in smiling to strangers with a concomitant rise in fear around 6 months. When the post-peak segments of the relatively homogeneous mean frequency and proportion smile age curve patterns were examined, a fairly constant level of smiling was noted through that upper age range for the Kibbutz and Family curves, while a systematic decline with age was noted for the Institution and Nursery curves.

A statistical test has indicated that the peak levels of mean smiling reached at 4 or 5 months by the three environmental groups were homogeneous, at an age before it could be assumed that various discriminative stimuli acquire much differential control over the smile response. Hence, it would appear that the levels of smiling found in the upper portions of the age range are not simple reflections of overall smile response strength. Rather it is thought one plausible explanation of the differences in level among the environmental age-group curves is that the pattern found is due to differences among the environments in the discriminative stimulus conditions that control infant smiles. These differences would be reflected in differences in the discriminative value or meaning of the standard stimulus for smiling that was used for Ss in each of these environments, namely O's unresponsive face. Thus, it is thought likely that the different mean curve levels reflect mainly the technical difference between the stimuli controlling caretaker behaviors and infant smiling in each environment *and* our test condition under which smiling could be evoked by O's unresponsive face. For example, in Kibbutz and Family environments, more than in the Institution or Day Nursery the near presence or distant sight of a caretaker or other adult, even with an unresponsive face, might cue S that some initiation (for instance, a smile) would be likely to lead to a reply by that person (e.g. a change in her face, like a smile). The caretaker's response might have reinforcer value sufficient to terminate the initiation, or it might imply that the interaction chain thus begun could culminate in a reinforcing consequence. On this assumed basis, there should be greater (stimulus) generalization from adults generally in the environment to O; and the two-minute presentation of O's appearance-face (standing as discriminative for reinforcing consequences) should evoke higher smile rates from Kibbutz and Family Ss than from Institution and Nursery Ss, through the post-peak age range. We are drawn to this more or less *ad hoc* explanation as a plausible and parsimonious basis for the pattern of differences found between environmental group smile curves in the upper portion of the age range studied.

Smiling, social responsiveness, 'satisfaction' and 'joy'

It would not seem parsimonious to think of the incidence of group smiling as having special implications for 'satisfaction with life' or 'happiness', and on this basis alone to conclude that some of the child-rearing settings studied are more wholesome or adequate than others. The point has been made that, before the discriminative stimulus control of smiling is reached, overall smile rate would reflect mainly conditioning history. Further, by 5-6 months, smile rate very likely has begun to come under close conditioned discriminative stimulus control and, thus, may reflect in social settings primarily the degree of an infant's involvement in social interaction sequences appropriate to those settings. (As a key response in those interaction sequences, the smile would be functioning in an instrumental or 'communicative' role there, with the appearance characteristics of persons functioning as the basic discriminative stimuli.) Infants for whom the appearance and behaviors of persons are not discriminative for reinforcement (i.e. those who are not 'dependent' upon others, or who do not 'relate' to persons) should exhibit to O relatively fewer smiles and other responses. Thus, we might expect fewer smiles to persons by Ss in environments characterized by low child-caretaker ratios and high personnel turnover; and it is on the basis of this limited responsiveness to persons displayed by those Ss that such environments might be evaluated as inadequate.

The smile has been thought also by some to reflect 'satisfaction' or 'joy', during reveries or after becoming anticipatory for the attainment of some reinforcing event, thus functioning in an 'expressive' role. (We have noted earlier that the infant's smile might communicate information to the person who could provide reinforcers, and also that it might function as a reinforcing stimulus for that person's behaviors.) Prior to conditioning, however, the infant's smile in the early social phase would seem to have minimal communicative meaning, and only in a limited sense to have expressive meaning. On the expressive point, aside from indexing smile threshold, the infant's smile could indicate that he was alert and fixating a stimulus, that he was not crying or fussing, and hence that he was not preoccupied with strong 'internal' stimuli (e.g. due to 'gas', hunger, fatigue, illness, or discomfort due to wet or soiled diapers). This pattern could provide information to an observer who might assume that an uncomfortable or bothered infant would not be likely to smile or even effectively to fixate stimuli. Outside the implication that smiling could index the absence of behaviors reflecting 'discomfort', there would seem to be no independent index of 'satisfaction' which might be related to the smile in the early months. The notion of the smile as 'expressive' may also reflect Pavlovian conditioning. Thus, if the discriminable appearance of a CS face is systematically followed by such activities as lifting or tickling (the US) which produce smiling or laughter, subsequent appearances of the face could elicit the smile response. These classically conditioned smiles or laughs might be thought by some to be expressions of the infant's 'joy', as e.g. at the approach of his father.

Comparison of our results with previous findings on the age course of smiling

Age of onset of social smiling. Even when based on our Institution Ss, the results on the 'proportion of a group smiling' index concur with reports that the smile response can be evoked by the human face at or before 4 weeks of age (Söderling, Bayley). M. C. Jones and Gesell

& Thompson reported social smiling at 6 weeks, Shirley at 7 weeks, and C. Bühler in the second month. The methods of Spitz & Wolf and of Ambrose did not begin to evoke social smiling until about

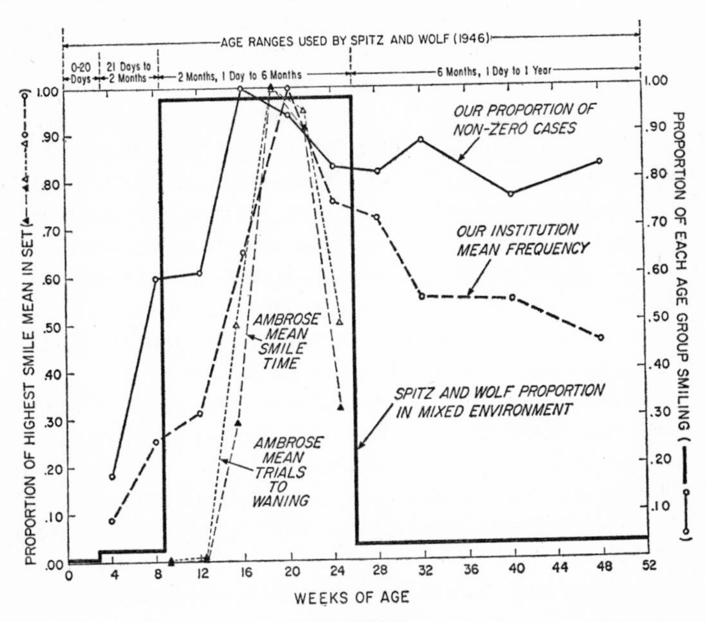

FIG. 26

Comparison of age curves for smiling from three investigations: (1) *the Spitz & Wolf* (1946) *study of an heterogeneous sample using as their measure the* Proportion of Ss who smiled in an age range; (2) *Ambrose's* (1961) *study of Institution infants using the measures* Mean smiling time per run *and* Mean number of presentations to waning; *and* (3) *This Study's age curves in the first* 48 *weeks* (12 *lunar months) for Institution infants using the measures* Mean frequency of smiles *and* Proportion of each age group smiling. *To make comparable the quantitative metrics of This Study and that of Ambrose, group means have been transformed into the proportions they constitute of the highest mean in their set; that highest mean is assigned the value* 1.00 (*left axis*). *The four age ranges covering the first year of life for Spitz and Wolf are defined at the very top of this chart. Their proportion values* (*right axis*) *are plotted as heavy horizontal lines through each age range; these are joined by vertical lines at range limits.*

the third month. The age curves of Figure 26 allow a visual comparison between the results of this study for Institution Ss in the first year and those of the latter two developmental studies on comparable groups; Ambrose's sample was made up of institution infants, and a significant proportion of that of Spitz & Wolf consisted of such Ss. It is seen that our results differ from those of the latter studies, for two of eleven of our Institution Ss were found to smile to a human face by 4 weeks, and more than half smiled by 8 and 12 weeks. When we bring to bear on this question of the age of onset of social smiling the results of the Ss from the other two environments studied at the early ages, Kibbutz and Town Family, the evidence for the early beginnings of social smiling is even more conclusive: five of six Kibbutz Ss smiled at 1 month, and eight of ten Family Ss smiled at 2 months, the earliest age at which the latter were represented. The difference in the early months between Spitz & Wolf and our results would seem to suggest that a moving and/or sound emitting face is not more effective as a stimulus for smiling than was our immobile unresponsive face. Indeed, it may be a less effective one.

Our dichotomous index of whether Ss smiled at least once in the first two-minute approach seems similar enough to the Spitz & Wolf index of whether Ss smiled to warrant comparing formally our results with those they present on page 73 of their monograph. Our 28-day month age-groups were combined roughly to cover the age ranges Spitz & Wolf used. It was assumed that their months were 30·5 days long. Only ·02 of 198 Spitz & Wolf Ss smiled in the period 61 days and below (our 1- and 2-month groups), while the proportions smiling in our three environments were ·50 of 46 Institution Ss, ·65 of 17 Kibbutz Ss, and ·80 of 10 Family Ss. Each of our three proportions is reliably higher at $P < \cdot 001$ than the ·02 of Spitz & Wolf, when subjected to chi square tests for fourfold tables (1 df, 2 tails).

Age of peak rate of social smiling. Even though Spitz & Wolf and Ambrose report a later onset of smiling, and a rapid, abrupt drop in smile rate from the peak month which we do not find, our mean frequency measure for Institution Ss reaches an apparent peak at 20 weeks, a point quite close to the point at which Ambrose found the peaks for the mean age curves of his two correlated measures; and, similarly, our Institution proportion smiling peak value of 1·00 (as well as our Family and Kibbutz proportions) at 16 weeks fall close to the value of ·98 at the smiling peak on the similar proportion measure employed by Spitz & Wolf, and is found near the mid-point of the gross age range (2 months 1 day through 5 months) in which they found their peak proportion of smilers. Thus, there is fair agreement between Ambrose's findings and ours on the peak month for mean smile rate, and gross agreement between the peak proportion found by Spitz & Wolf and ours.

The dichotomous smile data were again grouped in the broader age groupings used by Spitz & Wolf. Within each of our three environments, Ss were pooled across 3-, 4-, 5- and 6-months. It is noted that each of our three environments contains a somewhat lower proportion of those smiling in this range than the ·98 of 145 Ss reported by Spitz & Wolf. The differences are reliable at $P < \cdot 001$ (chi square, 1 df, 2 tail test) between their proportion (·98) and ·84 for 69 Institution Ss, and ·88 for 74 Kibbutz Ss. Our proportion of ·94 for 39 Family Ss did not differ reliably from their ·98. These results might be due to the possibility that proportionately more of the Spitz & Wolf sample in this range than of each of our environmental groups were of ages at or near the 4-month age of peak smiling that we have identified. Those authors do not publish monthly age distributions within their gross age ranges. Alternatively, the difference might be due to the possibility that the moving and/or sound-producing face of Spitz & Wolf constituted a more potent stimulus for smiling than did our unresponsive face for Ss of the age range in which peak smiling is found.

Decline of social smiling. It has been noted for both mean smile frequency and proportion smiling indices, in the portion of the age range after each peak smiling month, that response curves in our four environments all decline regularly and gradually, if they decline at all, and that none anywhere reaches a zero-level of responding. The proportion of Ss smiling in each of our four environments, pooled in the 6- through 12-month range (our 7-, 8-, 10- and 12-month groups), can be compared to the proportion ·03 found for 147 Ss in that age range by Spitz & Wolf. The proportions smiling in our four environments are ·63 of 52 Nursery Ss, ·81 of 83 Institution Ss, ·88 of 25 Family Ss, and ·90 of 93 Kibbutz Ss. Hence, each of our groups exhibits a proportion of Ss smiling in the 6- through 12-month range that is reliably greater at $P < \cdot 001$ (chi square, 1 df, 2 tail test) than ·03, the proportion found by Spitz & Wolf.

To the degree that the female face stimulus used in the present study was unfamiliar, even the Institution result pattern would run counter to the expectation that smile rate to unfamiliar faces should begin to decline to a near-zero level around 6 months (Washburn,

Spitz & Wolf, and the extrapolation from Ambrose's last age point). There could be various bases for this apparently discrepant result pattern, bases which do not depend on our different preliminary procedure. For instance, the Israeli groups studied might differ from previous samples in their reinforcement histories for smiling, or, in their experiences with strangers (which might in part determine their 'fear of strangers' and, hence, inversely their smile rates in our test setting). It is difficult to rule out still other bases for this finding. For a definitive picture, we must await, first, a complete replication of this study, and, second, the results of an investigation, with the same samples and ages, of smile rates (and 'fear' responses) to the approach of complete strangers. Until then we must content ourselves with the attempt that is made, in the final section of this report, to list a variety of possible bases for the discrepancy between the results of this and earlier studies, apart from the familiarization procedure used in this study.

It would seem parsimonious at this juncture to conceive of the absence of an abrupt decline in smile rate as due to the brief familiarization procedure we employed, prior to but not immediately preceding the observation proper, in which O exposed herself to Ss and in about 25 per cent of the cases made initiations or responses to them. To the extent that the familiarization procedure was successful with some Ss, the data could provide a valid picture of the strength of the smile response to the stimulus of a not totally unfamiliar woman's face, involving, we would imagine, rather little 'fear' of the strange. Because of the brief familiarization procedure employed to limit responses incompatible with smiling, such as 'fear', our data cannot bear directly on the question of whether a fear pattern emerges uniformly in Ss of the several environments, and, if it does emerge, at what month.

Even so, given the assumption that the smiling rate to familiar faces would remain constant or increase in all environments after 5 months, the systematic decline after that point in the smiling to a relatively unfamiliar face by Institution Ss (the only group represented in the early months for which curves appeared to decline steadily after reaching an apparent peak) may well index the onset of the capacity in the Institution infant to discriminate familiar from relatively unfamiliar faces, familiar faces being those discriminative for reinforcement and hence providing relevant cues for the occurrence of smiles. In the case of Kibbutz and Family Ss, the possibility cannot be ruled out that they could discriminate Os as strangers, but simply smile to strangers.

Comparison of our environmental group differences in smiling with comparable data from other investigations. In this section we compare our results for the groups from different child-rearing environments with those of other studies in which roughly similar groups were contrasted. In the section that follows, there will be examined potential bases for the discrepancies, in both Institution and other groups, between the findings of this investigation and the others. Our findings concerning different smiling patterns in different environments do not appear to agree with those of Spitz & Wolf (pp. 74-75), who reported no difference in smile rates in the first half-year between 'Institution' and 'Private-Home' (i.e. Family) Ss. Also, while they are not far off, our findings on timing do not agree precisely with those of Ambrose (1961) on the details of the age of onset of smiling and on the comparative age curve peaks for Institution and Family Ss. Further, it is not clear exactly how our results concerning environmental differences in early smiling are discrepant from those of Rheingold (1961). Comparing social behaviors of Institution and Family Ss at 3 to 4 months, Rheingold found Institution Ss more responsive to the examiner than Home Ss, as indicated by measures including 'time to first smile' and 'smile frequency'. It is recalled that at this age in the present study, Kibbutz and Family Ss smiled more than did Institution Ss. In the 8- through 16-week range, our Kibbutz and Family groups smiled on the average reliably more than did Institution Ss. However, at 20 weeks our Institution Ss appeared to exhibit a higher mean smile rate than did Family or Kibbutz Ss. At both 16 and 20 weeks, as large a proportion of Institution Ss appeared to smile as did Family Ss, and this proportion seemed slightly higher at both points than were the comparable proportions for Kibbutz Ss. However, none of the apparent differences in favor of Institution Ss are reliable. To the degree that Rheingold's 3-4 solar month Ss might have overlapped in age our 4- to 5-month (16- to 20-week) Ss, her finding might not be far different from ours.

Possible bases for the discrepancies between our findings and those of others

Aside from the brief familiarization or habituation procedure used in this study and not formally used in others, there might be other bases for the discrepancies between the findings of the present study and those of others, particularly those of Spitz & Wolf, Ambrose, and Rheingold. The first basis is technical. It is possible that some of those studies operated under a different *definition* of the smile than the one we employed, for extensive definitions of the smile response are not provided. Also, smile behavior categories might be of limited reliability when employed with Ss at some age points. Lastly, differences exist among the indices of smiling employed in the various studies. Examples of the diverse indices are: (1) the quantitative variables 'duration of smiles' and 'number of presentations to smile waning' of Ambrose; (2) the quantitative variables 'time to first smile' and 'number of smiles' of Rheingold; (3) the quantitative variable 'frequency of smiles' and the dichotomous variable 'proportion of a group who smiled' of this study; and (4) the dichotomous variable 'did or did-not smile on a given stimulus presentation' of Spitz & Wolf. Thus, while each of the variables is a plausible index of smiling, it is always possible that separately or in combination they would relate differently to age.

It is also conceivable that the *samples* for the various studies were drawn from different populations. Thus, the Institution samples of the different studies may have differed systematically in their reinforcement histories for smiling, or in some other significant way with respect to the stimuli which control smiling. Thus, also, for Western Hemisphere Indian infants in the second half-year of the Spitz & Wolf combined sample, a Caucasian stimulus face might have been relatively strange or it might have evoked 'fear' differentially. Environmental group age pattern differences in smiling found in this study, by Ambrose and by Rheingold, document the importance of working with homogeneous samples to study the course of smiling in early life. In the present context, we note that Spitz & Wolf drew their Ss from five diverse environmental groups and three races, a most heterogeneous sample.

The fact that our study was carried out in *Israel* suggests still another basis which might, at least in part, account for the differences between our results and those of others. First, it is likely that Israeli infants in all environments studied have, relative to their U.S. and British peers, considerable experience with familiar and stranger adults. Thus, for example, Town Family babies in Israel often receive care from non-parent adults, in addition to their mothers. Further, the Israel climate makes it possible for most babies there to spend relatively more of their time out-of-doors, where the highly urban condition would bring them in contact with many persons. Each of these factors could provide a basis, apart from the familiarization procedure used in this study, for the lack of a sudden decline after the peak in our age curves for smiling to a relatively unfamiliar face. Further, our sample of Family Ss might have differed from Rheingold's, which was made up of first-borns only who at age 3 to 4 months may have had much less experience than did our Family and Kibbutz Ss with adults other than their mothers. And it is possible, also, that the single institution Rheingold used was an exceptional one. In the present study, Ss came from six institutions, which followed various philosophies.

Another possible basis exists for the divergence between Ambrose's and our results. This involves the *sequence* and *duration* of stimulus presentation, and in particular the difference between our procedure of presenting the unresponsive stimulus face continuously for two minutes (for the data presented here) and Ambrose's procedure of presenting the stimulus face for thirty-second periods, interspersed by thirty-second pauses, until the smile response waned. Smiling might also have been inhibited somewhat in the Ambrose study through his use of thirty-second stimulus intervals, for the approach beginning each interval may have involved an abrupt quality. Also, Ambrose's male O stood four feet from S, putting his face at least four feet from S's, which is greater by two feet than the distance in our study between the faces of O and S. We note that in a preliminary study of the effect on smiles of two distances of O's face from S's, Ambrose (1960) found the average smiling time to be reliably greater at a two- than at a four-foot distance. However, this factor would have had to operate differentially with age to account for the differences in the 1- through 6-month age range between Ambrose's findings and ours. Another possible basis for the difference between the results of this study and Ambrose's may lie in the fact that he used a single male O, while we here report results from five women Os. This possibility is contraindicated to an extent by Ambrose's report (1961) that preliminary results similar to those he reported were obtained with his method by a woman O, though with longitudinal and not with cross-sectional data. His original study was cross-sectional.

Other factors might have been operating to determine the different results found in the various investigations. *Fear* which is incompatible with smiling might have been evoked in some Ss by the Spitz & Wolf procedure which involved the approach of a 'stranger' exhibiting an abrupt sequence of behavior. Although our Os were necessarily active when monitoring the timers and recording Ss' responses in the present study, they were never abrupt, and at least on that basis were unlikely to constitute fear stimuli.

A last basis for the discrepant result patterns between the present study and the others may lie in differences of *method.* One dimension of difference is in the stimulus conditions employed to evoke smiles. Thus, Ambrose and this study employed an unresponsive human stimulus face, while Spitz & Wolf employed a responsive stimulus face, moving and/or sound-producing. However, to the extent that Ambrose's results for the initial portion of the post-smile-peak age range begin to show a decline, and hence tend to agree with those of Spitz & Wolf, it would seem that the responsiveness of the stimulus face plays no role in accounting for the different results from ours they obtained in the upper portion of the range.

The possible impact of a second difference in stimulus context, involving the procedure of approach and pre-observation exposure and interaction, has already been considered at several points in this report. It is again taken up here to provide the basis for considering two points. The *first* is that because in this study only a cursory pre-observation exposure was generally used with Ss between 4 and 6 months, and the procedure was not required for Ss below 4 months, the difference in method could not readily be invoked to provide the entire basis of the apparent discrepancies between our results and those of Ambrose, Spitz & Wolf or Rheingold in the first half-year. The *second* point is that while familiarization procedures were not formally employed in these other studies, they might in effect have been involved to a degree in all of them. Thus, there is the possibility that Ambrose, and particularly Spitz & Wolf, might have employed procedures in their institution environments having elements in common with the exposure-familiarization aspect of our pre-observation method. Carrying out regular observations and other business in fairly limited environments, their Os very likely would be seen frequently, particularly by Ss between ages 5 and 12 months who could discriminate differentially. Further, while Spitz & Wolf write on their page 72 that they avoided touching, talking to, or even being in the presence of S before the observation proper, they also report on that page that each S was tested at different times both by a man and a woman O, and that all but 26 of their Ss were exposed to the 'smiling stimulus from 5 to 30 times during the critical period of the third, fourth, fifth and sixth months'. Further, Spitz & Wolf report on the same page that 147 Ss were 'followed' from 6 through 12 months, of which 108 had already been 'followed' from 3 to 6 months. If we understand their points correctly, their stimulus persons might not long have remained total strangers to Ss in those environments, and the cumulative effect of this process might constitute a 'familiarization' procedure even more intensive than the procedure employed in the present study, or at least not unlike it. To the extent that this reasoning would prevail, differences between their results and the results of this study would have to be explained on other bases than that we did employ, and Spitz & Wolf did not, a pre-observation familiarization-habituation procedure.

Summary

The smile response is centrally involved at all stages of social development and learning. We have presented a preliminary report of our attempt to chart the age course of the rate of smiling to the unresponsive face of a woman O, in the first 18 months of life, in groups of infant Ss from four diverse child-rearing environments in Israel. These environments seem to offer meaningfully different contexts for early development and learning. They include the Residential Institution (226 Ss), the middle-class Town Family (91 Ss), the Kibbutz or collective settlement (236 Ss), and the Day Nursery (105 Ss represented only in the 8- through 18-month range). Each S provides a score at a single monthly age point. A standard procedure of approach, observation, and recording in reliable behavior categories was employed. Prior to but not immediately preceding the observation, O subjected Ss to a brief familiarization procedure, which for about 75 per cent of the Ss consisted of their being passively exposed to her for thirty minutes, and in the remaining 25 per cent may have involved initiations to Ss as well as replies to their initiations. On a given approach, O presented for two minutes her unchanging unresponsive face two feet above S's. The forms of the age curves were examined for the '*mean* frequency of smiles' (and the '*proportion* of Ss in an age-group who smiled at all') and compared across the four environmental groups. On the assumption of no sex difference, sexes were pooled for the analysis. A preliminary evaluation of the consequences of possible experimental artifacts, involving known and assumed differences in the conditions of observation in the four environments, was made under three headings: (*a*) saliency of the evoking stimulus for smiling; (*b*) S's smile experience in the period directly preceding the observation proper; and (*c*) S's state. It was concluded that it would be discreet to emphasize in this initial report only a distinction between two smile age curve patterns: an Institution and Day Nursery pattern, relatively lower in initial and in final level; and a Family and Kibbutz pattern, relatively higher in initial and in final level. The major patterns identified in this preliminary analysis follow:

Age curves of the Mean Smile (and the Proportion Smiling) measures appeared most orderly. Infant smiles are evoked in Kibbutz and Institution Ss as early as 4 weeks, with a greater proportion of Kibbutz Ss smiling then. Kibbutz, Family, and Institution mean age curves are parallel in the first 4 months, and while Kibbutz and Family mean curves do not differ in height between 2 and 4 months, each is reliably higher in that range than the Institution mean curve. The Mean Smile age curve peak is reached at 20 weeks by Institution Ss, and at 16 weeks by Kibbutz and Town Family Ss. These peak means were found to be statistically homogeneous. (Comparable peaks of the Proportion Smiling curve are found at 16 weeks in all three environments.) In an heuristic analysis using concepts for the systematic impact of environmental conditions on smiling rates, the differences found between environmental group smile patterns in the early months were conceived to be a function of differences in the simple availability of stimuli which could elicit or evoke smiles, and which could reinforce them. At the same time, these different outcomes were referred to available conceptions of learning processes through which stimuli could have systematic, long term, impact on behavior. In particular, differences in the timing and pairing relationships into which such stimuli might enter with smiles, and the opportunities for the classical and operant conditioning of smiles which the patterns of these variables could constitute, were considered, while operant learning and the conditioned discriminative stimuli that could control smiling were the learning conceptions emphasized. The gross quality of our independent variables, 'age' and 'environmental group', precluded selecting from among the theoretical cases advanced those which best order our results.

In the post-smiling-peak range, extending from 4 or 5 months through 18 months, the Institution Mean Smile (and Proportion

Smiling) age curves seemed to decline regularly from their peak. This apparent pattern of decline was paralleled by the Nursery curves in the range where they are represented (8-18 months). The Kibbutz age curve seemed to decline little and the Family curve not at all, after their earlier 4-month peak. The distinct tendency of the environment Mean curves progressively to diverge, after appearing relatively homogeneous around 8 months, was tested by an analysis of variance of the linear regression coefficients fit to the 4 mean monthly curves in the 5- through 18-month range. These coefficients were found heterogeneous at $P < \cdot 001$, which indicated an Environment *by* Age interaction. The basis of this was that the Family curve showed reliably *less* linear decline than did the other three curves, while the Kibbutz curve declined reliably less than the Institution curve. This pattern of results was thought to be a function not of over-all smiling strength, but rather of the likelihood that smile (and other) responses emitted in the regular environment, in the presence of a caretaker or adult even when she would be displaying an unresponsive face, would initiate an interaction chain leading to reinforcement. Differences between environments in learning histories that might lead to such differential behavior patterns were considered.

There was an absence in all four environments of an abrupt decline in smile rate after their 4- or 5-month peaks. Such an abrupt decline, when found by Spitz & Wolf and others to a stranger's face as stimulus, was referred to the onset of a 'fear of strangers' or the 'eight-months anxiety' (Spitz, 1955). It was thought parsimonious in this report to conceive of the absence of the abrupt decline in all groups as due to the brief familiarization procedure employed prior to but not immediately preceding the formal observation. In this procedure Ss were exposed to O, and in about 25 per cent of the cases made minor initiations or responded to them. Even so, it was noted that the stimulus procedure of Spitz & Wolf and others who employed, presumably, complete 'strangers', appeared to have a number of aspects in common with our procedure. Hence, it was thought, our not finding the abrupt decline in smiling in the second half-year might be due to factors other than our habituation procedure. In this context, we attempted to understand our pattern of findings by scrutinizing various aspects of the method we employed to evoke smiles and their assumed roles in the results. The steps of our procedure were compared also with those in the procedures of earlier systematic studies of the age course of infant smiling, and some possible bases for our discrepant findings, other than the familiarization procedure, were identified.

Acknowledgements

This investigation was begun in 1960 while the writer was Visiting Professor of Psychology in the Hebrew University of Jerusalem. The University's Department of Psychology provided initial support which made possible the research program from which this is the first study reported. From the closing phases of data collection, this program has been supported by the U.S. National Institute of Mental Health. I owe much to Miriam K. Rosenthal's discriminating assistance, intelligent comments and suggestions, particularly in the early phases of this project. Rivka Landau was most reliable, dedicated, and alert in her supervision of the collection of the data in the latter phase of the project, and has been of great help in their processing and interpretation. Dr Hava Bonné Gewirtz was helpful in the pilot phase. Miriam Many, Tsvia Levi, Tamar Fisch and Hana Zauerbraun, in addition to Miss Landau and Mrs Rosenthal, served ably as observers. Their roles took them on short notice often and sometimes under difficult conditions of travel to sources of infants throughout the land of Israel. Administrative officials and professional caretakers of the 6 Baby Homes, 15 Day Nurseries and more than 70 Kibbutzim in which we worked in Israel were most cooperative. And the Kibbutz Central Committee on Child Research operating through the Seminar Hakibbutzim was unusually interested and well informed. This study owes much to the cooperation and advice of its members.

References

AHRENS, R. (1954) 'Beitrag zur Entwicklung der Physiognomie und Mimikerkennens' *Zeit für exp. und ang. Psychol.* **2(3)**, 414-54; and **2(4)**, 599-633

AINSWORTH, M. (1963) 'The development of infant-mother interaction among the Ganda' In B. M. Foss (Ed.) *Determinants of infant behaviour II* London: Methuen, pp. 67-104

ALTMANN, S. A. (1962) 'A field study of the sociobiology of rhesus monkeys, *Macaca mulatta*' *New York Acad. Sci.*, **102**, 338-435

AMBROSE, J. A. (1960) 'The smiling and related responses in early human infancy: an experimental and theoretical study of their course and significance' Ph.D. thesis, London University

AMBROSE, J. A. (1961) 'The development of the smiling response in early infancy' In B. M. Foss (Ed.) *Determinants of infant behaviour* London: Methuen, pp. 179-201

ARSENIAN, J. M. (1943) 'Young children in an insecure situation' *J. abn. soc. Psychol.* **38**, 225-49

BAER, D. M. & SHERMAN, J. A. Quoted in L. P. Lipsitt & C. C. Spiker (eds.) *Advances in Child Development and Behaviour*. New York; Academic Press, 1963, pp. 221-6

AUBLE, D. (1953) 'Extended tables for the Mann-Whitney statistic' *Bull. Dist. Educ. Res.* Bloomington: Indiana Univer.

BANDURA, A. & WALTERS, R. H. (1963) *Social learning and personality development* New York: Holt, Rinehart and Winston

BARABASH-NIKIFOROV, I. I. (1962) *The sea otter* Jerusalem: Israel Program for Scientific Translations (available from the Office of Technical Services, U.S. Dept. of Commerce, Washington, D.C.)

BARTHOLOMEW, G. A. (1959) 'Mother-young relations and the maturation of pup behaviour in the Alaska fur seal' *Animal Behav.* **7**, 163-71

BAYLEY, N. (1961) Personal communication

BEACH, F. A. (1939) 'Maternal behavior of the pouchless marsupial *Marmosa cinerea*' *J. Mammal.* **20**, 315-22

BEACH, F. A. & JAYNES, J. (1956a) 'Studies of maternal retrieving in rats. I: Recognition of young' *J. Mammal.* **37**, 177-80

BEACH, F. A. & JAYNES, J. (1956b) 'Studies of maternal retrieving in rats. II. Sensory cues involved in the lactating female's response to her young' *Behaviour*, **10**, 104-25

BEACH, F. A. & WILSON, J. R. (1963) 'Effects of prolactin, progesterone and estrogen on maternal reactions of nonpregnant rats to foster young' *Psychol. Rep.* **13**, 231-9

BENIEST-NOIROT, E. (1958) 'Analyse du comportement dit maternal chez la souris' *Monog. Francaises de Psychol.* **1**. Paris: Centre National de la Recherche Scientifique.

BERLYNE, D. (1958) 'The influence of the albedo and complexity of stimuli on visual fixation in the human infant' *Brit. J. Psychol.* **49**, 315-18

BIRCH, H. G. (1945) 'The relation of previous experience to insightful problem-solving' *J. comp. Psychol.* **38**, 367-83

BIRCH, H. G. (1956) 'Sources of order in the maternal behavior of animals' *Amer. J. Orthopsychiat.* **26**, 279-84

BOBBITT, R. A., JENSEN, G. D. & KUEHN, R. E. (1964) 'Development and application of an observational method: a pilot study of the mother-infant relationship in pigtail monkeys' *J. genet. Psychol.* **105**, 257-74.

BOURLIÈRE, F. (1954) *The natural history of mammals* New York: Knopf

BOWLBY, J. (1958) 'The nature of the child's tie to his mother' *Int. J. of Psychoanal.* **39**, 350-73

BRACKBILL, Y. (1958) 'Extinction of the smiling response in infants as a function of reinforcement schedule' *Child. Devel.* **29**, 115-24

BRUCE, H. M. (1961) 'Observations on the suckling stimulus and lactation in the rat' *J. Reprod. Fertil.* **2**, 17-34

BUCHSBAUM, R. (1948) *Animals without backbones* Chicago: Univer. Chicago Press

BÜHLER, C. (1933) 'The social behaviour of children' In C. A. Murchison (Ed.) *Handbook of Child Psychology* (2nd ed., revised) Worcester, Mass.: Clark Univer. Press

BURTON, M. (1957) 'Nature's wonderland, No. 8' *Illustrated London News*, March 2, 1957, 356-7

BUTLER, R. A. (1953) 'Discrimination by Rhesus monkeys to visual exploration motivation' *J. comp. physiol. Psychol.* **46**, 95-8

CALHOUN, J. B. (1953) 'The ecology and sociology of the Norway rat', *U.S. Public Health Service Publ.* no. 1008, 1-288.

CAUSEY, D. & WATERS, R. H. (1936) 'Parental care in mammals with especial reference to the carrying of young by the albino rat' *J. comp. Psychol.* **22**, 241-54

CLOUDSLEY-THOMPSON, J. L. (1960) *Animal Behaviour* London: Oliver and Boyd

COCKRUM, E. L. (1962) *Introduction to mammalogy* New York: Ronald Press

COMFORT. (1961) *Darwin and the naked lady* London: Routledge

COOLIDGE, H. J., JR. (1933) 'Notes on a family of breeding gibbons' *Human Biology*, **5**, 288-94

CORNWELL, A. C. & FULLER, J. L. (1961) 'Conditioned responses in young puppies' *J. comp. physiol. Psychol.* **54**, 13-15

COWIE, A. T. & FOLLEY, S. J. (1961) 'The mammary gland and lactation' In W. C. Young (Ed.) *Sex and internal secretions*, 3rd ed. Baltimore: Williams and Wilkins, pp. 590-642

CRAWFORD, M. P. & SPENCE, K. W. (1939) 'Observational learning of discrimination problems by chimpanzees' *J. comp. Psychol.* **27**, 133-47

CURIO, E. (1955) 'Der Jungentransport einer Gelbhalsmaus (*Apodemus f. flavicollis Melch.*)' *Z. Tierpsychol.* **12**, 459-62

DARLING, F. F. (1937) *A herd of red deer* Oxford: University Press

DARWIN, C. (1872) *The expression of emotion in man and animals* London: Murray. New York: Philosophical Library, 1955

DAVID, M. & APPELL, G. (1961) 'A study of nursing care and nurse-infant interaction' In B. M. Foss (Ed.) *Determinants of infant behaviour* London: Methuen

DAVIS, R. B., HERREID, C. F. II & SHORT, H. L. (1962) 'Mexican free-tailed bats in Texas' *Ecol. Monogr.* **32**, 311-46

DENNIS, W. (1935) 'An experimental test of two theories of social smiling in infants' *J. Soc. Psychol.* **6**, 214-23

DEVORE, I. (1963) 'Mother-infant relations in free-ranging baboons' In H. L. Rheingold (Ed.) *Maternal behavior in mammals* New York: John Wiley, pp. 305-35

EIBL-EIBESFELDT, I. (1955) 'Angeborenes und Erworbenes in Nestbauverhalten der Wanderratte' *Naturwissenschaften*, **42**, 633-4

EIBL-EIBESFELDT, I. (1958) 'Das Verhalten der Nagetiere' In J. G. Helmcke, H. v. Lengerken and D. Starck (Eds.) *Handbuch der Zoologie* Vol. 8, Lief. 12. Berlin: Walter de Gryter

EVERETT, J. W. (1961) 'The mammalian female reproductive cycle and its controlling mechanisms' In W. C. Young (Ed.) *Sex and internal secretions* 3rd ed. Baltimore: Williams and Wilkins, pp. 497-555

FISHER, E. M. (1940) 'Early life of a sea otter pup' *J. Mammal.* **21,** 132-7

FOSS, B. M. (1964) 'Mimicry in mynas (*Gracula religiosa*): a test of Mowrer's theory' *Brit. J. Psychol.* **55,** 85-8

FREEDMAN, D. G. (1961) 'The infant's fear of strangers and the flight response' *J. child Psychol. Psychiat.* **4,** 242-8

FREEDMAN, D. G. (1963) 16-mm. sound film: *Development of the smile and fear of strangers* PCR-2140, Penna. Psychol. Cinema Reg., University Park, Penna.

FREEDMAN, D. G. & KELLER, B. (1963) 'Inheritance of behavior in infants' *Science*, **140,** 196-8

FREUD, S. (1922) *Introductory lectures on psycho-analysis* London: Allen and Unwin

FULLER, J. L. & DU BUIS, E. M. (1962) 'The behaviour of dogs' In E. S. E. Hafez (Ed.) *The behaviour of domestic animals* London: Baillière, Tyndall and Cox, pp. 415-52

GESELL, A. & THOMPSON, H. (1934) *Infant behavior: its genesis and growth* New York: McGraw Hill

GEWIRTZ, J. L. (1959) 'Discussion of the use of operant conditioning techniques with children' In S. Fisher (Ed.) *Child research in psychopharmacology* Springfield, Ill.: Chas. C. Thomas, pp. 127-36

GEWIRTZ, J. L. (1961) 'A learning analysis of the effects of normal stimulation, privation and deprivation on the acquisition of social motivation and attachment' In B. M. Foss (Ed.) *Determinants of infant behaviour* London: Methuen, pp. 213-99

GEWIRTZ, J. L. (1965) 'The course of smiling by groups of Israeli infants in the first 18 months of life' In *Studies in psychology: Scripta Hierosolymitana*, **14**, Jerusalem: Hebrew University Press

GOLDSTEIN, K. (1957) 'The smiling of the infant and the problem of understanding the "other"' *J. Psychol.* **44,** 175-91

GOODPASTER, W. W. & HOFFMEISTER, D. F. (1954) 'Life history of the golden mouse, *Peromyscus nuttalli*, in Kentucky' *J. Mammal.* **35,** 16-27

GUILFORD, J. P. (1954) *Psychometric methods* 2nd ed. New York: McGraw Hill

HANSEN, E. W. (1962) 'The development of infant and maternal behavior in the rhesus monkey' Doctoral dissertation, University of Wisconsin

HARLOW, H. F. (1958) 'The nature of love' *Amer. Psychologist*, **13,** 673-85

HARLOW, H. F. (1961) 'The development of affectional patterns in infant monkeys' In B. M. Foss (Ed.) *Determinants of infant behaviour* London: Methuen, pp. 75-88

HARLOW, H. F. (1962) 'Development of the second and third affectional systems in macaque monkeys' In T. T. Tourlentes, S. L. Pollack and H. F. Himwick (Eds.) *Research approaches to psychiatric problems: a symposium* New York: Grune and Stratton, pp. 209-29

HARLOW, H. F. (1963) 'The maternal affectional system' In B. M. Foss (Ed.) *Determinants of infant behaviour II* London: Methuen

HARLOW, H. F., HARLOW, M. K. & HANSEN, E. W. (1963) 'The maternal affectional system of rhesus monkeys' In H. L. Rheingold (Ed.) *Maternal behavior in mammals* New York: Wiley, pp. 254-81

HATT, R. T. (1927) 'A gray squirrel carries its young' *J. Mammal.* **8,** 244-5

HAYES, K. J. & HAYES, C. (1952) 'Imitation in a home raised chimpanzee' *J. comp. physiol. Psychol.* **46,** 99-104

HEDIGER, H. (1955) *Studies of the psychology and behaviour of captive animals in zoos and circuses* (Trans. by G. Sircom) New York: Criterion Books

HINDE, R. A. (1962) 'Sensitive periods and the development of behaviour' *Lessons from animal behaviour for the clinician, Little club clinic in developmental medicine* **7,** 25-36

HINDE, R. A. & ROWELL, T. E. (1962) 'Communication in postures and facial expressions in the rhesus monkey (*Macaca mulatta*)' *Proc. zool. Soc. Lond.* **138,** 1-21

HINDE, R. A., ROWELL, T. E. & SPENCER-BOOTH, Y. (1964) 'Behaviour of socially living rhesus monkeys in their first six months' *Proc. zool. Soc. Lond.* **143**, 609-49.

HORNER, B. E. (1947) 'Parental care of young mice of the genus *Peromyscus*' *J. Mammal.* **28,** 31-36

HOWELL, A. B. & LITTLE, L. (1924) 'Additional notes on California bats; with observations upon the young of *Eumops*' *J. Mammal.* **5,** 261-3

HUESTIS, R. R. (1933) 'Maternal behavior in the deer mouse' *J. Mammal.* **14,** 47-9

HUMPHREY, G. (1921) 'Imitation and the conditioned reflex' *Ped. Sem.* **28,** 1-21

ITANI, J. (1959) 'Paternal care in the wild Japanese monkey, *Macaca fuscata fuscata*' *Primates: J. Primatology*, **2,** 61-93

JAMES, M. (1960) 'Premature ego development: some observations upon disturbances in the first three months of life' *Int. J. Psycho-anal.* **41**

JAY, P. (1962) 'Aspects of maternal behavior in langurs' *Proc. N.Y. Acad. Sci.* **102,** 468-76

JAY, P. (1963) 'Mother-infant relations in langurs' In H. L. Rheingold (Ed.) *Maternal behavior in mammals* New York: John Wiley, pp. 282-304

JENSEN, G. D. (1961) 'The development of prehension in a Macaque' *J. comp. physiol. Psychol.* **54,** 11-12

JENSEN, G. D. & TOLMAN, C. W. (1962a) 'Aspects of the mother-child tie in the monkey: the effect of brief separation and mother specificity' *J. comp. physiol. Psychol.* **55,** 131

JENSEN, G. D. & TOLMAN, C. W. (1962b) 'Activity level of the mother monkey, *Macaca nemestrina*, as affected by various conditions of sensory access to the infant following separation' *Animal Behaviour*, **10,** 228-30

JONES, M. C. (1926) 'The development of early behavior patterns in young children' *Ped. Sem. J. Genet. Psychol.* **33,** 537-85

KAILA, E. (1932) 'Die Reaktionen des Säuglings auf das manschliche Gesicht' *Annales Universit. Aboensis* Series B, **17,** 1-114

KINDER, E. F. (1927) 'A study of the nest-building activity of the albino rat' *J. exp. Zool.* **47,** 117-61

KING, J. A. (1958) 'Maternal behavior and behavioral development in two subspecies of *Peromyscus maniculatus*' *J. Mammal.* **39,** 177-90

KLOPFER, P. H. (1959) 'Social interactions in discrimination learning with special reference to feeding behaviour in birds' *Behaviour*, **14,** 282-99

KLOPFER, P. H. (1960) 'Observational learning in birds: the establishment of behavioural modes' *Behaviour*, **15,** 71-9

KOEHLER, O. (1954) 'Das Lächeln als angeborene Ausdrucksbewegung' *Zeit. f. Menschliche Vererbung u. Konstit.* **32,** 390-8

KRIS, E. (1962) 'Decline and recovery in the life of a three-year-old: or – data in psycho-analytic perspective on the mother-child relationship' *Psychoanal. study Child*, **17**

LABRIOLA, J. (1953) 'Effects of caesarean delivery upon maternal behavior in rats' *Proc. soc. exp. Biol. N.Y.* **83,** 556-7

LANG, H. (1925) 'How squirrels and other rodents carry their young' *J. Mammal.* **6,** 18-24

LEHRMAN, D. S. (1961) 'Hormonal regulation of parental behavior in birds and infrahuman mammals' In W. C. Young (Ed.) *Sex and internal secretions* 3rd ed. Baltimore: Williams and Wilkins, pp. 1268-1382

LEYHAUSEN, P. (1956) 'Verhaltensstudien an Katzen' *Z. Tierpsychol.* Beiheft 2

LOTT, D. F. (1962) 'The role of progesterone in the maternal behavior of rodents' *J. comp. physiol. Psychol.* **55,** 610-13

LOTT, D. F. & FUCHS, S. S. (1962) 'Failure to induce retrieving by sensitization or the injection of prolactin' *J. comp. physiol. Psychol.* **55,** 1111-13

LUNDIN, R. W. (1961) *Personality: an experimental approach* New York: Macmillan

MCGRAW, M. B. (1945) *The neuromuscular maturation of the human infant* New York: Columbia Univer. Press

MILLER, G. A., GALANTER, E. & PRIBRAM, K. H. (1960) *Plans and the structure of behavior* New York: Henry Holt

MILLER, N. E. & DOLLARD, J. (1941) *Social learning and imitation* New Haven: Yale Univer. Press

MIRSKY, J. A., MILLER, R. E. & MURPHY, J. U. (1958) 'The communication of affect in rhesus monkeys. I. An experimental method *J. Am. Psychoanalyt. A*, **6,** 933.

MOORE, J. C. (1957) 'Newborn young of a captive manatee' *J. Mammal.* **38,** 137-8

MOWRER, O. H. (1950) *Learning theory and personality dynamics* New York: The Ronald Press

MOWRER, O. H. (1960) *Learning theory and the symbolic process* New York: John Wiley

NEMTSOVA, O. L., MORACHEVSKAIA, E. V. & ANDREYEVA, E. I. (1958) 'Changes in the conditioned reflex activity of animals during pregnancy' *Pavlov J. Higher Nerv. Activity.* **8,** 223-33

NEWSON, J. & NEWSON, E. (1963) *Infant care in an urban community* London: Allen and Unwin

NICOLL, C. S. & MEITES, J. (1959) 'Prolongation of lactation in the rat by litter replacement' *Proc. Soc. exp. Biol. N.Y.* **101,** 81-2

ORR, L. W. (1930) 'An unusual chipmunk nest' *J. Mammal.* **11,** 315

PEARSON, O. P., KOFORD, M. R. & PEARSON, A. K. (1952) 'Reproduction of the lump-nosed bat (*Corynorhinus rafinesquei*) in California' *J. Mammal.* **33**, 273-320

PIAGET, J. (1952) *The origins of intelligence in children* New York: International Univers. Press

POURNELLE, G. H. (1952) 'Reproduction and early post-natal development of the cotton mouse, *Peromyscus gossypinus gossypinus*' *J. Mammal.* **33**, 1-20

PRECHTL, H. F. R. (1963) 'The mother-child interaction in babies with minimal brain damage' In B. M. Foss (Ed.) *Determinants of infant behaviour II* London: Methuen, pp. 53-9

PRICE, B. (1950) 'Primary biases in twin studies' *Amer. J. Hum. Genet.* **2**, 293-352

RHEINGOLD, H. L. (1961) 'The effect of environmental stimulation upon social and exploratory behaviour in the human infant' In B. M. Foss (Ed.) *Determinants of infant behaviour* London: Methuen, pp. 143-77

RHEINGOLD, H. L. (1963a) 'Controlling the infant's exploratory behaviour' In B. M. Foss (Ed.) *Determinants of infant behaviour II* London: Methuen, pp. 171-5

RHEINGOLD, H. L. (1963b) 'Maternal behavior in the dog' In H. L. Rheingold (Ed.) *Maternal behavior in mammals* New York: John Wiley, pp. 169-202

RICHARDSON, W. B. (1943) 'Wood rats (*Neotoma albigula*): their growth and development' *J. Mammal.* **24**, 130-43

RIDDLE, O., LAHR, E. L. & BATES, R. W. (1942) 'The role of hormones in the initiation of maternal behavior in rats' *Amer. J. Physiol.* **137**, 299-317

RIESS, B. F. (1950) 'The isolation of factors of learning and native behavior in field and laboratory studies' *Ann. N.Y. Acad. Sci.* **51**, 1093-1102

RIESS, B. F. (1954) 'The effect of altered environments and age in mother-young relationships among animals' *Ann. N.Y. Acad. Sci.* **57**, 606-10

RIOPELLE, A. J. (1960) 'Complex processes' Chap. 8 in R. H. Waters, D. A. Rethlingshafer and W. E. Caldwell (Eds.) *Principles of comparative psychology* New York: McGraw Hill

ROBERTSON, JOYCE (1962) 'Mothering as an influence on early development' *Psychoanal. study. Child,* **17**

ROSENBLATT, J. S., TURKEWITZ, G. & SCHNEIRLA, T. C. (1961)

'Early socialization in the domestic cat as based on feeding and other relationships between female and young' In B. M. Foss (Ed.) *Determinants of infant behaviour* London: Methuen, pp. 51-74

ROSENBLATT, J. S. & LEHRMAN, D. S. (1963) 'Maternal behavior of the laboratory rat' In H. L. Rheingold (Ed.) *Maternal behavior in mammals* New York: John Wiley, pp. 8-57

ROSS, S., DENENBERG, V. H., FROMMER, G. P. & SAWIN, P. B. (1959) 'Genetic, physiological, and behavioral background of reproduction in the rabbit. V. Nonretrieving of neonates' *J. Mammal.* **40,** 91-6

ROTH, L. L. & ROSENBLATT, J. S. (1964) 'Pregnancy changes in the self-licking patterns of rats' Paper presented at meetings of the American Psychological Association in Los Angeles

ROTHCHILD, I. (1960) 'The corpus luteum – pituitary relationship' *Endocrinology*, **67,** 9-41

ROWELL, T. E. (1960) 'On the retrieving of young and other behaviour in lactating golden hamsters' *Proc. Zool. Soc. London*, **135,** 265-82

ROWELL, T. E. & HINDE, R. A. (1962) 'Vocal communication by the rhesus monkey (*Macaca mulatta*)' *Proc. zool. Soc. London*, **138,** 279-94

ROWELL, T. E., HINDE, R. A. & SPENCER-BOOTH, Y. (1964) ' "Aunt"-infant interaction in captive rhesus monkeys' *Anim. Behav.* **12,** 219-26.

SALK, L. (1960) 'The effects of the normal heartbeat sound on the behavior of the new-born infant: implications for mental health' *World ment. Health*, **12,** 1-8

SANDER, L. W. (1962) 'Issues in early mother-child interaction' *J. child Psychiat.* **1,** 1

SCHALLER, G. B. (1963) *The mountain gorilla, ecology and behavior* Chicago: Univer. Chicago Press

SCHEFFER, V. B. (1945) 'Growth and behavior of young sea lions' *J. Mammal.* **26,** 390-2

SCHIFF, W., CAVINESS, J. A. & GIBSON, J. J. (1962) 'Persistent fear responses in rhesus monkeys to the optical stimulus of "looming" ' *Science*, **136,** 982-3

SCHNEIRLA, T. C. & ROSENBLATT, J. S. (1961) 'Behavioral organization and genesis of the social bond in insects and mammals' *Amer. J. Orthopsychiat.* **31,** 223-53

SCHNEIRLA, T. C. & ROSENBLATT, J. S. (1963) ' "Critical" periods in the development of behavior' *Science,* **139,** 1110-15

SCHNEIRLA, T. C., ROSENBLATT, J. S, & TOBACH, E. (1963) 'Maternal behavior in the cat' In H. L. Rheingold (Ed.) *Maternal behavior in mammals* New York: John Wiley, pp. 122-68

SCOTT, J. P. (1958) 'Critical periods in the development of social behavior in puppies' *Psychosomat. Med.* **20,** 42-54

SCOTT, J. P. (1962) 'Critical periods in behavioral development' *Science,* **138,** 949-58

SHIRLEY, M. M. (1933) *The first two years: a study of twenty-five babies: Vol. II. Intellectual development.* Minneapolis: Univer. of Minnesota Press

SILVER, I. A. (1956) 'Vascular changes in the mammary gland during engorgement with milk' *J. Physiol.* **133,** 65P-66P

SÖDERLING, B. (1959) 'The first smile: a developmental study' *Acta Paediatrica,* **48,** supplement 117, 78-82

SPITZ, R. A. (1955) 'A note on the extrapolation of ethological findings' *Int. J. Psychoanal.* **36,** 162-5

SPITZ, R. A. & WOLF, K. M. (1946) 'The smiling response: a contribution to the ontogenesis of social relations' *Genet. Psychol. Monogr.* **34,** 57-125

STANLEY W. C,. CORNWELL, A. C., POGGIANI, C. & TRATTNER, A. (1963) 'Conditioning in the neonatal puppy' *J. comp. physiol. Psychol.* **56,** 211-14

STELLAR, E. (1960) 'The marmoset as a laboratory animal: maintenance, general observations of behavior, and simple learning' *J. comp. physiol. Psychol.* **53,** 1-10

STURMAN-HULBE, M. & STONE, C. P. (1929) 'Maternal behavior in the albino rat' *J. comp. Psychol.* **9,** 203-37

SVIHLA, R. D. (1930) 'A family of flying squirrels' *J. Mammal.* **11,** 211-13

SVIHLA, A. & SVIHLA, R. D. (1930) 'How a chipmunk carried her young' *J. Mammal.* **11,** 314-15

TEVIS, L., JR. (1950) 'Summer behavior of a family of beavers in New York state' *J. Mammal.* **31,** 40-65

THORPE, W. H. (1956) *Learning and instinct in animals* London: Methuen

THORPE, W. H. (1961) *Bird-song: the biology of vocal communication and expression in birds.* Cambridge Monographs in Experimental Biology, 12. Cambridge: University Press

TINKELPAUGH, O. L. & HARTMAN, C. G. (1932) 'Behavior and maternal care of the newborn monkey (*Macaca mulatta* – "*M. rhesus*")' *Ped. Sem. & J. genet. Psychol.* **40,** 257-85

TOMILIN, M. I. & YERKES, R. M. (1935) 'Chimpanzee twins: behavioral relations and development' *Ped. Sem. & J. genet. Psychol.* **46,** 239-63

VAN HOOFF, J. A. R. A. M. (1962) 'Facial expressions in higher primates' *Symp. zool. Soc. Lond.* **8,** 97-125

WADE, O. (1927) 'Breeding habits and early life of the thirteen-striped ground squirrel, *Citellus tridecemlineatus* (Mitchill)' *J. Mammal.* **8,** 269-76

WAGMAN, W. E., CHRISTOFERSON, E. & FRIEDLICH, O. (1964) 'Self-licking and the maternal behavior of laboratory rats' Paper presented at the Eastern Psychological Association Meetings, Philadelphia, Penna.

WARREN, E. R. (1924) 'A muskrat moves its young' *J. Mammal.* **5,** 202-3

WASHBURN, R. W. (1929) 'A study of the smiling and laughing of infants in the first year of life' *Genet. Psychol. Monogr.* **6,** 397-535

WATSON, J. B. (1925) *Behaviorism* New York: Norton. (Revised ed. 1930)

WEISKRANTZ, L. & COWEY, A. (1963) 'The aetiology of food reward in monkeys' *Anim. Behav.* **11,** 225-34

WHARTON, C. H. (1950) 'Notes on the life history of the flying lemur' *J. Mammal.* **31,** 269-73

WIESNER, B. P. & SHEARD, N. M. (1933) *Maternal behaviour in the rat* Edinburgh: Oliver and Boyd

WOLF, K. M. (1953) 'Observations on individual tendencies in the first year of life' In M.J.E. Senn (Ed.) *Problems of infancy and childhood* New York: Josiah Macy, Jr. Foundation, pp. 114.

WOLFF, P. H. (1959) 'Observations on newborn infants' *Psychosomat. Med.* **21,** 110-18

WOLFF, P. H. (1963) 'Observations on the early development of smiling' In B. M. Foss *Determinants of infant behaviour II* London: Methuen, pp. 113-34

YOUNG, S. P. & GOLDMAN, E. A. (1944) *The wolves of North America* Washington, D.C.: Amer. Wildlife Inst.

YOUNG, W. C. (1961) 'The mammalian ovary. In W. C. Young (Ed.)

Sex and internal secretions 3rd ed. Baltimore: Williams and Wilkins, pp. 449-96

ZARROW, M. X., SAWIN, P. B., ROSS, S. & DENENBERG, V. H. (1962) 'Maternal behavior and its endocrine basis in the rabbit' In E. L. Bliss (Ed.) *Roots of behavior* New York: Hoeber, Harper, pp. 187-97

Index